# Ireland's Green Opportunity

*Driving Investment in a Low-Carbon Economy*

Peter Brennan

Published by Orpen Press
Upper Floor, Unit K9
Greenogue Business Park
Rathcoole
Co. Dublin
Ireland

e-mail: info@orpenpress.com

www.orpenpress.com

© Dr Peter Brennan, 2012

Reprinted 2019

Paperback ISBN: 978-1-78605-075-5
ePub ISBN: 978-1-871305-75-3
Kindle ISBN: 978-1-871305-76-0

All rights reserved. No part of this publication may be reproduced,
stored in a retrieval system or transmitted in any form or by any
means, electronic, mechanical, recording or otherwise, without
the prior, written permission of the publisher.

This book is sold subject to the condition that it shall not, by
way of trade or otherwise, be lent, resold, hired out, or otherwise circulated without the publisher's prior consent in any form
than that in which it is published and without a similar condition including this condition being imposed on the subsequent
purchaser.

Printed in Dublin by SPRINTprint Ltd

*For my parents, Joe and Patricia*

# Contents

# Contents

# Introduction

About €500 billion in potential green economy investments in Ireland and the UK over the next decade have been announced. This is against the backdrop of a global green economy market which has been estimated at €3.5 trillion with the potential to grow by more than 4 per cent per annum to 2015.[1] That is a lot of potential business. However, translating investment intentions into 'shovel-ready' projects is never easy and perhaps more so in the renewable energy, energy efficiency, forestry, water and waste sectors that comprise the 'green economy'.

This book provides an overview of this growing sector; discusses the policy drivers and the strategic issues influencing investment decisions; and gives specific insights into individual sub-sectors of the green economy. The main drivers are EU policy on climate change and renewable energy, sustainability and the price of energy.

Understanding this agenda will help you better appreciate where the challenges lie but, more importantly, where there are already significant business opportunities. It will be of interest not only to Ireland's 240 cleantech companies but to potential investors and project promoters.

My keen interest in climate change dates from 2006 when I approached Brendan Halligan, chairman of the Institute of International and European Affairs (IIEA), and suggested that Ireland needed to start taking this topic seriously and asked whether consequently the Institute would support a project that would bring the country's stakeholders together to prepare a report on the issues, options and challenges. Replying almost instantly in the affirmative, Brendan appointed me chairman of the IIEA's Climate Change Research Group. We delivered what we promised and more importantly cajoled nearly 60 diverse

Introduction

stakeholders to work in unison.² In the intervening years the
IIEA has organised dozens of events attended by national and
international experts on climate change. I think it is fair to say
that there is a large consensus in Ireland about the absolute
requirement to first articulate and then implement a far-
reaching national climate change/low-carbon strategy thanks
in no small measure to the IIEA's ongoing work.

By understand the science, politics and economics of climate
change one can get a much better appreciation of the investment opportunities that will be part of Ireland's transition to
a low-carbon economy over the coming decades. This is not
to say that many countries, regions, islands, businesses and
households will not suffer the negative consequence of climate
change; they undoubtedly will and many are already affected by
extreme weather events. My focus is quite different: I look at the
opportunities. Linking climate policy with enterprise policy is an
over-arching theme of the book.

The mitigation measures and adaptation strategies that
Ireland and other countries need to put in place will require
significant public and private investment. Depending on what
choices are made, business opportunities will arise and, once
investments are in the pipeline, jobs will be created.

As I see it, climate change and the green economy are two
sides of the same coin. It is therefore necessary to understand the
dynamics and drivers of both. For example, a potential investor
in an energy-efficiency or bio-energy project would benefit from
a broader understanding as to how this type of project fits into
the overall climate change/low-carbon economy picture and the
Government's priorities. And that is a key objective of this book.
I sincerely hope I provide a good overview, a strategic perspective and enough background information to inform prospective
investors. If you are looking for a job in the green economy or
wish to start your own 'green' project I hope the book will help
you fast track your way forward. There are dozens of grants and
schemes already in place to promote new investments. I argue
that additional and more targeted incentives are needed if the
green economy is to reach its potential within a shorter time
frame than is currently envisaged.

A secondary aim is to provide researchers, public policy-
makers and anyone interested in climate change and renewable
energy policy with a library of up-to-date source material.
Acknowledging that the literature is vast, I have gone to

considerable lengths to identify the most relevant and topical reports relating to each subject matter. The bibliographical material is therefore not only extensive but easy to access through hyperlinks and endnotes. I appreciate that I may have missed some contributions to the literature and for that my apologies.

The third aim, by way of providing evidence, is to create a better awareness of the huge potential of the green economy not just in Ireland but in export markets. As the Government is in the process of revising Ireland's policies on sustainable development, climate change, renewable energy all in the context of Ireland moving to a low-carbon economy, the book offers some new perspectives for our policy-makers. The harsh reality is Ireland is playing catch-up. Despite the rhetoric, and our world-class renewable resources (of which we currently use just 1 per cent of the total potential) Ireland is largely a policy and technology recipient and not a key influencer. We are not yet at the cutting edge (with some notable exceptions). This is where we want to be. This is where we should be. If this book does nothing else I hope it will open the minds of our key policy-makers to take a 'whole of government' approach to the twin issues of climate change and the green economy. Yes, we have to address the constraints imposed upon us by the EU–IMF programme, but that should not stop us from planning and facilitating investment and export opportunities.

The book's two sections are largely self-contained. So if you want to find out about the science, politics and economics of climate change and the policies underpinning Europe's and Ireland's transition to a low-carbon economy then you will be interested in Part 1. Part 2 deals with specific green economy business opportunities.

**Part 1** will take you through the science, politics and economics of climate change. The issues are global; but the responses are local. In Ireland's case, almost all of our policy response is a direct consequence of what is agreed at EU level. Irish climate scientists have already mapped out the potential impacts. At global level there is near universal consensus that a business-as-usual approach to climate change is no longer an option. The missing ingredient is an international agreement to set binding greenhouse gas (GHG) emission-reduction targets. To date, the UN's climate change negotiators have failed to build a sufficient consensus between the developed and developing world to keep the Earth's temperature from rising by no more than 2°C – the limit beyond which potential catastrophic consequences will inevitably result.

Part 1 also outlines the key elements of the EU's climate mitigation and energy security response: the so-called 20–20–20 package, which requires Ireland and the other (26) Member States to reduce GHG emissions by 20 per cent by 2020 and to invest in renewable energy and energy efficiency. One key policy instrument is the EU's emissions trading scheme (ETS) as it covers over 10,000 energy-intensive installations across Europe. By creating a market for carbon, the EU is endeavouring to incentivise these operators (in what is called the 'trading sector') to invest in low-carbon technologies. Ireland is not going to find it easy to comply with the national target set for the non-trading sectors (i.e. the sectors not covered by the EU's ETS) not least because of the above EU average emissions from our agriculture and transport sectors. On the other hand, with suitable investment carbon mitigation will result. Thanks to the Environmental Protection Agency we have a good handle on not only who emits what under the EU ETS, but what precisely needs to be done to transition Ireland (like all other Member States) to become a low-carbon economy. This strategic objective – a key policy objective of government – will bring about fundamental changes in personal, household and corporate behaviour. Within several decades, for example, electricity generation will be largely carbon neutral, greater energy efficiency will be mandatory, and the green economy will achieve the same priority status as the other key sectors of the Irish economy.

The Government has got the message loud and clear. By the end of 2012, Ireland will have a (much) revised national climate change/low-carbon strategy, a national adaptation strategy, a revised energy policy and a strategy on sustainable development. Once these are in place, with supporting budgets, then perhaps the green economy will begin to achieve its true potential.

**Part 2** sets the scene in terms of identifying potential business opportunities as it draws on the very latest thinking and trends at global level. While Ireland cogitates, the rest of the world is investing record amounts in renewable energy and water. China, India, Germany and the UK are among the countries that have prioritised such investments. As a consequence they are becoming technology leaders and thankfully as a result of these investments the cost of some critical infrastructure components is beginning to fall. Ireland has a tentative green economy strategy but not as relatively ambitious as these global players. There are plenty of promoters with shovel-ready projects, some investments are already at full tilt (in the onshore wind sector for example) and even more are seeking export opportunities. The main sub-sectors where the book identifies specific opportunities include on and offshore wind, tidal and ocean energy, solar, bio-energy, geothermal, energy efficiency, forestry, water and waste.

In common with other European countries, we are about to embark on a national strategy to create a low-carbon economy by 2050, which will inevitably see the rapid deployment of new technologies, significant behavioural change and a host of business opportunities here and in export markets.

We cannot negotiate with nature. But we can position Ireland as a niche player in a growing global green economy.

I hope the readers of this book come to the same conclusion.

# Acknowledgments

I am very grateful to Gina Hanrahan, Senior Researcher at the Institute of International and European Affairs, Dr Brian Motherway, Chief Executive Officer, Sustainable Energy Authority of Ireland, Professor John Sweeney, NUI Maynooth, Dr Ken Macken, Dr Seán O'Riordáin, Public Policy Advisors Network, Dr Robert Geraghty, Enterprise Ireland, Alan Quirke, Environment Policy Analyst, Forfás, and Dr Neil Walker, Head of Environment and Energy Policy, IBEC, who kindly reviewed a working draft of the material and gave me great feedback (mostly in a personal capacity). I really appreciate their insights and advice. Obviously the views expressed are mine alone.

# Glossary of terms

**Adaptation (to climate change)**: The taking of measures to cope with the effects of climate change, rather than the action taken to reduce emissions. Adaptation benefits are the avoided damages or the realised benefits following the adoption and implementation of adaptation measures.

**Afforestation**: The act or process of establishing a forest on land that has not been forested for 50 years.

**Allowances units**: That entitle the holder to emit 1 tonne of $CO_2e$. These include Assigned Amount Units (AAUs), ERUs (from JIs), CERs (from CDM projects), and RMUs (from LULUCF). For compliance, units must be surrendered in amounts equal to actual emissions over the commitment period.

**Annex 1 Parties**: Countries, members of the OECD, and economies in transition, and countries from central and eastern Europe. Non-Annex 1 countries are developing countries.

**Assigned amount unit (AAUs)**: Under the Kyoto Protocol, participating Annex B Parties are allocated AAUs, each equivalent to 1 tonne of $CO_2e$. For compliance, at the end of the commitment period, these AAUs must be surrendered by the Parties in an amount equal to their actual covered emissions over the period.

**Auctioning**: An approach by which emission allowances are distributed by governments to operators covered by an emissions trading scheme (ETS).

**Banking**: Parties may save excess emission allowances or credits from the first commitment period for use in a subsequent commitment period i.e. post-2012.

**Base year**: The year against which commitments are to be measured. For example, 2005 is the EU's base year for determining EU and national targets to 2020.

**Cap and trade**: A scheme that sets a cap on emissions and allocates a number of emission rights to installations to cover their emissions. These operators can use the emission rights to demonstrate compliance and can trade these emission rights among themselves.

**Carbon capture and storage (CCS)**: The capture of $CO_2$ from large point sources, compression, transportation and injection into underground geological formations.

**Carbon leakage**: Happens where a portion of the cuts in greenhouse gas (GHG) emissions by countries trying to meet mandatory carbon limits may reappear in other countries not bound by such limits. This raises potential competitiveness issues.

**Carbon market**: A trading system through which countries may buy or sell units of GHG emissions.

**Carbon sink**: Natural or man-made systems that absorb $CO_2$ from the atmosphere and store them.

**CDM**: Clean Development Mechanism – a flexible instrument under the Kyoto Protocol through which developed countries may finance GHG emission reduction or removal projects in developed countries and receive credits for doing so.

**CERs**: Certified emission reductions representing 1 tonne of $CO_2e$ achieved through a CDM project.

**Climate change**: Change in climate attributable to human activity arising from the release of GHGs into the atmosphere and that is additional to natural climate variability.

**CO2**: Carbon dioxide, the main GHG arising from human activities and also naturally occurring.

**CO2e**: Carbon dioxide equivalent, where gases other than $CO_2$ are referred to for comparison purposes. These are converted to their equivalence in global warming terms to $CO_2$.

**Commitment period**: The Kyoto Protocol provides that Parties' targets are to be achieved over the five-year period 2008–2012 (the first 'commitment' period). Targets at international level for subsequent periods have yet to be negotiated.

**COP**: Conference of the Parties (to the UNFCCC), which is the negotiating body for global climate change talks.

**Credits**: Emission entitlements generated in offsetting or carbon crediting mechanisms that can be used for compliance in a cap and trade scheme.

**Emission rights**: Emission entitlements generated in a cap and trade scheme. They include AAUs and EU Allowances (EUAs).

**Emissions cap**: A mandated restraint, within a scheduled time frame, that puts a ceiling on the total amount of GHG emissions that can be released into the atmosphere.

**Emissions permit**: The non-transferable or tradable entitlement bestowed by government upon an entity to emit a pollutant within specified constraints.

**ERUs**: Emission reduction units representing 1 tonne of $CO_2e$ GHG emission reductions achieved through a JI project.

**EU effort sharing**: The agreement reached at EU level to jointly meet their commitments post-2012 by reallocating emissions at national level in the non-traded sector i.e. emissions not covered by the EU ETS.

**EU ETS**: The EU's emissions trading scheme, which allows those operators reducing GHG emissions below what is required to use or trade the excess reduction to offset emissions at another source inside or outside the country.

**EUAs**: European Union allowances distributed to installations under the EU's ETS corresponding to 1 tonne of $CO_2e$.

**Flexible mechanisms**: There are three such mechanisms provided for under the Kyoto Protocol: CDM; JI; and inter-party ETS.

**Fungibility**: Refers to the possibility that one unit can be exchanged for, or replaced by, another.

**Greenhouse gases (GHG)**: A gas from the atmosphere that freely allows radiation from the sun through to the Earth's surface, but traps the heat radiated back from the Earth's surface towards space and reradiates it back to the Earth's surface. The main anthropogenic GHGs are carbon dioxide ($CO_2$), methane ($CH_4$) and nitrous oxide ($N_2O$).

**Gt**: Gigatonne i.e. a thousand Mt.

**GWP**: Global Warming Potential.

**IEA**: International Energy Agency.

**IPCC**: Set up in 1988, the Intergovernmental Panel on Climate Change is the authoritative scientific source on climate change.

**JI**: Joint Implementation, or jointly implemented projects in developed countries that limit or reduce emissions.

**Kyoto Protocol**: The global agreement on climate change, which set binding limitation and reduction targets for developed countries. It covers emissions in the period 2008–2012.

**MACC**: The marginal abatement cost curve, which identifies the least cost measures that could be introduced to reduce GHG emissions.

**Marrakech Accords**: The agreements reached that set down the rules for operating the more complex provisions of the Kyoto Protocol.

**Methane (CH4)**: One of the basket of six GHGs controlled by the Kyoto Protocol.

**Mitigation**: Actions resulting in reductions to the degree or intensity of GHG emissions.

**National registry**: Accounts for the holding of allowances by the Parties.

**Non-ETS**: Those sectors that are outside the EU ETS.

**REDD**: Emissions from deforestation and forest degradation.

**RMU**: Removal units are generated in Annex B Parties by LULUCF activities and used to help these countries meet their Kyoto Protocol commitments.

**Sequestration (of carbon)**: The removal of $CO_2$ from the atmosphere and the storage of the carbon, generally by growing plants. It also includes forestry sinks and the storage of carbon in associated soils.

# Table of acronyms

| | |
|---|---|
| AAUs | assigned amount unit |
| ACA | accelerated capital allowances |
| ACES | American Clean Energy Security Act 2009 |
| AD | anaerobic digestion |
| AER | alternative energy requirement |
| AFOLU | agriculture and forestry land use |
| ARRA | American Recovery and Reinvestment Act 2009 |
| BAU | business as usual |
| BER | building energy rating |
| BERR | Department for Business, Enterprise and Regulatory Reform |
| BES | business expansion schemes |
| BEST | Berkeley Earth Surface Temperature |
| BGE | Bord Gáis Energy |
| CAP | Common Agricultural Policy |
| CBA | community-based adaptation |
| CCS | carbon capture and storage |
| CDM | clean development mechanism |
| CDP | Carbon Disclosure Project |
| CEJAPA | Clean Energy Jobs and American Power Act |
| CEMEP | Commission on Environmental Markets and Economic Performance |
| CER | certified emission reduction |
| CER | Commission for Energy Regulation |
| CFL | compact fluorescent lighting |
| CHP | combined heat and power |
| CIF | climate investment fund |
| CIM | community-wide implementation measure |
| CITL | community independent transaction log |
| COFORD | Council for Forest Research and Development |

| | |
|---|---|
| COMETR | Competitive Effects of Environmental Tax Reforms |
| COP | Conference of the Parties |
| CSP | concentrating solar power |
| CSR | corporate social responsibility |
| DBO | design, build and operate |
| DCENR | Department of Communications, Energy and Natural Resources |
| DCHP | domestic-scale combined heat and power |
| DECC | Department of Energy and Climate Change |
| DECLG | Department of Environment, Community and Local Government |
| DEFRA | Department for Environment, Food and Rural Affairs |
| ECEEE | European Council for an Energy Efficient Europe |
| ECF | European Climate Foundation |
| ECO | energy company obligation |
| EMAS | environment management systems |
| EMCE | European Marine Energy Centre |
| ENRTP | Environment and Natural Resources Thematic Programme |
| ENTSO-E | European Network of Transmission System Operators in Electricity |
| EPA | Environmental Protection Agency |
| EPBD | Directive on Energy Performance in Buildings |
| ERU | emission reduction unit |
| ESCO | energy service company |
| ESD | Energy Services Directive |
| ETS | emissions trading scheme |
| EU | European Union |
| EUA | EU allowances |
| EUEI | EU Energy Initiative |
| EUTL | European Union Transaction Log |
| FCPF | Forest Carbon Partnership Facility |
| FDI | foreign direct investment |
| FIT | feed-in tariff |
| FiTCfD | feed-in tariff with contract for difference |
| FLEGT | forest law enforcement governance and trade |
| FYP | five-year plan |
| GCCA | Global Climate Change Alliance |
| GCM | global climate models |
| GEEREF | Global Energy Efficiency and Renewable Energy Fund |

## Table of acronyms

| | |
|---|---|
| GHG | greenhouse gas |
| GJ | gigajoules |
| GPP | green public procurement |
| GRI | Global Reporting Initiative |
| Gt | gigatonne |
| GWP | global warming potential |
| IAE | Irish Academy of Engineering |
| ICAP | International Carbon Action Partnership |
| IEA | International Energy Agency |
| IEI | International Environmental Issues |
| IFSC | International Financial Services Centre |
| IIEA | Institute of International and European Affairs |
| IIED | International Institute for Environment and Development |
| IMF | International Monetary Fund |
| INC | International Negotiating Committee |
| IPCC | Intergovernmental Panel on Climate Change |
| ISLES | Irish–Scottish Links on Energy Study |
| ITL | international transaction log |
| IVCA | Irish Venture Capitalist Association |
| IWMA | Irish Waste Management Association |
| JPA | joint procurement agreement |
| JSG | joint steering group |
| LDCs | least developed countries |
| LIEN | large industry energy network |
| LULUCF | land-use, land-use change and forestry |
| MACC | marginal abatement cost curve |
| MBT | mechanical biological treatment |
| MDG | millennium development goals |
| MEF | major economies forum |
| MOTR | mineral oil tax relief |
| MRFCJ | Mary Robinson Foundation - Climate Justice |
| MRV | measuring, reporting and verification |
| MSW | municipal solid waste Mt     million tonnes |
| Mtoe | million tonnes of oil equivalent |
| MWh | megawatt/hour |
| NAMAs | nationally appropriate mitigation actions |
| NAP | national allocation plan |
| NAPA | National Adaptation Programme for Action |
| NCCS | National Climate Change Strategy |
| NDP | National Development Plan |
| NEEAP | National Energy Efficiency Action Plan |

| | |
|---|---|
| NGCT | natural gas carbon tax |
| NGO | non-governmental organisation |
| NIAER | Northern Ireland Authority for Utility Regulation |
| NREAP | National Renewable Energy Action Plan |
| OEM | original equipment manufacturer |
| OREDP | Offshore Renewable Energy Development Plan |
| PEEP | power generation, energy efficiency and pharma |
| Ppmv | parts per million volume |
| PSO | public service obligation |
| QELROs | quantified emission limitations and reduction objectives |
| RBMP | river basin management plans |
| REDD | emissions from deforestation and forest degradation |
| REFIT | renewable energy feed-in tariff |
| RES | renewable energy sources |
| RMU | removal units |
| RWSS | regional water supply schemes |
| SCC | social cost of carbon |
| SDR | special drawing rights |
| SEAI | Sustainable Energy Authority of Ireland |
| SET-PLAN | Strategic Energy Technology Plan |
| SEWG | Sustainable Energy Working Group |
| SIDS | small island developing states |
| SRES | Special Report on Emissions Scenarios |
| UNCED | UN Conference on Environment and Development |
| UNEP | United Nations Environment Programme |
| UNFCCC | UN Framework Convention on Climate Change |
| WAIS | West Antarctic Ice Sheet |
| WFD | Water Framework Directive |
| WMO | World Meteorological Organisation |
| WRAP | Waste and Resources Action Programme |

# Part I

# The science, politics and economics of climate change

**Chapter 1**

# The science of climate change

Will those responsible for decisions in the field of climate change at the global level listen to the voice of science and knowledge, which is now loud and clear?

R.K. Pachauri, chairman of the IPCC, Oslo, December 2007 (accepting the Nobel PeacePrize)

## Introduction

This chapter introduces the science of climatology, which is so fundamental to our understanding of climate change. The literature on this subject is vast for those who require more detailed explanations and insights than is provided by this brief overview.

The science is not exact. Nobody has yet claimed to be infallible when it comes to predicting in precise detail what will happen decades hence. Although climate forecasts are uncertain and will remain so, the broad conclusions of climate science which are based on many lines of evidence – including ice cores from a depth of 3 km in the Antarctic – give a high degree of confidence to scientists' predictions. Thus there is an overwhelming consensus about the causes of climate change and potential impacts; the over-arching conclusion is that warming of the climate system is unequivocal as is now evident from observations of increases in global average air and ocean temperatures, widespread melting of snow and ice and rising global average sea levels.

Thus understanding the basics of the science of climate change is the best starting point for a fuller understanding of the dynamics of climate change and the often turbulent debates about the degree to which climate change will impact on the global economy and what should be done to mitigate the worst effects. That said, bear in mind that scientists are concerned with probabilities, never with certainties or consensual agreement. The scientists tell us if GHG emissions continue at business-as-usual levels significant sustainability issues will arise in every part of the planet.

While a lot has been written about the impacts of climate change at a global level there is far less awareness of the likely impacts in Ireland. Thanks to the efforts of Irish scientists some of the risks associated with climate change have been identified and are set out below.

## Some definitions

Given that we are talking science let us get a few key definitions on the table.[3]

**Climate change** means a change of climate that is attributed directly or indirectly to human activity that alters the composition of the global atmosphere and that is in addition to natural climate variability observed over comparable time period.[4]

**Weather** on the other hand refers to variables such as temperature and rainfall that fluctuate naturally from day to day, between seasons and from year to year; an altogether shorter time frame.

The main **greenhouse gases** (GHG) include water vapour, $CO_2$, methane (which is more potent at capturing heat energy than $CO_2$), nitrous oxide and some industrial gases such as chlorofluorocarbons. These gases act like an insulating blanket keeping the Earth's surface warmer than it would be if they were not present in the atmosphere. As they increase in the atmosphere, the extra heat they trap leads to **global warming**. This warming, in turn, places pressure on the Earth's climate system and leads to climate change.

**Albedo** is the amount of sunlight reflected by a planetary surface. Albedos range from 1 for complete reflection to 0 for complete absorption. Global heating reduces ice, snow and some cloud cover, which leads to lower planetary albedo: a greater absorption of sunlight and even more global heating. The importance of this can be seen from the fact that one-third of all energy reaching Earth from the sun is reflected back to space by white surfaces.

A **carbon sink** is a reservoir that accumulates and stores carbon. Oceans are a carbon sink; they absorb some 48 per cent of all carbon emitted. Interestingly, the oceans vary in their ability to absorb carbon. Cold sea water can hold more $CO_2$ than warm seawater, so as the ocean warms it becomes less able to absorb the gas. The process by which carbon sinks remove $CO_2$ from the atmosphere is known as carbon **sequestration**.

## Overview

The science of climate change reflects a mixture of atmospheric physics, chemistry, oceanography, hydrology, biology and geology. Thus the interdependencies between these varied disciplines define the debate on the science of climate change.

Thus it should come as no surprise that while considerable progress has been made, it is not possible to provide definitive answers to many of the questions that are being asked about climate change.

We can thank French scientist Jean-Baptiste Joseph Fourier for our understanding of the greenhouse effect. In his work in the early part of the nineteenth century (1824), he observed that energy reaches the Earth from the sun mainly in short wavelengths such as visible sunlight. It is absorbed and then radiated back into space as long-wave radiation, mainly in the infrared part of the electromagnetic spectrum. He used the analogy of the glass in a greenhouse to describe the radiative warming of the Earth's surface due to these gases. In theory, when calculating the differential between the energy coming in and infrared radiation the planet should be frozen. However, Fourier correctly concluded that the atmosphere acts as a mantle keeping a proportion of the heat in and so making the Earth liveable. He found that $CO_2$ could act as a blanket in the atmosphere trapping heat close to the surface causing temperatures to increase; the first suggestion that global warming could occur. The Irish scientist John Tyndall, a native of Leighlinbridge, County Carlow, confirmed this assertion in 1860. He measured the absorption of infrared radiation by $CO_2$ and water vapour and established the radiative properties of these gases.

What is known is that the Earth's thermostat, a delicate and complex mechanism, has been around 14°C for the past 14,000 years, with small changes of less than 1°C. At the heart is $CO_2$, a colourless and odourless gas, which plays a critical role in maintaining the balance necessary to all life. It is also a waste product of the burning of fossil fuels that we all use for heat, transport and energy requirements.

The role of GHG in the atmosphere is qualitatively well understood. It is known that increasing the atmospheric concentration of the principal anthropogenic GHG, $CO_2$ leads to higher mean global surface temperatures. It is also accepted that $CO_2$ has increased very substantially during the last century to the highest levels seen in the past 800,000 years, and that this increase is primarily of anthropogenic origin i.e. it is related to or a result of the influence of human beings. It is beyond reasonable doubt that $CO_2$ emissions from human activities remains in the atmosphere for a long time.

When the Earth's orbit is strongly elliptical (which it is not at present) during its 100,000-year cycle the planet is carried both

### The greenhouse effect

The greenhouse effect is the heating effect exerted by the atmosphere on the Earth's surface because of the presence in the atmosphere of certain gases (greenhouse gases) that trap some of the long-wave radiation being emitted upward by the surface and re-emit it back to the surface. The long-wave radiation is heat radiation of the kind emitted by a warm object, which we can feel at a distance from the object but our eyes cannot see. In contrast, the sun's radiation is mainly short-wave radiation that we can both feel and see. This radiation passes downward through the atmosphere largely unimpeded and is absorbed by the surface, tending to raise the surface temperature. If there were no greenhouse gases in the atmosphere, a long-term equilibrium temperature would be reached where the downward moving solar radiation would be balanced by the upward moving long-wave radiation at the surface, with all the long-wave radiation being lost to space. The mean temperature at the surface would then be about 33°C colder than the temperature we know, and the whole Earth would be covered with ice. The presence of the naturally occurring GHGs, trapping some of the long-wave radiation and preventing it from being lost to space, is thus essential for life on Earth as we know it. It is the enhanced greenhouse effect due to extra man-made GHGs, mainly $CO_2$, being emitted into the atmosphere that is the cause for concern.

closer and further away from the sun, meaning that the intensity of the sun's rays reaching the Earth varies by as much as 30 per cent. The tilt of the Earth's axis to the sun also has an impact on radiation levels (about two-thirds of the sun's rays reaching the planet are absorbed, while the remaining third is reflected back into space). Sunspots too affect the planet. However, how these often small variations in radiation affect climate change is not always clear.[5] Certainly the astronomical changes in the Earth's orbit are conclusively linked to radical changes in climate associated with the planet's oscillation between glacial and interglacial modes over the past two million years.

From the poles to the equator the Earth spans a range of temperatures between 40°C below zero to 40°C above. Air at 40°C can hold 470 times as much water vapour as air at -40°C. Hence the poles are frozen deserts. However, for every 1°C of warming the world experiences there is an average 1 per cent increase in rainfall, which is not evenly distributed.

## Climate change is not new6

Over the past 4.5 billion years, since the Earth was formed, the global climate has changed dramatically many times.[7] During the past million years, the average temperature of the Earth's surface has risen and fallen by about 5°C through ten major ice age cycles. Twice – around 710 million and again at 600 million years ago – Earth crossed a threshold that all but exterminated life, freezing the planet right to the equator. The oldest climate aberration, discovered in November 2003 from a study of ice cores, happened some 55 million years ago when, accompanied by an unexplained release of GHGs into the atmosphere, there was an abrupt rise in surface temperature by as much as 10°C. Other rapid changes of a similar dimension were recorded at the end of the last ice age over a few decades as a result of the sudden collapse of ice sheets or changes in ocean currents.

Past temperature changes affected the world dramatically. For instance, only 14,000 years ago we were in an ice age where glaciations at times extended as far south as the Alps in Europe. More worryingly, in what is the fairly recent past, the sea level was 100 metres lower than today. In even earlier times, several million years ago, global temperature was several degrees higher than today and warm, tropical oceans may have reached much further from the equator, causing significant changes to atmospheric flow patterns. The last 8,000 years have been relatively stable at the warmer end of this temperature range.[8]

Fast forward to the Medieval Warm Period (AD 800–1300) and the Little Ice Age (AD 1500–1800) – two well-known climate episodes during the past thousand years. The northern hemisphere may have been warmer by up to 1°C on average during the former period than during the latter. Several assessments indicate that northern hemisphere average temperatures over the past 50 years have been warmer than during the Medieval Warm Period, and temperatures during the last decade are warmer still.

The largest global temperature changes evident in the geological record have typically occurred fairly slowly over tens of thousands of years, but much more gradually than the warming over the past century. The rate and scale of change over the past 20,000 years where the Earth warmed by as much as 5°C is the focus of much of the scientific analysis. Some predictions suggest that we are facing a rate of change some 30 times faster than the last significant period of change.

Another recent discovery is that once the glaciers started to melt some 19,000 years ago, there were very sharp rises in sea levels (by as much as 15 metres within 500 years). In the case of Ireland, such were the volumes of cold water released that this disrupted the Gulf Stream. Why? Heat is borne in a stream of warm salty water. As it gives up its heat the water sinks because, being salty, it is heavier than the water around it, and this sinking draws more warm salty water northwards. If the Gulf Stream's saltiness is diluted with fresh water from the Greenland glaciers it no longer sinks as it cools, and no more warm water is drawn northwards in its wake. This is not theoretical as the Gulf Stream has stopped flowing as recently as 8,000 years ago.[9] Ice cores from Greenland indicate that as the Gulf Stream slowed in the past the island experienced a massive 10°C drop in temperature in less than a decade. The possibility of a slow collapse of the Gulf Stream is one of the main 'tipping points' that scientists are aware of.[10]

## Scientific forecasts

The Intergovernmental Panel Climate Change's (IPCC) Synthesis Report is based on the assessment carried out by three working groups and provides an integrated view of climate change at global level as the final part of the IPCC's Fourth Assessment

Report (AR4).[11] The Fifth Assessment Report is underway and is scheduled to be published in October 2014.

Observed decreases in snow and ice extent are also consistent with warming. Satellite data since 1978 shows that annual average Arctic sea ice extent has shrunk by an average of 2.7 per cent per decade, with larger decreases in summer of an average of 7.4 per cent per decade. Mountain glaciers and snow cover on average have declined in both hemispheres. Observational evidence from all continents and most oceans shows that many natural systems are being affected by regional climate changes, particularly temperature increases.

According to the IPCC, it is *very likely* (a quantified probability) that over the past 50 years cold days, cold nights and frosts have become less frequent over most land areas, and hot days and hot nights have become more frequent. It is *likely* that heat waves have become more frequent over most land areas, the frequency of heavy precipitation (i.e. rain) events has increased over most areas, and since 1975 the incidence of extreme high sea level has increased worldwide. Average northern hemisphere temperatures during the second half of the twentieth century were *very likely* higher than during any other 50-year period in the last 500 years and *likely* the highest in at least the past 1,300 years.

The AR4 has confirmed the assertion that 'warming of the climate system is unequivocal' and that most of the observed twentieth century increase in globally averaged temperatures is *very likely* due to the observed increases in anthropogenic GHG concentrations. A discernible human influence on the climate system is now apparent and extends to oceanic warming, temperature extremes and wind patterns. The IPCC's scientists concluded that concentrations of the main GHGs are higher than at any time in the past 650,000 years. $CO_2$ concentrations are presently (2012) over 393 ppmv (parts per million volume) compared with pre-industrial levels of 280 ppm, while methane concentrations have already doubled from their pre-industrial values. In the absence of strict emissions controls, a doubling of atmospheric concentrations of $CO_2$ is likely by the end of the present century. As a consequence, global temperatures are projected to increase by between 1.8°C to 4°C over the same period depending on the climate sensitivity to increased levels of GHG. Some of these predictions are captured in Figure 1 overleaf.

**Figure 1: Changes in temperature, sea level and northern hemisphere snow cover**

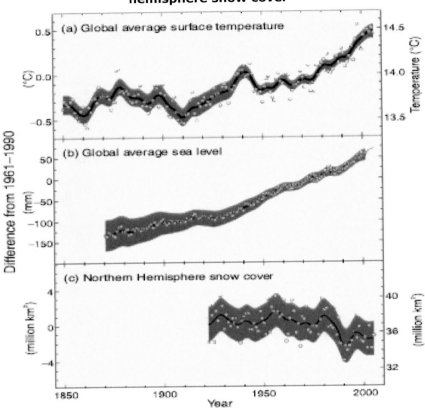

*Source:* IPCC (2007), *Fourth Assessment Report.*

The rate of warming also appears to be increasing with the linear warming trend of the last 50 years almost double that for the last 100 years. Twelve of the last thirteen recent years (1995–2007) rank as the warmest years on record since the 1850s, while seven of the eight warmest years have occurred since the turn of the century. The period 2001–2007 was warmer, by 0.21°C, than the previous decade of the 1990s (1991–2000), which had constituted the warmest decade of the warmest century of the last millennium based on a combination of instrumental and proxy records.[12] Changes in regional precipitation have also been found to be occurring over the period 1900–2005. A significant increase in precipitation amounts has been detected in eastern parts of North and South America, northern Europe and northern and central Asia, while a tendency for increased drying has been observed in the Sahel, the Mediterranean, southern Africa and parts of southern Asia. Changes in extremes have also been found to be occurring with the frequency of intense precipitation events having increased over most land areas, while more intense and prolonged droughts, particularly in the tropics and sub tropics, have been observed since the 1970s. These changes are likely being driven by a combination of factors such as changes in humidity, atmospheric circulation patterns and increased storm activity, all of which are likely to change as a consequence of global warming. Changes in precipitation and evaporation over the oceans have also resulted in the freshening of mid- and high-latitude waters with increased salinities apparent in low-latitude waters.

## Global climate change

According to the IPCC if current rates of emissions continue $CO_2$ concentrations are likely to be double those of present day concentration levels by the end of the century. If one includes the global warming potential (GWP) of all GHG, or the warming potential of a GHG converted to the effective warming of 1 tonne of $CO_2$, a doubling of effective $CO_2$ levels is likely to occur much earlier. Current atmospheric concentration levels of all GHG, calculated according to their global warming potential, equates to approximately 425 ppmv $CO_2$ equivalent. As a consequence of the radiative forcing due to the increased levels of these gases in the atmosphere, global climate models (GCMs) project that the surface averaged global temperatures are likely to increase by between 1.8°C to 4.0°C by 2080–2099, relative to 1980–1999 (Figure 2), depending on which emissions scenario is considered likely.

### SRES (Special Report on Emissions Scenarios)

The **A1** storyline and scenario describes a future world of very rapid economic growth, global population that peaks in mid-century and declines thereafter, and the rapid introduction of new and more efficient technologies. Major underlying themes are convergence among regions, capacity building, and

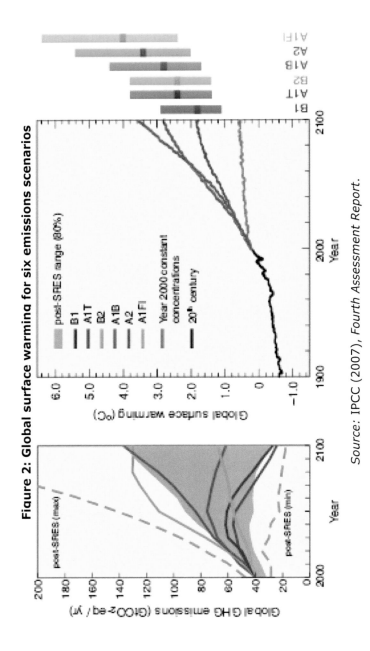

**Figure 2: Global surface warming for six emissions scenarios**

*Source: IPCC (2007), Fourth Assessment Report.*

increased cultural and social interactions, with a substantial reduction in regional differences in per capita income. The A1 scenario develops into three groups that describe alternative directions of technological change in the energy system. The three A1 groups are distinguished by their technological emphasis: fossil intensive (A1FI), non-fossil energy sources (A1T), or a balance across all sources (A1B).

The **A2** storyline and scenario describes a very heterogeneous world. The underlying theme is self-reliance and preservation of local identities. Fertility patterns across regions converge very slowly, which results in continuously increasing global population. Economic development is primarily regionally oriented and per capita economic growth and technological change are more fragmented and slower than in other storylines.

The **B1** storyline and scenario describes a convergent world with the same global population that peaks in mid-century and declines thereafter as in the A1 storyline, but with rapid changes in economic structures towards a service and information economy, with reductions in material intensity, and the introduction of clean and resource-efficient technologies. The emphasis is on global solutions to economic, social, and environmental sustainability, including improved equity, but without additional climate initiatives.

The **B2** storyline and scenario describes a world in which the emphasis is on local solutions to economic, social, and environmental sustainability. It is a world with a continuously increasing global population at a rate lower than in A2, intermediate levels of economic development, and less rapid and more diverse technological change than in the B1 and A1 storylines. While the scenario is also oriented towards environmental protection and social equity, it focuses on local and regional levels.

*Source*: IPCC (2007).

Widespread reductions in the terrestrial storage of water, coupled with the thermal expansion of the oceans, are projected to increase sea level by between 0.28 m and 0.43 m by the end of the present century relative to 1980–1999 (Figure 3).

**Figure 3: Projected global average surface warming and sea level rise at the end of the twenty-first century**

| Case | Temperature change (°C at 2090–2099 relative to 1980–1999) | (m at 2090–2099 relative to 1980–1999) | Sea level rise |
|---|---|---|---|
| | Best estimate | *Likely* range | Model-based range excluding future rapid dynamical changes in ice flow |
| Constant year 2000 concentrations | 0.6 | 0.3 – 0.9 | Not available |
| B1 scenario | 1.8 | 1.1 – 2.9 | 0.18 – 0.38 |
| A1T scenario | 2.4 | 1.4 – 3.8 | 0.20 – 0.45 |
| B2 scenario | 2.4 | 1.4 – 3.8 | 0.20 – 0.43 |
| A1B scenario | 2.8 | 1.7 – 4.4 | 0.21 – 0.48 |
| A2 scenario | 3.4 | 2.0 – 5.4 | 0.23 – 0.51 |
| A1FI scenario | 4.0 | 2.4 – 6.4 | 0.26 – 0.59 |

*Source:* IPCC (2007), *Fourth Assessment Report.*

While not contributing to sea level rise, Arctic sea ice extent is likely to decrease with summer sea ice completely disappearing within a few decades according to some model projections. While this may open up the possibility of new shipping routes, it will have a significant impact on Arctic ecosystems and is likely to affect air and ocean circulation systems.

## Dangerous climate change

The ultimate objective of Article 2 of the UN Framework Convention on Climate Change (UNFCCC) is to stabilise GHG concentrations in the atmosphere at a level that would prevent dangerous anthropogenic interference with the climate system. The Convention also outlines the following conditions in relation to the time frame and level of stabilisation as sufficient to allow ecosystems to adapt naturally to climate change, to ensure food production is not threatened and to enable economic development to proceed in a sustainable manner. 'Dangerous' in the context of Article 2 is related to both impacts of climate change and also levels of GHG concentrations that are responsible for this climate change.

The IPCC's Third Assessment Report 'reasons for concern' concept offers further insight as to what is 'dangerous'. This highlights the relationship between increases in global mean temperature and the risk of adverse impacts including those to unique and threatened systems, risk from extreme events, distribution of impacts, aggregation of impacts and risk from future large-scale discontinuities (Figure 4).

### Figure 4: Dangerous climate change

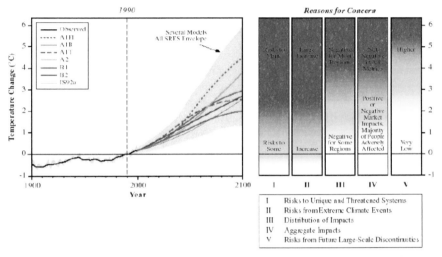

*Source:* Mastrandrea, M.D. and S.H. Schneider (2004), 'Probabilistic Integrated Assessment of "Dangerous" Climate Change', *Science*, 304: 571–5.

Determining what constitutes dangerous anthropogenic inter-ference with the climate system in relation to Article 2 of the UNFCCC involves value judgements. Science can support informed decisions on this issue, including by providing crite-ria for judging which vulnerabilities might be labelled 'key'. Key vulnerabilities may be associated with many climate-sensitive systems, including food supply, infrastructure, health, water resources, coastal systems, ecosystems, global biogeochemical cycles, ice sheets and modes of oceanic and atmospheric circu-lation. Many risks are identified with higher confidence. Some risks are projected to be larger or to occur at lower increases in temperature.

However, there is still considerable uncertainty with respect to the definition of what is termed 'dangerous', and at what level GHG concentration levels should be stabilised and the specific time frame to do it in. What is 'dangerous' climate change is open to much deliberation. Understanding what constitutes dangerous climate change is important for both scientific analysis and policy decisions.[13] It is based on value judgements that may be perceived differently based on location and assessment of vulnerabilities.[14] For some it is based on a trigger point for abrupt change in the physical climate system while for others it is based on socio-economic impacts that might apply in a climate that changes gradually.[15]

Impacts of climate change as a result of increasing global mean temperatures can be classified in two ways. Impacts as a result of gradual or smooth warming of the climate system are relatively predictable and allow systems time to adapt. Impacts as a result of abrupt climate change have a likelihood of much greater impact, but lower probability of occurring. Such abrupt changes in climate have occurred in the past and are likely to do so in the future. For example, a research report by McElwain and Sweeney highlighted major changes that occurred in Ireland about 8,000 years ago when a relatively sudden influx of fresh water from melting ice in northern Canada is considered to have temporarily reduced the strength of the North Atlantic component of the Gulf Steam. This resulted in an abrupt and widespread cooling event in and around Ireland.[16]

High impact events are by their nature difficult to predict. They are largely non-linear singular events that occur when a specific threshold is crossed. Examples include the collapse or weakening of the Gulf Stream (Thermohaline Circulation), disintegration of the West Antarctic ice sheet (WAIS), or melting of the Greenland ice sheet. These events would have significant global and regional effects with possible irreversible impacts.[17] A global mean temperature increase of 2°C or greater above pre-industrial levels could trigger these events. For example, studies on the WAIS have found that recent thinning and ice shelf loss have not been reproduced in climate models, and thus may be more sensitive to warming than suggested by current models. A number of authors believe that the threshold beyond which the ice shelves are vulnerable to collapse could be passed by 2100.[18] Oppenheimer and Alley have also found that global warming of 2–4°C could cause destabilisation of the WAIS.[19]

16

## Why a temperature target?

A limit to global mean temperature has been defined as it can be easily related to impacts and vulnerabilities. Other options included an atmospheric GHG concentration level, a combined target of change in mean global temperature with sea level rise, changes in regional climate variables and changes in extreme events. However, global mean temperature was preferred as it can be directly related to changes in GHG, impacts of concern such as sea level rise and changes in extreme events can be directly linked to global temperature rise and it is more understandable to the general public.[20]

At current GHG levels the Earth's surface is already committed to further warming of 0.4–0.7°C.[21] Based on warming since pre-industrial levels of 0.7°C, this means that we are already committed to a warming of 1.1–1.4°C, greater than half of the EU climate protection target. Climate sensitivity is the expected increase in global mean temperature following a doubling of $CO_2$ concentrations above pre-industrial levels. Current ranges of climate sensitivity are between 1.5 and 4.5°C based on current climate models. This means that the 2°C target may be reached at varying levels of $CO_2$ equivalent concentrations depending on actual climate sensitivity. At 550 ppmv $CO_2$ equivalence the risk of temperature rise greater than 2°C is very high.[22] At 650 ppmv $CO_2$ equivalent there is only a one in sixteen chance of staying within the target.[23] At current levels there is a two in three chance of staying within the 2°C target. To be confident of staying safely within the 2°C target, $CO_2$ concentrations would need to be stabilised at levels much lower than 550 ppmv, more probably at levels closer to 400 ppmv. Nations taking part in the Conference of the Parties in Durban (December 2011) reaffirmed their intention to take steps to remain within this target temperature rise of 2°C. Furthermore, delaying action to stabilise GHG concentration levels will ensure that greater action will need to be taken in the future and less confidence can be placed in remaining within the target level.

## Sea rise

Contraction of the Greenland ice sheet is projected to continue to contribute to sea level rise until well after 2100. Some scenarios suggest the virtually complete elimination of the Greenland ice sheet and a resulting contribution to sea level rise of about seven metres if global average warming were sustained in excess of 1.9–4.6°C relative to pre-industrial values. The corresponding future temperatures in Greenland are comparable to those inferred for the last interglacial period 125,000 years ago when palaeoclimatic information suggests reductions of polar land ice extent and 4–6 metres of sea level rise.

Current global model studies project that the Antarctic ice sheet will remain too cold for widespread surface melting and will gain mass due to increased snowfall. However, net loss of ice mass could occur if dynamical ice discharge dominates the ice sheet mass balance. Partial loss of ice sheets on polar land could imply metres of sea level rise, major changes in coastlines and inundation of low-lying areas, with greatest effects in river deltas and low-lying islands. Such changes are projected to occur over millennial time scales, but more rapid sea level rise on century time scales cannot be excluded.

Sea level rise as a result of warming is inevitable. Thermal expansion would continue for many centuries after GHG concentrations have stabilised, for any of the stabilisation levels assessed, causing an eventual sea level rise much larger than projected for the twenty-first century. The eventual contributions from Greenland ice sheet loss could be several metres, and larger than from thermal expansion, should warming in excess of 1.9–4.6°C above pre-industrial be sustained over many centuries. The long time scales of thermal expansion and ice sheet response to warming imply that stabilisation of GHG concentrations at or above present levels would not stabilise sea level for many centuries.

## Gaia

Gaia – the idea that the Earth's biosphere behaves as though it were a single organism – was the insight of what many believe to be the world's most original and influential living scientist, James Lovelock. He believes that our species is now putting the Earth under unprecedented stress and that climate change could lead to a world with a much impoverished ecology that is barely habitable by humans. He claims that the 'point of no return' may have already been passed.[24]

He makes the observation: 'If we fail to take our planet seriously we will be like children who take their homes for granted and never doubt that breakfast starts the day.' Lovelock's core argument is that the root cause of climate change is that there are too many people, pets and livestock – more than the Earth can carry – and no voluntary effort can act to reduce our numbers fast enough even to slow climate change. These exhalations of breath and other gaseous emissions are responsible for 23 per cent of all GHG emissions. If you add fossil fuel burnt in the food production cycle this adds up to about half of all $CO_2$ emissions; a vegetarian diet is the only solution!

His prediction, which is disturbing, is that as a consequence of humans not having the slightest understanding of the seriousness of the Earth's plight there is the possibility that global warming may all but eliminate people from the planet. Lovelock disputes the smooth curves of the latest IPCC forecasts and cites the September 2007 discovery that all but 40 per cent of the ice floating on the Arctic Ocean has melted. He reckons the summer Arctic Ocean will be almost ice-free within fifteen years; or 35 years ahead of the IPCC's estimates. This is because ice reflects some 80 per cent of the sunlight that strikes it whereas sea water reflects only 20 per cent, which adds to the Earth's heat load. Lovelock also points to the progressive decline in the population of ocean algae. Algal growth acts to cool the Earth by removing $CO_2$.[25] On the basis of recent observations, another eminent climate scientist, James Hansen, head of NASA's Goddard Institute for Space Studies (New York), has called for a far greater reduction in $CO_2$ than previously proposed.

The key issue is the trigger point that will cause a sudden rise in temperature. Compare the Earth with an iced drink, which stays cool until the last of the ice melts, and so to some extent it is with the Earth. A great deal of the heat of global heating has gone into warming the ocean and into melting ice. According to Lovelock's model not much happens initially once $CO_2$ is added but as abundance approaches 400 ppm signs of instability appear. This amplification, between 400 ppm and 500 ppm could cause a 5°C rise in temperature; remember the Earth's atmospheric greenhouse is now well above 400 ppm $CO_2$ equivalent.

Lovelock argues that sea level rise is the best available measure of the heat absorbed by the Earth because it comes from only two main causes: the melting of glaciers on land and the expansion of the ocean as it warms. In other words, sea level is a thermometer that indicates true global warming.

The melting of ice does not significantly raise sea levels but makes a huge difference to the quantity of heat received by the Earth from the sun. Sea level rise will proceed as it has been doing since 1989, nearly twice as fast as predicted. When significant sea level rise occurs it will happen relatively quickly and could account for several metres.

According to Lovelock, some parts of the world may escape the worst consequences of climate change. The northern regions of Canada, Scandinavia, Siberia, New Zealand, the UK and Ireland will be among the least affected by global warming due to their oceanic position. These regions and countries will be able to sustain agriculture and may become a lifeboat for humanity. Saharan conditions will extend into southern Europe, as they are currently experienced in Australia and Africa.[26] So the gravest dangers for much of the western world are not from climate change itself, but indirectly from starvation, competition for space and resources and related tribal wars. In his usual cheerful manner Lovelock speculates that the climate war could kill nearly all of us and leave the few survivors living a Stone Age existence.

Lovelock casts the gravest of doubts about politicians' talk about a world in 2050 fit for eight billion people living on a 2°C hotter Earth with the temperature stabilised and emissions regulated. He believes the range of forecasts is so large that it is difficult to believe that they are reliable enough to be used by governments to plan policy for ameliorating climate change. Business as usual (BAU) is not therefore an option.

The Gaia model is not without its critics.

## Critics of the science

Over the past decade there have been many claims that the evidence proving the impact of climate change was false or exaggerated and that attempts were made in the scientific literature for example, to keep reports that opposed the mainstream opinion on the science from publication.

The origin of the most recent story, broken by the *Guardian* newspaper, is based on the publication of hacked emails from the University of East Anglia that revealed how climate scientists acted to keep research papers they did not like out of academic journals. The paper suggested that climate scientists were, in effect, trying to censor their critics. The *Guardian* quoted one scientist who said 'I need a hard case for rejecting [a paper]'. The scientists involved disagreed with any suggestion of interference. But after their private emails had been published, the emails also revealed that one of the most influential data sets in climate science – the following 'hockey stick' graph of temperature over the last 1,000 years – was the subject of con-siderable controversy within the climate science community; with evidence produced that claims: 'the 20th century is neither the warmest century over the last 1,000 years, nor is the most extreme' (Figure 5).

### Figure 5: The Hockey Stick Graph

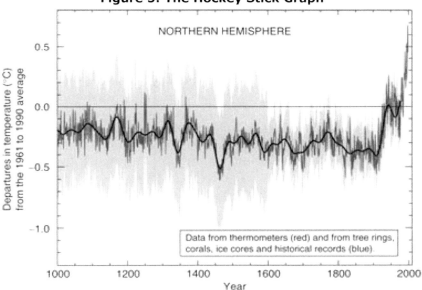

*Source:* Mann, M.E., Bradley, R.S. and Hughes, M.K. (1999), 'Northern Hemisphere Temperatures during the Past Millennium: Inferences, Uncer-tainties, and Limitations', *Geophysical Research Letters*, 26 (6): 759.

The graph was a pioneering attempt by Professor Mike Mann of Pennsylvania State University in 1998 to put together data from hundreds of studies of past temperatures using 'proxies' from analysing things like tree rings. It has become a symbol of the conflict between mainstream climate scientists and their critics. The deniers say it is a lie. Climate scientists stand by it. What few commentators have pointed out is that this disagreement dates back a full decade.

The IPCC is supposed to be the gold standard of independent peer-reviewed work on the science of climate change. Any chink in its armour has the potential to undermine its credibility and trust in the science of climate change. The way the IPPC operates is that panels of scientists, who are generally not paid for the work, anonymously review papers submitted to scientific journals, which are then relied upon by the IPCC in drawing conclusions about all aspects of climate change. The AR4, a key document that informed the current climate change negotiations, was prepared on this basis.

The nub of the issue is that the IPCC used 'grey literature' – sources outside peer-reviewed academic journals, including reports from campaign groups – as a basis for the rather important statement that the Himalayan glaciers would be gone within 35 years; a relatively short time frame. The environmental NGO, the World Wildlife Fund, was in fact the author of the inaccurate research that found its way into the IPPC report. There have been allegations that the IPCC failed to act when this alleged error came to light before the Copenhagen meeting of climate change negotiators (in December 2009). The implication was that a claim of such importance would influence the Chinese and Indian negotiators to adopt a more flexible position at the talks.

There has been a torrent of criticism about the IPCC's role. For example, Lü Xuedu, the Deputy Director General of the Chinese National Climate Centre, is reported to have said that the organisation should be reformed to 'prevent political interference, to improve research and to reduce western bias'. The Chinese accept that the glaciers in Urumqi in north-east China and indeed elsewhere are shrinking but not at the pace suggested by the IPPC.

The IPCC issued a statement that expressed regret for the mistake. IPCC chairman, Dr Rajendra Pachauri (who visited Dublin in June 2007 as a guest of the Institute of International and European Affair's Climate Change Group), admitted the mistake had seriously damaged the IPCC's credibility and boosted the efforts of climate sceptics. He said 'an isolated mistake' had been made, down to human error, and totally out of character for the Panel. He was quite annoyed at insinuations made, without any evidence being produced, about his salary and lifestyle. Thus the controversy moved from an attack on one error (albeit important) to the head of the IPCC, and by extension to the very credibility of the IPCC, which is the primary source of the scientific evidence that informs policy-makers. A review of the IPCC has been undertaken. Various investigations have also exonerated the scientists concerned.

This spat among climate scientists comes at a time when the IPCC is beginning work on its next assessment report. While attempts may have been made by a minority to sanitise scientific articles in the past, there will much closer scrutiny in the future. Is it time to peer review the peers? Furthermore, it will be essential to hear more evidence from the climate scientists based in the countries most affected by climate change; that is the emerging economies and the less developed world as to date the majority of inputs have come from academics from developed countries.

The global community needs to support the IPCC. The city of Southampton spends more on street cleaning – some £8 million – than the world does on the IPCC – £3.6 million.

## Recent research

The Berkeley Earth Surface Temperature (BEST) project is an effort to resolve criticism of the current records of the Earth's surface temperatures by putting online an open database and analysis of these temperatures and temperature trends. The BEST scientists concluded that the warming trend is real and that over the past 50 years the land surface has warmed by 0.91°C. These results mirror those obtained by the US National Oceanic and Atmospheric Administration, the Hadley Centre and NASA's GISS Surface Temperature.

The Swedish Commission on Sustainable Development's report (May 2009) on climate change science concludes that some of the effects of continued global warming are more severe than previously thought and that future climate warming may be greater than previously estimated. The research makes the point that the dramatic reduction in Arctic sea ice cover in 2007 and 2008 could be the first observed 'tipping point' in the climate system. The level of sea rise should be no more than 1 metre over the next 100 years.

While the IPCC found that the Antarctic was the only continent where no evidence of global warming has been observed, more recent observations point to a noticeable warming effect especially on the western part of the continent. Increased signs of melting of Greenland ice have also been observed. The next IPCC assessment report is not due before 2014. However, scientists have already published preliminary findings that show that $CO_2$ levels (at 393 ppmv in 2012) are at a higher level than previously estimated and are increasing more rapidly; there has been an extensive thinning on the margins of Greenland and Antarctica; and there is a more than expected rapid loss of Arctic sea ice with the Northwest Passage again free from ice last summer (2011).[27] The World Meteorological Organisation has concluded Arctic ice could disappear altogether by 2050.[28]

Climate sceptics would do well to read the IPCC report presented prior to the latest climate change negotiations.[29] Climate scientists have concluded it is 'virtually certain' the world will have more extremes spells of heat and fewer cold spells. Heat waves, which will occur more frequently, could be as high as 9°C hotter by 2100 according to the latest predictions; thirteen of the hottest years on record have occurred over the past fifteen. Incidences of heavy rainfall are also likely to increase and severity levels will be higher than are currently experienced.

Climate scientists working for the United Nations Environment Programme (UNEP) estimate that GHG emission levels of approximately 39–44 Gt of $CO_2$ equivalent ($GtCO_2e$) within a decade or so would be consistent with a 'likely' chance of limiting global warning to 2°C; picking a precise date such as 2020 is not feasible.[30] However, under a business-as-usual scenario (i.e. no additional measures are implemented) global emissions could reach 52–57 Gt in the relatively short term. The implications of a 5–9 Gt 'emissions gap' will no doubt be the focus of further scientific scrutiny in the years ahead.

## Climate change research in Ireland

Significant changes are projected to occur in Ireland's climate over this century.[31] The research outputs are aimed at strengthening data and the information base and filling gaps in knowledge about the impacts of climate change. Lead author, Professor John Sweeney, NUI Maynooth, pointed out:

We are looking at changes in extremes at both ends of the spectrum, more rain and more intense rainfall at one end and then heat waves and droughts at the other. However, considerable uncertainty still remains in several areas, particularly in relation to rainfall. A risk management type approach to adaptation will be required to take account of these uncertainties.

The projections, as follows, are in line with earlier reports provided by Professor Sweeney and his team at ICARUS at the National University of Ireland, Maynooth.[32]

## Climate impacts in Ireland

- Mean annual temperatures in Ireland have risen by 0.7°C over the past century.

- Average temperatures will rise by 1.4°C–1.8°C by 2050, and be in excess of 2°C relative to the 1961–1990 baseline by the end of the century.

- Summer and autumn are projected to warm faster than winter and spring, with the midlands and east warming more than coastal areas.

- Winter rainfall is projected to increase by 10 per cent, while reductions in summer rainfall of 12 per cent to 17 per cent are projected by 2050.

- The largest winter rainfall increases are expected to occur in the midlands.

- By 2050, reductions in summer rainfall of between 20 per cent and 28 per cent are projected for the south and east coast, increasing to between 30 per cent and 40 per cent by 2080.

- The main challenges to Irish agriculture will come from wetter winter and drier summer soils, but the impacts will not be uniform across the country.

- There will be impacts in relation to water resources, with the phenomenon of a 'ten-year flood' likely to occur every three years.

- Changes in the frequency of extreme events will accompany these climate changes. Longer heat waves and drought may occur, which will be especially important for the east and south.

The NUIM findings have established future climate change scenarios for Ireland that can now be used by policy-makers to plan adaptation measures specific to Irish circumstances.

## Overview[33]

There has been a linear increase of 0.7°C in the Irish temperature records over the 1890–2004 period.[34] Warming was found to have occurred in two periods, 1910–1949 and 1980–2004. The rate of warming in the latter period of 0.42°C/decade is nearly double that of the earlier period. While the Irish records were found to display a large degree of inter-annual variability they are largely consistent with the global data.

Mean annual temperatures were found to have increased significantly at all stations. The greatest seasonal increases have occurred in winter temperatures at most stations, while autumn temperatures display the lowest rate of increase. Increases in seasonal mean maximum and minimum temperatures were also found to be occurring. The greatest increases in mean maximum temperature was found to be occurring during the winter months, in contrast to global trends, where increasing minimum temperatures are associated with increased night time cloud cover during this season. Since 1961, annual mean maximum temperature has increased by 1.1°C.

Changes in precipitation amounts and intensity have also been found to be occurring in Ireland, consistent with European precipitation trends towards increased receipts at mid- to high-latitudes and reduction evident in low-latitudes. Annual precipitation at Malin Head has increased by 40 per cent between the 1890s and 1990s, with four of the five wettest years on record at Malin Head having occurred since 1990. Analysis also suggests that inter-annual variability is increasing with two of the lowest annual totals occurring since 2000. An increasing trend in winter precipitation at locations in the north and west of the country is in contrast to a decreasing trend in summer precipitation for locations in the south and east, over the period analysed, leading to a changing seasonal and spatial distribution of precipitation in Ireland.

While the Irish climate records display a large degree of variability on time scales from annual to multi-decadal, largely due to our Atlantic location, changes occurring in the key climate variables are consistent with those at the global scale. The identified changes in the Irish climate should give cause for concern particularly if these trends continue over coming decades.

While increased temperatures may facilitate new opportunities, particularly in the agricultural sector, the rate of increase may prove too quick to allow time for natural systems, such as ecosystems and habitats, to adjust. The character of Irish precipitation, which has traditionally been associated with long duration and low intensity events, is increasingly being characterised by more intense, short-lived precipitation events and is likely to result in increased incidence of flooding during all seasons and give rise to water quality issues. Many of the problems associated with more intense precipitation have become more apparent in recent years, as was evident during the summer months of 2007 and 2008 and the autumns of 2009 and 2011.

## Regional climate projections in Ireland

A number of methodologies have been developed that translate the large-scale output from GCMs to regional or local scale. Two of the most widely employed approaches are dynamical and statistical downscaling, both of which are employed by the C4I and ICARUS GCM centres, located in Met Éireann/UCD and NUI Maynooth, respectively, as well as in a number of other modelling centres around Ireland. Despite the different methodologies and GCMs employed by these centres, output from both modelling centres indicate projected changes in the Irish climate of a similar order of magnitude, suggesting a degree of confidence with regards to the regional scenarios produced.

The C4I temperature projections for mid-century show warming everywhere relative to the present, the warming being accentuated in summer and autumn (1.2–1.4°C warmer). The warming shows a spatial gradient, with the greatest temperature increases projected for the south and east. The projections for precipitation show increased values in autumn and winter (5–10 per cent wetter) and decreases in spring and summer (5–10 per cent drier). Unlike the temperature projections, however, the precipitation projections show no distinct spatial gradient.

Based on the multi-model ensemble model derived by Fealy and Sweeney, projections for Ireland suggest that, over the present century, this warming rate is likely to increase to between 0.2–0.3°C/decade. As a consequence, an increase of between 0.7–1°C is likely to occur in all seasons by the 2020s.[35] This increase is projected to be more or less uniform across Ireland. By the 2050s, mean seasonal Irish temperatures are projected to increase by between 1.4 and 1.8°C, with the greatest warming in the autumn months. This increase is likely to be associated with a greater warming of the interior of the island resulting in an enhanced 'continental effect'. Coastal areas are likely to be slightly cooler than inland areas in summer due to the presence of sea breezes during the summer months. This continental effect becomes further enhanced by the 2080s, with temperature increases of between 2°C and 2.7°C. Changes in precipitation over the course of the present century are likely to have a greater impact on Ireland, than changes in mean temperature, due to the potential of increased flooding during the winter months and reductions in stream flow during the summer months.

By the 2050s, winter increases are suggested to be in the order of +12 per cent, with a similar order of magnitude reductions likely during the summer months. An increasing seasonal and spatial disparity also becomes apparent by this time period, with greater winter increases likely to be experienced in the midlands and north west of the country, while the greatest decreases in summer, in the order of 20–30 per cent, are likely for regions along the south and east coasts, though considerable uncertainty persists in terms of spatial differences in seasonal rainfall projections. The seasonal contrast in precipitation receipt, between winter and summer, is likely to become further enhanced by the 2080s, with winter increases of +15 per cent projected with reductions of almost -20 per cent projected for the summer months. Extreme precipitation events are likely to increase in all seasons in the future.

While a reasonable degree of confidence exists as regards temperature projections, greater uncertainty characterises the projected changes in precipitation. Winter rainfall increases of approximately 10 per cent and summer reductions of approximately 25 per cent for some parts by the 2050s constitutes the most important aspect of future climate change for Ireland. Changes in the frequency of more extreme events will also have significant impacts. A substantial reduction in the number of frost days, lengthier rainfall events in winter, and more intense downpours in summer are projected together with an increasing summer drought problem, especially for eastern and southern parts of Ireland. Arising from these projected changes a number of key impacts can be anticipated.

## Water resources

Modelling of catchments using the projected climate scenarios described earlier is inevitably a process entailing uncertainties. These arise from uncertainties in future global emissions, the reliability of GCM outputs and the uncertainties existing in hydrological modelling itself.[36]

Robust increases in winter and spring stream flow are apparent. This typically amounts to about 12–15 per cent extra by mid-century, especially pronounced in the wetter west where significant implications for flood management are implied. For the A2 emission scenario, for example, catchments such as the Boyne, Moy and Suck show substantial increases in the magnitude of the 50-year flood. In the case of the Boyne this increase is of the order of 50 per cent by mid-century.

As might be expected, higher peak flows result in a reduction in return periods for floods of a particular magnitude. Almost all the catchments studied confirm a decrease in return periods. In the case of the River Barrow for example the once-in-a-50-year flood has fallen to an 18-year event by mid-century, and for the Blackwater to just over an 11-year event by mid century. These changes raise concerns regarding the integrity of flood defences, the capacity of urban storm drainage systems, the need for greater caution concerning planning and development of vulnerable areas as well as insurance implications for commercial and private properties. In a situation where more frequent winter flooding is likely, concerns regarding the maintenance of water quality also arise.

Reductions in summer rainfall are likely to have a significant influence in reducing storage and ultimately stream flow in most catchments. The extent of these decreases is largely dependent on the soil characteristics of individual catchments. Soils with a lower capacity to hold moisture will show the greatest sensitivity to climate change. Soil moisture deficits will begin earlier and end later in the year while reductions in groundwater recharge and lower groundwater levels during critical times of the year are likely to alter the nature of groundwater–surface water dynamics for entire rivers. By mid-to-late century, significant reductions in groundwater storage during the recharge period will increase the risk of severe drought, as the failure of winter or spring precipitation may result in prolonged drought periods where the groundwater system is unable to recover.

Water quality management is likely to be more problematical as a result of both direct and indirect impacts of climate change. Direct effects include increased water temperatures and the contamination of coastal aquifers from saline intrusion, while indirect effects relate to increasing demands placed on limited resources from human pressures, especially during times of low flow.

## Agriculture

Climate change will impact on Irish agriculture both directly and indirectly. Directly, increased $CO_2$ in the atmosphere is beneficial to most agricultural crops and acts as a form of fertiliser, stimulating growth. Indirectly, the changes in climatic parameters such as temperature and rainfall may either enhance or negate the direct $CO_2$ influence. Ultimately, these impacts will also be tempered by the extent of adaptive responses taken by farmers e.g. in storing water for irrigation, changing crop types, seed varieties and planting/harvest dates or by changing management practices such as paddock rotations, animal housing etc.

Using the projected climate scenarios to drive crop growth models reveals that changes are likely in the distribution and viability of current agricultural crops in Ireland, though most of the present crops will continue to be viable in a changing climate.[37] Spring wheat and barley productivity will continue to be maintained though water stress in the south east may be problematical. Future yields will be closely linked to precipitation. However, it is likely that reductions in fertiliser inputs will be possible without having a detrimental effect on yields in many cases, thus enabling profitability to hold up. Maize will also suffer some water stress, but will show significant yield increases and extend its distribution markedly as climate changes. Its suitability as a high energy forage crop will further boost its popularity, particularly west of the Shannon where more summer rain will be available than in the south east. Soya bean, currently a sub-marginal crop, will make modest inroads into the maize area later in the century. Potatoes are projected to have an irrigation requirement in the driest parts of the east and may become commercially unviable due to increased competition for water resources. Elsewhere, in areas such as Donegal and south Cork, irrigation may not be required, but high nitrogen applications may be required instead.[38] Harvesting is likely to become more problematical due to the onset of winter rains in October as is planting in wet soils in spring and possible increases in pest and diseases.

For livestock production the critical consideration is grass productivity. Drought losses are likely to be most marked in the east and south of the country. Should housing requirements increase as a result of wetter soils in spring (and even on occasion periods of summer housing may be required as pastures dry) more land will have to be given over to fodder production. Stocking rates may not increase much in this situation. Again the west will be less disadvantaged and livestock production will dominate more west of the Shannon with arable production concentrated in the east.

## Coastal environments

An acceleration in the current rate of global sea level rise of 3.1 mm/year is expected over the present century as warming induces expansion of the oceans and land-based glaciers continue to melt. Global sea level is projected to rise by between 0.28 and 0.43 m over the course of the present century though considerable uncertainties persist as regards the contributions that will eventually result from key areas such as Antarctica.

In addition to sea level rise, significant increases in wave heights have been observed from ships and buoys in the North Atlantic in recent decades.[39] Storminess changes in the northeast Atlantic are however most likely to be related to natural variability and a sustained spell during that the North Atlantic Oscillation (an index of westerliness) was in strongly positive mode.[40] Some regional climate models however suggest that the frequency of intense storms over the North Atlantic area in the vicinity of Ireland is projected to increase by approximately 15 per cent by mid-century.[41]

For hard rock coastlines such as predominate along much of the west coast this is not of major concern. However, for coasts composed of unconsolidated glacial materials and sand, which exist most commonly along the east coast, increased vulnerability exists. Such coasts typically exhibit marked annual retreat. In the case of some parts of the Wexford coast this may amount to up to two metres per annum. About 20 per cent of Ireland's coast is at risk of increased erosion and it is estimated that the current rate of coastal erosion and the current economic impact can be expected to treble or quadruple over the next 100 years.[42] However, material eroded from a location on the coast, if not held in near-shore or offshore deposits, may provide material for deposition elsewhere along the coast. Ultimately, occurrence and rates of erosion or deposition will depend on whether or not the coastline is in equilibrium with the amount of energy coming into the coastal zone environment and whether or not there is an adequate supply of material.

The combination of higher sea level and more intense storminess raises the probability of some coastal locations around Ireland being subjected to increased flooding (Figure 6) and erosion risks.

Coastal inundation may become a more frequent event because of the combination above. Low lying areas close to the coast will be the principal areas of concern, especially the Shannon Estuary and the rias of the south and west. Coastal wetlands and salt marsh areas are also vulnerable and some cities that have grown seaward on reclaimed land (such as Dublin) also merit risk analysis. Approximately 300 km² of land has a greater than 50 per cent chance of being flooded over the coming decades.

A practical case study illustrates the challenges facing, in this case, the International Financial Services Centre (IFSC). In its (2005) *Dublin Coastal Flood Protection Report*, Dublin City Council identified that flood defences were well below that required for future predicted sea levels and could lead to serious flooding over a wide area. The proposal envisaged the erection of a 900 mm high concrete retaining quay wall faced with granite or brick 1.8 metres from the edge of the quay wall at a length of some 1,300 metres along the south campshires from the Millennium Bridge to the Macken Street Bridge. The wall is designed to deal with a sea rise of some 3.7 metres. Some 32 hectares are at risk between the Liffey and the railway line, including major streets south of the campshires such as Townsend Street, Lombard Street and Sandwith Street Lower, Pearse Street and Macken Street. As the EIS notes:

The consequences of flooding in this area is severe with extensive damage to properties and infrastructure and with

## Figure 6: Probability of inundation associated with a sea-level rise of 0.48 metres and a storm surge of 2.6 metres

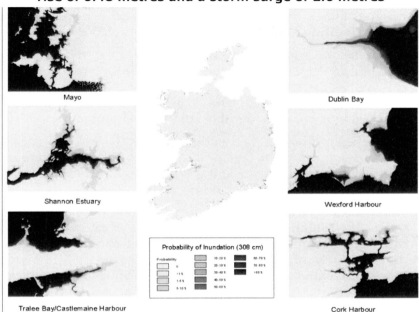

Mayo

Dublin Bay

Shannon Estuary

Wexford Harbour

Tralee Bay/Castlemaine Harbour

Cork Harbour

*Source:* Fealy, R. (2003), 'The Impacts of Climate Change on Sea Level and the Irish Coast' in Sweeney et al., *Climate Change: Scenarios and Impacts for Ireland*, EPA.

the risk of personal injury......in view of the high likelihood of flooding, the risk is now unacceptably high. Should climate change alter mean sea levels, flooding is inevitable.

While an environmental impact statement has been published (June 2011), there is no commitment to public funding to meet the capital costs of this climate change adaptation project. Those who objected to the proposed sea wall at Clontarf presumably had due regard to the risks of flooding that were identified.

### Other impacts

Among the more important impacts are:

- Impacts on Irish forests from reduced winter chilling, increased $CO_2$, changed frost and wind regimes and changed incidence of pests and disease. Pests such as the green spruce aphid, the pine weevil, the great spruce bark beetle, the European sawfly, and fungal infections such as honey fungus, fomes and Phytophthora, may pose an increasing threat to productivity.[43]

- Impacts on aquaculture and the marine environment. Salmon production in Ireland is near the southern range of the species distribution and temperature increases, together with changes in the incidence of algal blooms, pests and diseases, may have considerable commercial impacts.

- A marked reduction in heating degree days will occur in milder winters with a less pronounced winter peak demand for electricity and gas. Ongoing tightening of building insulation standards will further reinforce this trend.

- Considerable reductions in winter cold-related mortality will occur in Ireland as warming proceeds. Heat wave-related mortality in summer will not counteract this to any extent and adjustment to health service provision will be necessary to exploit this favourable situation. Other adverse health impacts may however increase in importance such as increases in the incidences of water- and food-related diseases.

## Summary

It is likely that the greatest impacts of climate change in Ireland will arise from changes in the seasonal distribution of precipitation rather than from changes in temperature. Increased winter precipitation, particularly in the midlands, north and west of the country is likely to result in an increased frequency of flood events, particularly if the current observed trends towards more intense precipitation events continue throughout the present century. Significant reductions in precipitation are likely to be experienced during the summer months. This is likely to give rise to reductions in water availability. Reductions in soil moisture availability are also likely due to the projected increases in temperatures giving rise to increased evaporation during the summer and autumn months. Ironically, a decrease in total precipitation but accompanied by an increase in convective precipitation may give rise to an increase in the number of local summer flooding events.

It is clear from the scientific findings outlined above that the impacts of climate change will be profound in many sectors.

Figure 7 summarises the potential impacts and vulnerabilities for Ireland associated with various increases in global temperatures. If global temperatures can be maintained below the 'guard rail' of 2°C above pre-industrial times, it may be possible to limit the severe impacts of global climate change. However, the potential for catastrophic or 'dangerous' impacts of climate change become ever more likely as we approach or exceed this 'guard rail'. While there are many uncertainties with regard to thresholds and targets above which dangerous climate change may occur, it is arguable that the precautionary principle approach should be the main guide in assessing at what level global mean temperature rise should be limited and stabilisation of GHG concentrations achieved. The prediction of occurrence and timing of high-impact, low-probability events is not currently possible but it is evident that warming above 2°C may make these events more likely.

**Figure 7: Summary of potential impacts for Ireland for various increases in global surface averaged temperature**

| Up to 1°C | Up to 2°C | Greater than 2°C |
|---|---|---|
| Longer growing season | Increased likelihood and magnitude of river flooding | Sea level rise due to thermal expansion of oceans, melting of the GIS, collapse of the WAIS |
| Potential for new crops, e.g. soybean | Reduced soil moisture and groundwater storage | Loss of coastal habitats due to inundation and increased erosion |
| Increased production of existing cereal and grass crops | Water shortages in summer in the east which will impact upon reservoirs and soil management | Increased incidence of coastal flooding |
| Earlier breeding and arrival of birds | Increased demand for irrigation | More intense cyclonic and extreme precipitation events |
| Heat stress will have an impact on human and animal health | Change in distribution of plants and animals, e.g. decline and possible extinction of cold Arctic species | |
| Negative impact upon water quality, e.g. reduction in quantity of water to dilute pollution | Fisheries could be affected as fish stocks are sensitive to small changes in temperature | |
| | Increased frequency of forest fires and pest infection | |

*Source*: McElwain, L. and Sweeney, J. (2007), 'Implications of the EU Climate Change Target for Ireland', EPA.

Chapter 2

# The geopolitics of climate change[44]

> After 2020, developing country emissions will overtake
> those of the developed world. In the meantime, the
> rate of growth of overall developed country emissions
> should start to fall, followed by an overall absolute
> reduction from 2020 onwards.
>
> European Commission, Communication on Limiting
> Global Climate Change to 2° Celsius, January 2007

## Introduction

While climate change is a problem that requires a worldwide
response, countries (all of whom are emitters of GHG) have different levels of responsibility, ability and incentives to tackle the
problem.

This chapter discusses the broad characteristics of the
climate change problem and what has been done to date to
reach agreement through the UN as the international body
responsible for climate change.

The issue of reducing GHG emissions goes the root of vital
national interests and seeking political consensus on such a
sensitive issue as climate change has been a major challenge to
say the least. For example, it took almost eight years from the
formal adoption of the Kyoto Protocol to secure its ratification.

Climate change negotiators are persistent, persuasive and
patient; they need to be.

Slowly, very slowly, there appears to be a movement towards the next phase of the game i.e. the replacement of the Kyoto Protocol with a successor agreement or an arrangement that will see most of the world's major emitters pledge and deliver on GHG emission-reduction targets.

## Characteristics of the climate change problem

Climate change presents a unique set of challenges for policy-makers. Highlighting certain characteristics of the problem allows for a greater understanding of why this might be the case.

Climate change is a pronounced and wide-ranging form of market failure, as described in the Stern Review.[45] The pricing of global resources does not take appropriate account of their scarcity value or of the services they provide. Actors in the global economic system do not have the information or ability to act in the long-term collective interest of the planet. As with other kinds of market failure, climate change requires governments to intervene with policies and measures that benefit society as a whole. Government intervention can correct this market failure by providing an enabling framework, through legislation, incentives and, above all, the predictability of conditions for forward planning.

No country, however, has the incentive unilaterally to implement policies to control the exploitation of this resource because the negative consequences of climate change would still occur, while the self-imposed restriction would entail additional costs for the country in question. Under these conditions, no country acting in its own self-interest would choose to control emissions. In the long run, dangerous climate change would still occur with negative impacts arising globally.

On the global level, a rational political response would be for all countries to build an international regime to regulate access to this resource in order to avoid a long-run sub-optimal outcome. Several factors, however, militate against the development of such a regime.

First, the intergenerational cost–benefit implications of unchecked emissions have to date retarded effective political responses. The negative consequences of climate change will, by and large, be felt by future generations while the cost of action is borne by the current generation. Because policy-makers tend to prioritise short-run impacts, generating the political will necessary to reduce GHG emissions is problematic.

Second, the impact of climate change is projected to be asymmetric geographically. Developed countries, which have the greatest levels of historic responsibility for the problem, will suffer less relative to developing countries from the negative impacts of climate change and have at their disposal the political and economic resources to adapt more successfully. Consequently, the negative impacts are perceived as distant, not only temporally but also geographically, and the incentive for developed countries to take action on climate change is low.

Finally, deciding the rules of an international climate change regime is extremely complex for a number of reasons. Countries' per capita emissions vary greatly. Yet emissions per capita are not a good measure of responsibility because some countries industrialised earlier than others and have been polluting far longer. Many advanced developing countries now accept that climate change is having an impact on their economies and therefore they too have to make a contribution.

## Early policy responses

Although anthropogenic climate change has been with us for the past century, until the 1980s political responses to the threat of climate change were muted and international efforts to respond to the threat were weak. This can, to some extent, be attributed to the degree of uncertainty surrounding the science of climate change and the impact of human activity on the environment.

The political debate on climate change is fundamentally underpinned by a developing consensus among the scientific community on the causes and effects of climate change. The journey to consensus on the science, and the increasing ability to communicate that consensus, was an essential precursor to the early policy responses to the threat of climate change.

In 1985, a seminal conference on climate change, organised by the World Meteorological Organisation and the UN Environmental Programme (UNEP) led to the establishment in 1988 of the Intergovernmental Panel on Climate Change (IPCC). It was given a remit to assess the magnitude and timing of weather variations, the socio-economic consequences arising and to propose realistic policy responses. Its modus operandi is to synthesise the available peer-reviewed research and to compile the results into periodic assessment reports. By virtue of their comprehensive nature these reports have come to be accepted as the consensus of scientific opinion on climate change. For example, the Fourth Assessment Report (AR4) provided a stark warning to policy-makers of the dangers of a business-as-usual approach to GHG emissions as well as an evaluation of the viability of different policies and measures that might be employed to mitigate emissions.[46] The IPCC reports have been decisive in encouraging policy-makers to take into account the long-term implications of policy, and difficult decisions can be justified by referring to this consensus of scientific opinion.

## Towards an international framework

The UNEP/WMO conference of 1985 also led to the establishment of the International Negotiating Committee (INC) with a mandate to establish an international convention on climate change. The First IPCC Assessment Report, published in 1990, added impetus to the process. As a result, the UN Framework Convention on Climate Change (UNFCCC) was opened for signature at the Earth Summit in Rio de Janeiro, Brazil in 1992.

The Convention was an attempt to overcome the barriers to communication between countries by establishing an overall framework for intergovernmental efforts to respond to climate change. It recognised that the atmosphere is a shared resource, the stability of which can be affected by human-related emissions of $CO_2$ and other GHGs. It established the overall objective of 'stabilisation of greenhouse gas concentrations in the atmosphere at a level that would prevent dangerous anthropogenic interference with the climate system'. No definition was offered for 'dangerous anthropogenic interference' and this therefore remains a contested term.

The important principle of common but differentiated responsibility was also enshrined in the Convention. This principle is based on the understanding that the largest share of historical and current global emissions of GHG has originated in developed countries and as a consequence that developed countries should take the lead in combating climate change. A clear onus was thereby placed on developed countries to take the first step towards a global solution.

Under the UNFCCC, governments committed to the following measures:

- Establishing inventories and reporting standards for GHG measurement;
- Sharing information on emissions and mitigation measures;
- Launching national strategies for addressing GHG emissions; and
- Cooperating in preparing for adaptation to the impacts of climate change.

The UNFCCC also established a Conference of Parties (COP) as the supreme body of the UNFCCC charged with overseeing its implementation. It meets annually, with extraordinary sessions to be held at other times as deemed necessary. The COP was also given the right to adopt protocols to the Convention.

The UNFCCC contained no specific commitments, but rather sought to create a designated international forum for the climate change debate that would bring the main parties together. It was hoped that specific commitments would follow. Because developed countries and those with economies in transition (referred to as Annex I Parties) effectively undertook to bear the compliance costs of developing countries (referred to as non-Annex I Parties), and because of the recognition of common but differentiated responsibilities, the UNFCCC was ratified relatively quickly and came into force in March 1994.

## Kyoto

At the first COP, held in Berlin in April 1995, a group with a mandate to negotiate a protocol specifying emissions reduction obligations for Annex 1 Parties was formed. This mandate was fulfilled at COP 3 in Kyoto, Japan, in 1997, when legally binding emission-reduction targets were agreed. The EU played a leadership role by insisting that all Annex 1 Parties set quantified emissions limitations and reduction objectives (QELROs) within a defined time period.[47] Annex I Parties, in recognition of their historical responsibility and greater economic resources, undertook to reduce their 1990 GHG emissions levels by an aggregate 5.2 per cent by 2012.

This aggregate target was differentiated among developed countries; the major emitters were apportioned targets as follows: the US -7 per cent, Russia -8 per cent, Japan -6 per cent, and the EU -8 per cent. The terms of the Kyoto Protocol allowed for groups or 'bubbles' of countries (such as the EU) to manage their efforts in unison. This in itself was a controversial proposal; the US and Canada argued that it was inequitable because it allowed for wide differentiation between EU Member States but not for other Annex 1 countries.

The non-Annex I countries, including those with substantial emissions, such as China, India and Brazil, were not required to make any stabilisation commitments under the terms of the Protocol, as had been envisaged in the UNFCCC. It was hoped that the Annex I countries, by moving first to control emissions, could convince developing countries to follow in the future, thereby breaking the vicious circle of inaction.

Many groups and commentators argued that the commitments were too distant (2008–2012) and lacked in ambition on the grounds that targets made under the commitment period, even if reached, would be more than offset by rising emissions in the developing world. In defence of the Kyoto Protocol, it was argued that it was justifiable as an attempt to establish the international architecture and instruments to tackle climate change that could be enhanced and built upon by future agreements.

The Kyoto Protocol broke new ground by defining three flexible mechanisms that had the potential to reduce the cost of meeting emission-reduction targets in developed countries. In justifying these mechanisms, it was argued that the cost of limiting emissions varies considerably from region to region, while the benefit is the same irrespective of the location of the emissions reduction. The three mechanisms are Joint Implementation (JI), the Clean Development Mechanism (CDM) and (international) emissions trading. JI allows an Annex I country to implement an emission-reducing project in another Annex I country; the emissions reductions units (ERUs) achieved count towards meeting the Kyoto target of the first party. The CDM allows for Annex 1 Parties to fund emissions reductions projects in Annex II countries to offset their own emissions; this allows Parties not included in Annex I to benefit from project activities resulting in certified emissions reductions (CERs). The third mechanism, (international) emissions trading, allows for the transfer to, or acquisition from, other Annex I Parties of assigned amount units (AAUs). However, according to the protocol, 'any such trading shall be supplemental to domestic actions for the purpose of meeting quantified emission limitation and reduction commitments under that Article'.[48]

## Ratification process

The road to ratification proved difficult. In 1997, the US Senate unanimously passed the Byrd–Hagel Resolution, which stated that the Senate would not be a signatory to any protocol that did not also include binding targets for developing countries that otherwise might harm the American economy.

The Kyoto Protocol received a major setback with the election of George W. Bush as President of the US in 2000. In March 2001, the new President announced that Kyoto would not be ratified, describing it 'as a lousy deal for the American economy'.[49] One of the main arguments used against US ratification was that the competitive position of the US would deteriorate vis-à-vis the developing countries, which had not taken on any commitments. Higher energy prices resulting from emissions trading, carbon taxes and other measures that would be needed to meet emission-reduction targets, it was argued, would make goods less competitive, damaging exports and jobs. Carbon leakage – the migration of energy-intensive economic activity from one country to another as a result of policy – would result in no net emissions reductions occurring. The US was primarily concerned with increased competition from fast-growing developing countries such as China.

Despite this major setback, delegates at COP 7 in Marrakech, Morocco in 2001 managed to breathe new life into the Kyoto Protocol by reaching an agreement on a number of outstanding issues, including rules governing the use of the flexibility mechanisms, reporting, land use, land use change and forestry (LULUCF), compliance measures and support mechanisms. The EU also played a leadership role in keeping Kyoto alive as the EU and its Member States ratified the Kyoto Protocol on 31 May 2002. With Russia's ratification in November 2004, the protocol reached the 55 per cent coverage of global emissions it required and came into force in February 2005.

## Looking beyond 2012

Global emissions continue to rise by an average of 3 per cent per annum.[50] A small number of developed countries are responsible for more than 50 per cent of global emissions. On average, their per capita emissions are more than five times higher than those of developing countries. On a BAU basis, it has been estimated that the developed countries will need to cut GHG emissions by 60 per cent to 80 per cent by 2050 to achieve the EU's target to limit average global temperature increases to no more than 2°C of pre-industrial levels. However, a contribution will also have to be made by advanced developing countries as they too are now part of this global problem. China is now the world's biggest emitter.

Developed and developing countries take markedly different approaches to climate change negotiations. Given emissions projections in the medium term, both will have to take action to control emissions if the problem is to be adequately addressed. No agreement has yet been reached on how this might be achieved in a universally acceptable manner.

The task of negotiating a successor agreement to Kyoto that would be acceptable to all Parties is well advanced. At the G8 meeting in Heiligendamm in Germany in June 2007, the G8 countries agreed to launch negotiations on climate change under the UN's umbrella.[51] Under the UNFCCC, environment ministers from around the world, supported by more than a thousand national experts, have been working on a new accord for several years.

A roadmap to begin negotiations on an accord to succeed Kyoto was agreed at the Bali COP in December 2007. It comprised the following main elements:[52]

- An agreement to develop a shared vision on a long-term global goal for emissions reductions based on the principle of common but differentiated responsibility, respective capabilities and socio-economic conditions

- Enhanced national and international action on mitigation

- Enhanced national action on adaptation technology development and the provision of financial resources and investment

- Enhanced national action on technology development and transfer to support mitigation and adaptation efforts

- Enhanced action on the provision of financial resources and investment to encourage mitigation, adaptation and technological development, and

- The setting of targets with reference to the IPCC's AR4.

- It was envisaged that a new deal could be concluded by December 2009 at the COP in Copenhagen. This would allow for outstanding issues to be resolved in time for ratification to take place the following year.

## COP 15 Copenhagen

One clear message emerged from the talks held in Bangkok – the penultimate meeting before the Copenhagen COP 15 that took from 7–18 December 2009 – everyone was lowering expectations. Climate change negotiators left Bangkok with a poorly structured 170-page document with as many blanks as texts to be agreed in square brackets.

There was a growing (but misguided) consensus that Plan B would see the global climate change negotiations extended to the first half of 2010. The Bangkok meeting was useful in that delegations' 'red line' issues were put on the table. The US tabled its proposals on inter alia the Global Adaptation Fund (under the auspices of the World Bank), the use of technology and much stricter provisions in relation to the measuring, reporting and verification (MRV) of emissions.

Among the key sticking points was whether the Kyoto Protocol should be adapted or replaced, with the US not at all keen to sign up to a Kyoto-type deal. The US made it clear that they wanted to make progress but not on the basis of an adaptation to the Kyoto Protocol.

Aside from procedural issues, many participants, apart from the EU and Japan, tabled GHG reduction offers in the ballpark of what is needed to keep global warming to around 2°C. There was some limited support for a formula whereby Parties would pledge to reduce GHG emissions by an absolute amount but that this would not become binding via an international treaty.

While it got limited attention, a salient issue was clearly the amount of money the developed countries were prepare to pay to less developed ones to help them finance adaptation measures and, if such a mechanism was agreed, what was the optimum institutional set up.

The EU held a strong view that the sum of the proposals submitted by developed countries to date for mid-term GHG emission reductions was insufficient and would not meet the cuts that science requires.

The outcome of the COP, the Copenhagen Accord, which is not legally binding, is a 'bottom-up' pledge and review process for national mitigation targets. Negotiated by 28 countries, it has been legalised within the UN by its 194 members, with the exception of Bolivia.

Concluding a legally binding successor to the Kyoto Protocol proved a step too far. On the other hand, the fact that global leaders (for the first time) signed up to an aspirational 2°C target for global temperature rise was a significant outcome as this provided a point of reference for the submission of national mitigation pledges lodged with the UNFCCC Secretariat. However, in sum, these national efforts would lead to a global warming of around 3.2°C if fully implemented; not exactly what the COP intended. Grave doubts have been cast, therefore, as to whether these pledges are worth anything more than the paper they are written on.

Other issues that were progressed include adaptation, MRV of emissions mitigation in developing countries, technology transfer, capacity building, and reduced emissions from deforestation and forest degradation (REDD+).

During COP 15, participants acknowledged the need for scaled-up, new and additional resources to support developing countries' capacity to deal with the negative effects of climate change as well as to prepare for the effective and efficient implementation of a new climate regime. The Copenhagen Accord included a number of new financial elements:

- A 'fast start finance' commitment was made by developed countries to provide new and additional resources, approaching US$ 30 billion for the period 2010–2012, with balanced allocation between adaptation and mitigation.

- A long-term finance commitment by developed countries to jointly mobilise US$ 100 billion a year by 2020 to address the needs of developing countries, and in the context of meaningful mitigation actions and transparency on implementation. Funding will come from a variety of sources, public and private, bilateral and multilateral, including alternative sources of finance.

- A high-level advisory group on climate change financing was established to study the potential sources of revenue, including alternative sources of finance, towards meeting this goal.

- A Copenhagen Green Climate Fund to be established as an operating entity of the financial mechanism of the Convention to support projects, programme, policies and other activities in developing countries related to mitigation including REDD+ (including conservation, sustainable management of forests and enhancement of forest carbon stocks), adaptation, capacity-building, technology development and transfer.

The EU lost its leadership role at Copenhagen. As a consequence, and subsequently, there had to be a rethinking of policy in advance of the Cancún (and Durban) COPs given the changed (and more negative and less constructive) US position and the almost unanimous view that a legally binding successor to the Kyoto Protocol is a political non-runner.

The main lesson learned is that the much acclaimed bottom-up approach (involving national pledges) does not work.

## COP 16 Cancún

The negotiations took place in Cancún, Mexico, from 27 November to 10 December 2010. The mood was quite different.[53] The frantic atmosphere of COP 15 was replaced by a more pragmatic, businesslike approach to negotiations, which proceeded at a 'glacier' pace.[54] Gone too were the high expectations of previous years. This was borne out in the conclusions, which left many confused. The COP managed to keep the climate change negotiations alive after Copenhagen, where trust in the process was dinted due to the lack of transparency and non-inclusive manner in which the accord was drawn up and presented as a fait accompli.

Again China was the main player and, despite its low profile, showed flexibility and was clearly facilitative.

The EU's view is that the Cancún Agreements (despite the vagueness of the final conclusion) were positive and forward looking and they 'pave the way for immediate and concrete actions on the ground, and provide a solid basis for a comprehensive legally-binding post-2012 framework'.[55]

Other commentators described the outcome as a floor and not a ceiling in the level of ambition.[56] On the other hand, the level of expectation was almost zero. The Adaptation Framework (and Adaptation Committee) has been welcomed by African nations in particular (who emit just 4 per cent of global emissions). However, Cancún failed to translate the good intentions to set up a climate fund into concrete commitments.

The reality is that Cancún did not bring any progress on actual emission-reduction targets, nor has a process been established to close the 5–9 Gt GHG emissions gap i.e. the quantum of global emissions that needs to be reduced in order to meet the 2°C target.

The consensus is that COP 16 was a qualified success in the light of the political fallout after the Copenhagen COP; it saved the process and not the planet. The UNFCCC is still in charge and the Parties are still talking.[57]

The Cancún Agreements confirmed the goal that developed countries will mobilise US$ 100 billion in climate funding for developing countries annually by 2020, in the context of meaningful mitigation actions and transparency on implementation, and established the Green Climate Fund through which much of the funding will be channelled.

Fast-start finance will support immediate action on climate change and has the potential to kick start mitigation and adaptation efforts in developing countries. Transparency about fast-start financing plays a crucial role in building confidence in the international climate change negotiations. According to Christiana Figueres, Executive Secretary of the UNFCCC, fast-start finance is 'a central key to unlocking the door to success in Cancún'.

The EU and its Member States committed to contributing a total of €7.2 billion over the period 2010–2012 as part of their fast-start effort. In 2010, the EU had already mobilised €2.3 billion. The EU and its Member States are deploying these funds around the world and the results of these efforts will increasingly become visible on the ground in the months and years to come. EU fast-start finance will, however, neither reduce nor divert the amount of funding provided to fight poverty and contribute to achieving the Millennium Development Goals. Furthermore, many of the Member States and the Commission have published detailed information of their ongoing initiatives. This information will make an important contribution to trust-building in the context of international negotiations.

The European Commission pledged a total of €150 million additional grant funding as its contribution to fast-start finance in the period 2010–2012. In 2010, the Commission mobilised €50 million, half of which is to be spent on adaptation in the least developed countries (LDCs) and small island developing states (SIDS) under the Global Climate Change Alliance (GCCA).

The other half is foreseen for capacity building related to MRV of GHG emissions; low-emission development strategies; REDD+; carbon market mechanisms; and technology cooperation involving a wide range of developing countries in Africa, Latin America and Asia. Most of this funding will be deployed through existing and already operational cooperation instruments and initiatives to ensure timely and efficient delivery. In addition to fast-start finance, the EU provides significant funds to climate financing through its regular development cooperation programmes. The European Commission's fast-start funding comes on top of preliminarily programmed support for climate-relevant actions in developing countries in the period 2010–2012 in the order of €900 million.

In summary, Cancún was seen as an interim step towards a global climate change treaty.[58]

## COP 17 Durban

The seasoned climate change negotiators were among the 12,000 participants who travelled to South Africa in December 2011 to try and settle what has become one of the most politically divisive and complex areas under discussion at multilateral level. As the host nation, South Africa saw its primary role as that of a bridge builder; 'middlepowermanship' as it was called.[59]

While Cancún may have seen the negotiations get back on track, many difficult questions were nowhere near agreement in advance of the Durban COP 17, for example the legal form of the agreement; a second commitment period; the future of the Kyoto Protocol; the design of the technology mechanism, as well as rising concerns on the economic impact of climate change given the current economic climate.

The main conclusions of the Durban COP were as follows:[60]

- The Kyoto Protocol and its flexible mechanisms will continue until 2017 or 2020 (with the EU favouring 2020).

- A new working group will develop a new climate architecture involving all countries by 2015 for implementation by 2020.

- The operationalisation of the following initiatives agreed during the Cancún COP: Green Climate Fund, the Technology Executive Committee and the Adaptation Committee.

Japan, Canada and Russia (representing some 40 per cent of global GHG emissions) have announced they will not participate in a second commitment period. Most of the countries that went along with a second commitment period had already agreed to reduce their emissions by domestic legislation. Emission reduction commitments and the distribution of such efforts were not resolved. During 2012, the Annex I countries will continue talks about their reduction commitments, the treatment of Kyoto units between the commitment periods and importantly how to treat the use of carbon credits generated by forestry projects.

A high level dialogue on CDM was launched at Durban.[61] CDM is the main source of income for the Adaptation Fund, which will finance projects in non-Annex 1 countries. CDM and JI will continue to operate until at least 2017 (and probably 2020). What happens after that depends on what is decided about the use of 'new market mechanisms' (yet to be defined) under a successor to the Kyoto Protocol. From 2013, the EU will not allow CERs that originate from the destruction of certain industrial gases such as HFC 23. In addition, under EU ETS rules, purchases will only be allowed from LDC projects. A review process about the future of CDM has been launched.[62] The review will undoubtedly address some of the problems that have been identified.[63]

## New market mechanisms

These market-based mechanisms were defined in the COP conclusions and are a part of the work programme for 2012. In practical terms, and from an EU perspective, the key aim is to build a larger more cost-effective instrument than CDM based on trading and crediting. There will be a move away from project to sector specific programmes and as a consequence it is expected that private finance will be better leveraged. Developing countries will be asked to prepare national implementation plans that will set out the sectors and GHGs to be covered, monitoring, reporting and verification protocols in line with IPCC guidelines, and a baseline emissions pathway. Each country will have the flexibility to determine if a limited cap and trade scheme should be included. Several issues have surfaced that need to be addressed, including the link to the roll-out of Nationally Appropriate Mitigation Action plans and the relationship with CDM projects. The EU wants the core set of rules to ensure environmental integrity of the national implementation of the new market-based mechanisms and comparability between the Parties' commitments. The December 2012 COP in Doha is expected to adopt decisions thus allowing this initiative to begin from early 2013.

The Durban Platform for Enhanced Actions also agreed that a roadmap for a new legal framework should be established by 2015. Specifically, a protocol, another legal instrument or an agreed outcome with legal force under the UNFCCC applicable to all Parties, will be developed. Thus China did not close the door to the possibility of limiting its emissions. The principle of 'common but differentiated responsibilities' appears to have been weakened. Even the US Climate Envoy, Todd Stern, acknowledged that 'everyone understands we are talking about a legal agreement of some sort or another'.

While the institutional details of the Green Climate Fund (to benefit developing countries' efforts) were agreed the sources of funding remains an open issue. There is an expectation that the Fund will become operational in 2014.

The COP adopted a decision regarding the accounting of emissions from LULUCF and from forest sinks of developed countries during the second commitment period. Of interest to the farming community was the inclusion of emissions from revegetation, cropland management, grazing land management and wetland drainage. It is unlikely that the REDD+ afforestation programme to help developing countries will be operational before 2014.

The COP also agreed to set up a Technology Executive Committee to provide analysis and to network the various institutions responsible for technology development and transfer.

The Durban conference succeeded in putting back on track an agreement for 2015 that was supposed to have been achieved in Copenhagen in 2009. Finalising the terms of the second commitment period and clarifying post-2012 commitments are the two most urgent issues on the table.

In the context of the second commitment period agreed, the EU was to present its QELRO by 1 May 2012. Preliminary technical work suggests that a QELRO of 80 per cent will be tabled.[64]

From Ireland's perspective the Durban COP was a qualified success not least because some 40 decisions were taken as part of a balanced package. COP 18 in Doha (December 2012) will have agriculture, one of Ireland's 'red line' issues, on the table. The EU played a far more central role on this occasion because its policy position was agreed well in advance and it secured many allies to its positions. There is a strong sense of expectation that the Commission will bring forward proposals to move beyond the current 20 per cent emission-reduction target (see the chapter on the EU's 20–20–20 package for more details) and in relation to forest carbon. Over the next four years not only will Irish and EU negotiators seek to reach a final conclusion on a replacement for the Kyoto Protocol rules but will want to ensure that the decisions taken at the recent COPs are in fact implemented. The global climate change negotiations will be a significant issue for Ireland's 2013 EU presidency.[65]

## Conclusion

For a decade investors have called on world leaders for policy certainty so that the international carbon market can develop its full potential. In addition, investors want a clear regulatory environment informed by a long-term policy framework. Post-Durban we are not quite there. In fact, and being realistic, it will be at least three to four years before an international legal agreement provides the certainty investors and policy-makers require.

There is a consensus in the international community that climate change must be addressed and that the requisite institutional architecture be put in place. A critical issue for Ireland is whether the European Commission – in the context of Europe's low-carbon strategy 2050 – will propose tougher GHG emission-reduction targets. There appears to be no particular pressure from Member States at least in the short term for the EU unilaterally to bring forward a more ambitious set of targets.

A new coalition of the willing needs to take leadership of the talks in advance of the Doha COP in December 2012 otherwise they are doomed to failure. The agenda must include measures whereby developed and developing nations can move at different speeds – ideally by way of a legally binding agreement – but with an over-arching common objective to take whatever steps are considered necessary to keep GHG emissions below 2°C.

The years ahead will be busy for the climate change policy community.

**Chapter 3**

# Perspectives on climate change[66]

Business as usual is dead – green growth is the answer to both our climate and economic problems.

Anders Fogh Rasmussen, Danish PM, The International Scientific Conference on Climate Change, Copenhagen, March 2009

## Introduction

This chapter sets out the perspectives of three quite different sets of countries. The EU in common with many developed countries has taken a leadership role primarily on the basis that they are currently implementing binding emission-reduction targets as part of their commitments under the Kyoto Protocol.

Emerging economies, China and India notably, have a significant impact on global climate change policy not least because of their push to modernise their growing economies. China, as the world's largest emitter, is at the forefront in terms of investment activity in the areas of energy efficiency and renewable energy.

The poorest and least developed countries who can least afford the impacts that climate change is already inflicting on their economies want the developed and emerging economies to do more.

This chapter sets out the position of the main players. Their views are constantly evolving so what is presented should be seen as a 'snapshot' of current trends and opinions.

## Developed countries' responsibilities[67]

All developed countries are signatories to the UNFCCC, and thus – at least in theory – subscribe to the notion of 'common but differentiated responsibility' i.e. they have primary responsibility to take first action to reduce emissions. Industrialised countries have, however, different levels of responsibility for climate change, different potentials for mitigation, different levels of economic resources to adapt to the impacts of climate change, and different levels of exposure (or perceived exposure) to competition from the developing world. It is not surprising, therefore, that approaches to negotiating a post-2012 agreement differ widely among these countries. Differences of perspectives on the role of mandatory emission-reduction targets, the role of developing countries in international agreements, and the prospective role of an international emissions trading scheme, are pronounced.

Developing countries have consistently refused to adopt emission-reduction targets, arguing that their per capita emissions are only a fraction of those in the developed world. While some would argue it is inconceivable that developing countries would agree to take on emission-reduction targets in the early post-2012 commitment period, it is possible they may agree interim intensity targets. The main issue becomes how to integrate developing countries into an international framework to reduce emissions without requiring them to commit to mandatory emissions targets in the short term.

The following table demonstrates the power of this argument. The contrast between the US and China is noteworthy.

### Table 1: Per capita emissions of GHG

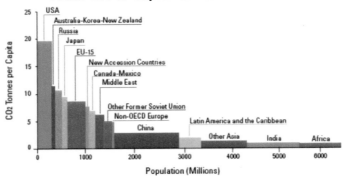

*Source:* United Nations (2010), *Environmental Indicators*.

## The EU

Europe is responsible for 10 per cent of global GHG emissions and the EU-25 has an overall 8 per cent emission-reduction target for 2008–2012 on the 1990 baseline under the Kyoto Protocol.[68] The EU is playing a global leadership role in post-2012 climate change negotiations. In March 2007, the European Council agreed a unilateral commitment to a 20 per cent emissions reduction on the 1990 level by 2020 and a 30 per cent emissions reduction if other developed countries make a comparable commitment.

Meeting on 21 October 2010, EU environment ministers adopted comprehensive conclusions about the EU's negotiating position for COP 15. These conclusions were endorsed by the EU heads of state and government when they meet on 29–30 October 2010. As a consequence, the EU, unlike the US, had set out what it believed to be the framework for a deal at Copenhagen and subsequent COPs. This mandate has largely informed the EU's policy stance since as can be seen from the EU's mandate agreed before the Durban COP.

Ireland and the other Member States have agreed as follows:

**Targets:** All OECD countries should adopt the following targets:

• Global emission reductions of at least 50 per cent by 2050 compared to 1990 levels

• Aggregate developed country emission reductions of at least 80–95 per cent during this period

• The EU will cut its emissions by 30 per cent by 2020 compared to 1990 levels provided that other developed countries commit themselves to comparable emission reductions

• Average GHG emissions per capita should be reduced to around 2 tonnes of carbon equivalent by 2050.

**Emerging economies**: Advanced developing countries should commit to appropriate mitigation action, reflecting their common but differentiated responsibilities and respective capabilities.

**MRV**: The EU will require stricter measuring, reporting and verification (MRV) of nationally appropriate mitigation actions (NAMAs).

**Business opportunities**: Incentives should be introduced to engage the private sector in technology cooperation; R&D must be substantially scaled up; global technology objectives set; and safe and sustainable technologies diffused.

**Financing**: The EU accepts that the net incremental costs of mitigation and adaptation in developing countries will be in the region of €22–€50 billion from public sources by 2020 and in the range €5–€7 billion between 2013 and 2015. The EU has signaled it will make a contribution (unspecified), subject to: 1) a fair burden being agreed between the Parties (with the exception of the LDCs) at global level in line with the distribution key to be agreed; 2) a governance arrangement; and 3) and delivery of specific mitigation actions as detailed in country-specific low-carbon development plans.

**CDMs**: The current arrangement will be reformed and sectoral crediting and trading mechanism gradually introduced.

**Land use**: The importance of LULUCF was stressed in developing countries, with a call that a performance-based mechanism that recognises verified emission reductions should be established.

**Carbon leakage**: The list of sectors and sub-sectors deemed to be exposed to a significant risk of carbon leakage in the context of the EU ETS was identified.

**Aviation/maritime**: Both these sectors will be brought within the international agreement on the basis of global agreements to be developed by ICAO and the IMO respectively. Part of the revenues raised (from the auctioning of allowances) will be directed to the benefit of climate change purposes in developing countries.

---

### EU's climate change policy aims

- Binding GHG emission reductions by all industrialised countries based on comparable effort

- Appropriate action by developing countries to limit emissions

- A framework for action on adaptation to climate change

- Action to reduce deforestation and promotion of sustainable forest management in tropical regions

- New accounting rules for emissions from land use, land-use change and forestry

- An expanded international carbon market to generate financial support for developing countries
- A comprehensive package on technology cooperation and funding to accelerate development of a low-carbon global economy.

In short, the EU had a comprehensive mandate to negotiate at the Copenhagen and subsequent COPs. The only area where the EU (and indeed G20 finance ministers) has yet to reach agreement concerns the developed world's precise commitment to help LDCs meet the challenges of climate change.

The EU's immediate policy priorities include adoption of a Directive on Energy Efficiency, increasing investment in the energy sector (in the context of the Energy 2050 Roadmap), and boosting efforts to fight climate change (in the context of the Low Carbon 2050 Roadmap).[70]

While Europe continues its debate, the US and other developed countries are also redefining their climate change and low-carbon policies.

## US climate change policy

The national debate was completely transformed with the election of President Obama as he campaigned for a cap and trade scheme and an 80 per cent GHG emission-reduction target by 2050. The (initial) acceptance by the political leadership of the serious implications of the effects of climate change galvanised the new administration into action. There was clear policy intent and a supporting stimulation package already in place. Also the President had proactively engaged on the climate change agenda at international level.[71] However, once the Senate blocked the American Clean Energy and Security Act (2009) as part of the Republican resurgence during the 2010 mid-term elections and given the Republican's bill to prohibit the Environmental Protection Agency from regulating GHGs, all has changed. The US negotiators have no mandate to conclude a legally binding successor to the Kyoto Protocol. There is limited political support for federal measures to tackle climate change. More and more people have become sceptical about the dangers and even the reality of global warming. With revenue from the proposed cap and trade scheme no longer a prospect in the short term, proposed federal spending on clean energy development (some $83 billion by 2019) has been severely reduced. As a consequence the US has lost is leadership role on climate change.

Under the Clean Air Act, the EPA is responsible for vehicle emission standards, for the mandatory reporting of GHG emissions by all operators emitting more than 25,000 tonnes and carbon capture and storage. The EPA regulates power plants and vehicle emission standards because not to do so would be a risk to public health and welfare.[72] On 23 September 2009, President Obama signed an executive order requiring some 10,000 operators, accounting for some 85 per cent of US emissions, and each federal agency to measure GHG emissions for the first time and to set GHG emission-reduction targets by 2020.[73] In the absence of legislation the EPA will endeavour to 'do its own thing' and regulate the power companies without reference to the Kerry–Boxer Bill and, as a consequence, not include many of the protections and flexibilities written into the draft legislation. The power of the EPA under the Clean Air Act was clarified by the US Supreme Court in June 2011.

The State Department takes the lead in the UNFCCC negotiations. It has, for example, convened the Major Economies Forum (MEF) outside the COP process whereby the world's largest emitters share views on emerging policy options. The MEF's third meeting in L'Aquila concluded that there should be at least a 50 per cent reduction of global emissions by 2050, and that developed countries should reduce their emissions in aggregate by 80 per cent or more by 2050 as part of that goal.[74] At the MEF, the US has made it clear it has no intention of financing the development of China, India and Brazil. The Department of Energy is also a key player and is driving a number of key programmes. Implementation of other measures is generally handled by the line departments as (apart from the EPA) as there are no significant federal agencies responsible for the coordination and delivery of climate change programmes. Both the US and the EU support the MEF initiative to establish a 'global partnership to drive transformational low-carbon climate-friendly technologies'.[75]

Many states wanted US climate change legislation to provide for the construction of additional nuclear plants (which account for 20 per cent of electricity generation) and a resumption of offshore drilling. While 'energy independence' was a clarion call justifying support for climate change legislation, this is clearly empty rhetoric given the US dependency on fossil fuels. The EU–US Energy Council has had mutual business opportunities in the clean/green technology sector on the agenda.[76]

Another important factor is that the Senate, in the light of the experience with the Kyoto Protocol, is very suspicious of the administration engaging in international negotiations affecting US interests where they do not have the final say. The Senate rejected the Kyoto Protocol on the grounds that developing countries had not made any commitments to reduce their GHG emissions. This legacy issue has not been forgotten.

The US expects to be in a position to sign up to a global compromise deal on all the main issues, short of this agreement being enshrined into a legally binding text. The maxim in Washington is: 'we will agree internationally only what we can agree domestically'. Senator John Kerry declared that the US must take a leadership role in the COP negotiations.[77] How this wish can be achieved in practice in the absence of a final US position on the outstanding issues is hard to reconcile. Also the US position has to be seen against the background that the US has a poor record in ratifying international treaties. The US starting point is that many aspects of Kyoto were a failure, in particular the absence of any GHG emission-reduction commitments from developing countries. Many of the senior State Department negotiators at the time are still in place and are therefore insistent that they cannot agree to anything that could jeopardise the adoption of US climate change legislation. These negotiators are very much bruised from the memory that the deal they did in Kyoto was resoundingly rejected by the Senate.

## ARRA

The American Recovery and Reinvestment Act 2009 (ARRA) (the Stimulus or The Recovery Act) was signed into law in February 2009. It envisaged a doubling of the production of alternative energy within three years, largely as a consequence of the availability of $80–100 billion voted under the provisions of the Act. There is now a clear policy shift to introduce measures to promote energy efficiency (with programmes targeted at federal buildings and homes).

The following are among the programmes that were earmarked for funding as part of the proposed $787 billion package (in spending and tax cuts):

- Smart Grid Investment Programme ($11 billion)
- State Energy Efficiency Programme ($6.3 billion)
- $6 billion for loans for renewable energy projects
- $2.5 billion in research grants awarded on a competitive basis
- Advanced battery Grants Programme ($2 billion) and $400 million for electric vehicle projects
- $500 million to retrain workers to avail of jobs in the green economy.

Despite many promises of shovel-ready projects, ARRA has not yet delivered the quantum of investment expected. However, funding has been approved for offshore wind, hydropower, smart meters and smart grid projects.

## ACES

By a narrow margin (219–212), the House of Representatives voted on 26 June 2009 to pass the American Clean Energy Security Act 2009 (ACES) that would (if adopted) have created a cap and trade scheme and limited GHG emissions to 17 per cent below 2005 levels by 2020 and to 83 per cent by 2050. This Waxman–Markey Bill was abandoned when it got to the Senate.

Critical complementary measures included requirements on power companies to generate more electricity from renewable energy; strict energy-efficiency targets; and, the delivery of a wide variety of programmes at federal and state level. At the time, the passing of the ACES by Congress was seen as a significant victory for President Obama as he had placed energy high on the list of his domestic policies. Senator Ed Markey described this legislation as 'dramatic' and a direct response to the acknowledgment by the political leadership of the science of climate change. He said ACES was 'as good as US politics can possibly deliver on climate change at this point in time'.

Senators Barbara Boxer (D-CA) and John Kerry (D-MA) introduced their 821-page Clean Energy Jobs and American Power Act (CEJAPA) on 30 September 2009. In many respects it mirrored the ACES/Waxman–Markey Bill. A significant complication was that many influential committees had jurisdiction over the Bill. For example, the Finance Committee had major influence over budget provisions; the Foreign Relations Committee's main role was in relation to the Copenhagen mandate; and the Environment and Public Works Committee oversaw the provisions about the EPA. In addition, widely divergent regional, sectoral and constituency issues bore down on senators' voting intentions. Major efforts were made to obtain a bipartisan approach and thereby to secure the required votes needed to ensure its passage on the basis that it is easier for the President to sign a bipartisan bill. Hence there was much public and positive comment about an op-ed column by Senators (Democrat) Kerry and (Republican) Graham published in the *New York Times* on 11 October 2009 in which they committed to work together to reach agreement on climate change. Key issues were flexibilities in emissions trading/cap and trade; coal state senators' concerns (e.g. CCS); agriculture and forest offsets; introduction of a border tax on carbon intensive goods; offshore drilling; additional incentives to promote nuclear energy and investing in developing countries CDM projects. The Kerry–Boxer Bill was centre stage of the debate in the US on climate change. The fact that it was deficit neutral was a main selling point, so too were the numbers of green jobs that the senators claimed would be created. The prospect of greater energy independence was another key selling point. The border adjustment proposal was, in the minds of many senators, a significant 'red line' issue as they believed US manufacturers needed protection from carbon-ntensive imports that would not be subject to mitigation measures such as a cap and trade scheme.[78]

The US bottom line position in Copenhagen was to be very much informed by the progress reached in the Senate in considering the Kerry–Boxer Bill. The fact that the Senate voted 35–25 against the legislation was a major blow to the administration. As the US administration failed to get their domestic legislation through there is no expectation of major climate change legislation for the foreseeable future not least because many new members of Congress are climate change sceptics. Therefore the US cannot sign a new legally binding climate change treaty regardless of its content. With this knowledge, the US has lost its leadership role at the COP. Its negotiators will be constructive but they will not determine the outcome.

## China

China – now the world's largest emitter – is very serious about climate change, not least because it already has set aggressive targets, including a 20 per cent reduction in energy intensity by 2020, strict energy-efficiency standards, renewable energy goals (15 per cent by 2020), and vehicle fuel economy stand-ards.[79] President Hu Jintao is committed to reducing the carbon intensity of the Chinese economy but by how much remains to be revealed. However, there are many who doubt that China has the capacity to deliver, measure and verify whatever commit-ments it makes.

Commentators anticipated that China would use the COPs to demonstrate its global leadership role in relation to climate change and this certainly happened at the Durban COP.

China, despite being the world's biggest emitter, and in common with many economies in transition, will not be asked to commit to absolute cuts in emissions before 2020.

China wants the developed countries to commit to spending 1 per cent of GDP (some $400 billion) on a financial adaptation package.

A significant number of the senior echelon within the public sector in China are scientists/engineers. They do not need any convincing on the science of climate change. Hence given the background of the country's negotiators, China did not surprise the international community by adopting a strong leadership role during COP 17. China appears to support the US view that binding GHG emission-reduction targets should not be made in a post-Kyoto treaty. However, if China decided to change its position and table a binding GHG emission-reduction target by 2020 – on foot of its call to Annex 1 countries to announce more aggressive GHG emission cuts – this would change the dynam-ics of the COP negotiations.[80]

According to the UN's latest statistics, China and US emis-sions of $CO_2$ are roughly equal in absolute terms, but per capita emissions of $CO_2$ are only 4.9 tonne in China compared to 19.7 tonne in the US (and 10.9 tonne in Ireland). Emissions are, however, rising exponentially; by 166 per cent between 1990 and 2007 (the latest year for which statistics are available). In 2006, China added 102 gigawatts of electricity generation – equal to the entire grids of the UK and Belgium combined, 90 per cent of it coal-fired.[81]

Given that 76 million rural Chinese are living in extreme poverty there will clearly be a strong incentive for China to prioritise growth over other policy objectives for some time to come.

Within China there is an increasing recognition, however, of the potential negative impacts of unmitigated climate change and other environmental damage. The National Climate Change Assessment Report foresees higher temperatures causing droughts, spreading deserts and reducing water supplies.[82] Most alarmingly, its projections suggest that production of rice, corn and wheat could fall by 10 per cent by 2030, and by up to 37 per cent during the second half of the century. 'If we do not take action, climate change will seriously damage China's long-term grain security', the assessment pointed out. The report concluded nevertheless that China should not risk slowing its economic growth by curbing the growth of GHG emissions.

China has responded to the challenge in a number of ways:

- It launched a drive to use energy more efficiently, a move some analysts say could have a similar impact to an emissions cap.
- It invested heavily in nuclear, wind, hydro and bio-fuel power generation, and has acted to control the use of methane gas from coal beds.
- An extensive reforestation programme is underway.
- It has become the largest generator of CDM projects.

China continually puts the onus on developed countries to lead the way on emissions reductions. It also hopes that the developed countries can provide financial and technological support to developing countries to better meet their needs for technology transfer and cooperation, particularly in climate change observation and monitoring, reduction of GHG and adaptation to climate change. This was a position reiterated to members of a European Parliament's delegation to China in November 2007. The delegation concluded that China was politically committed to tackling climate change, though not willing (then) to accept quantitative emission-reduction targets.[83]

China is keen to participate in global initiatives on energy efficiency, the development of renewables and carbon capture and storage technologies. According to Yu Jie, Climate Advisor of the Heinrich Boll Foundation in Beijing, the Chinese Government is deeply concerned about climate change, but is waiting for US action. According to Ms Yu, 'China will be a follower if the US leads'.[84] The US is very sensitive to what China wants and is paying close attention to the climate change policy of the largest purchaser of US Treasury bills.

As a lead member of the BASIC (Brazil, South Africa, India and China) negotiating group that drew up the Copenhagen Accord, China will not agree to any measures that constrain its capacity for development. Thus it prefers a voluntary approach based on the UN principle of 'common but differentiated responsibilities'. China has pledged as part of the Eleventh Five Year Plan (FYP) to reduce the emissions intensity per unit of GDP by between 40 and 45 per cent by 2020 on a 2005 baseline; to achieve a 20 per cent improvement in energy efficiency per unit of GDP by 2010 (compared to 2005); and to increase the share of non-fossil fuel to 15 per cent. The Twelfth FYP identifies the country's low-carbon strategy as a key priority and has been described as 'the greenest FYP in China's history'.[85] The energy-efficiency and renewable energy industries are listed as 'strategic emerging sectors'. Five provinces and eight cities have been selected as pilot areas for low-carbon development.

China has openly criticised the US for failing to meet its climate change commitments.[86] Instead it is taking a leadership role in clean energy investment, far outstripping both the US and EU's efforts.[87]

## India

India is the world's fourth biggest emitter and produces about 4 per cent of global $CO_2$ emissions. Emissions rose by about 133 per cent between 1990 and 2007. With poverty more prevalent in India than China, per capita emissions are only 1.4 tonnes; about a third of those in China. Growth in emissions is likely to continue into the foreseeable future as the Indian economy continues to expand. In June 2007, India's National Council on Climate Change agreed to draft national policy but made no commitment to mandatory emissions targets. Several domestic measures have been taken including a tree-planting programme, and projects to improve energy efficiency, fuel usage, industrial processes and management of solid waste. India and China agree that developed countries need to make stronger emissions reductions commitments. This position was articulated clearly by India's (then) Environment Minister, Prad-ipto Ghosh, before the G8 met at Heiligendamm (2007) when he said that, 'reducing greenhouse gas emissions is likely to have significant adverse impacts on GDP growth of developing countries, including India, and serious implications for our pov-erty-alleviation programmes'.[88]

In June 2008, Prime Minister Manmohan Singh launched India's first National Action Plan on Climate Change. The plan outlines eight national missions for sustainable development: solar energy; energy efficiency; creating a sustainable habitat; conserving water; preserving the Himalayan ecosystem; creating a green India; creating sustainable agriculture; and establishing a platform of strategic knowledge for climate change. The plan lacks a budget and plan of action at this point, but a Council on Climate Change, with stakeholders from the Government, industry, and civil society, has been formed to come up with directives and funding. Among the eight missions, the strongest focus seems to be on solar power. The plan contains no ref-erence to emission-reduction targets. In the meantime a Low Carbon Committee has been set up to identify various options that India could pursue.

Like the other BASIC countries, India wishes to retain the Kyoto Protocol's clear distinction between developed and devel-oping countries. However, while India favours a multilateral approach and wants to see the UNFCCC at centre stage, its negotiators could go along with solutions outside the UN frame-work. At the Durban COP India adopted a clear, consistent and compassionate strategy and was satisfied with the outcome as according to the Indian Environment Minister 'this decision does not imply that India has to take binding commitments to reduce its emissions in absolute terms in 2020'. Under the Copenhagen Accord, India has pledged a (voluntary) 20–25 per cent reduction in GHG emission intensity per unit of GDP by 2020 (from a 2005 base); with the emissions-intensive agricul-ture sector not included.

## Japan

Japan is responsible for 5 per cent of global emissions of $CO_2$ and is the world's fifth largest emitter. While Japan signed and ratified the Kyoto Protocol and undertook to reduce emissions by 6 per cent by 2012, its emissions had risen 14 per cent by 2007.

The 2005 Kyoto Protocol Target Achievement Plan (revised in March 2008) sets out the Government's strategy. Japan made headlines at the UN General Assembly in September 2009 when its newly elected Prime Minister, Yukio Hatoyama, pledged to reduce his country's emissions in 2020 by 25 per cent from 1990 levels.

The main domestic policy measure is a voluntary ETS established in 2005. Some 34 companies and corporate groups have been selected as participants. Under the scheme, the Government subsidises the installation cost of $CO_2$ emissions reductions equipment to help businesses that are actively attempting to reduce GHG emissions. In exchange for the subsidy the participants are required to commit to a certain reduction in their $CO_2$ emissions. The scheme also allows them to trade $CO_2$ emissions quotas to meet their reduction targets. The total government budget for the subsidy is $23.6 million.

As a large industrialised country, Japan plays a key role in international negotiations and was central in brokering a compromise between the EU and US at Kyoto in 1998. Japan is one of the world leaders in the development of climate-friendly technologies. For example, the Honda and Toyota hybrid electric vehicles are driving innovation in this new sector.

Former Japanese Prime Minister Shinzo Abe's main contribution to the COP negotiations was a proposal to reduce global emissions by 50 per cent by 2050 in an agreement that would include all the world's major emitters, including China. According to the (then) Executive Secretary of the UNFCCC, Yvo de Boer, however, this proposal is 'not a great deal more than empty talk'.[89] It is thought that Japan is increasingly concerned with the emergence of China and wishes to avoid measures that might result in the leakage of carbon-intensive industry to its competitor.

Following the country's massive earthquake, Prime Minister Naoto Kan announced in May 2011 that Japan's future energy policy will be based on the pillars of renewable energy and energy efficiency; a strategic shift from dependence on fossil fuels and nuclear. The closure of the earthquake-struck Kashiwaki-Kariwa nuclear power plant will add a further 2 per cent annual increase in emissions as the lost capacity is replaced by oil and coal-power generation.

Although a signatory to the Kyoto Protocol, Japan's efforts at cutting emissions have been of limited success. Japan is expected to struggle to meet its Kyoto targets and is likely to have to rely on the global carbon market in which it will be a key player.[90] At the Durban COP Masahiko Horie, Japan's climate envoy, told Reuters that 'the Kyoto Protocol in not the right path' and Japan will not renew its Kyoto commitments that expire in 2012. On the other hand, Japan has invested in 600 projects in 100 countries under the 'fast-start' finance initiative.

Japan sees the business opportunities that will flow in a low-carbon economy and its climate change policy reflects its wish to be centre stage of the COP negotiations. Hence its emission-reduction target is more ambitious than the EU and many other developed countries.[91]

## Australia

The Australian Government has taken a robust approach to climate change. Its Clean Energy Future Programme includes: 1) the introduction of a carbon price; 2) promoting innovation and investment in renewable energy; 3) encouraging energy efficiency; and 4) creating opportunities in the land sector to cut pollution. The CSIRO, Australia's Bureau of Meteorology, is forecasting more extreme and severe weather events as a consequence of global warming. This threat to homes, business, communities and vital industries such as agriculture is the main driver behind the Government's politically ambitious programme. So too is its relatively high per capita GHG emissions (which are high because electricity is mainly generated from coal).

Australia has committed to cut GHG emissions by at least 5 per cent compared with 2000 levels by 2020, which will require a net reduction of 23 per cent in GHG emissions by 2020. In common with most of the developed world, Australia has set a GHG emission-reduction target of 80 per cent by 2050. Some 500 of the country's largest emitters will be required to buy and surrender to the Government a permit for every tonne of emissions at an initial price of AUS \$23 (€17.22), with 50 per cent of the revenue raised to be used to cut taxes and increase payments to some 6 million households.[92] The balance will be used to support jobs and competitiveness and build a new clean energy future. The supporting legislation – a package of 18 Bills – was introduced to parliament on 19 September 2011 and approved by the Senate on 8 November thus paving the way for what is seen as one of the most important environmental and economic reforms in Australia's history.

Australia's Department of Climate Change and Energy Efficiency is actively promoting new energy-efficiency programme. The country's Clean Energy Regulator was appointed in April 2012. Consultations are underway on several initiatives including the Australian National Registry of Emissions Units and changes to its Renewable Energy Target scheme rules.

## New Zealand

As Australia breaks new ground in tackling climate change, its neighbour New Zealand has decided to slow down the scheduled implementation of its ETS by delaying full entry of the energy, transport and industrial sectors and covering agriculture emissions only if technologies are available to reduce the burden on farmers. In accepting the findings of the Doing New Zealand's Fair Share report, Climate Change Minister Nick Smith, said: 'climate change policy comes down to a difficult choice between how much and how quickly we want to reduce emissions and how much households and businesses are prepared to pay'.

Forestry was the first sector to join the domestic ETS (on 1 January 2008), with liquid fossil fuels, stationary energy and industrial processes joining in July 2010. The ETS is New Zealand's primary means of incentivising the long-term behavioural change that is required to reduce emissions. In carrying out its review as to how the ETS should evolve after 2012, an expert panel noted that the uncertainty about the future of international climate change agreements is likely to continue in the short to medium term and this heavily influenced their findings. An over-arching consideration is that a clear signal should be given by government to businesses and households to assist with their long-term investment and purchasing decisions. As a consequence, a number of important decisions have been taken including:

- The current obligation for businesses to surrender 1 NZ emissions unit (NZUs) for every 2 tonnes of emissions will be phased out over three years so that in 2015 businesses will have to surrender 1 NZU for each tonne of emissions.

- The price cap, currently NZ $25 per NZU, is to be increased by $5 per annum in 2013 and beyond i.e. €16.46.

- The point of obligation should be at the farmer level, rather than at the processor level as is currently legislated.

## Developing countries' perspectives

It is widely accepted that climate change affects everybody, but not equally. The degree to which its impacts are felt depend on people's capacity to cope with its consequences.[93] The poor live in vulnerable areas. Their livelihoods are closely linked to natural resources. They have limited savings and security; limited access to technology; and limited opportunities for employment in less vulnerable occupations.[94] The biggest impacts that are being felt **now** in the developing countries of Africa, Asia and Latin America include:

- Significant seasonal changes in weather
- Unstable and erratic rainfall rates, with significant changes in rainfall patterns prevalent
- Much higher temperatures, with summer temperate of 4–5°C higher forecast for the north west regions of Asia (by 2055)
- Extreme weather events (droughts, floods, storms), now common features of everyday life.

Changing weather is affecting:

- **Agriculture and food**: with even small changes resulting in severe impacts as regards planting for example. Lower harvest yields are likely.
- **Water scarcity**: water availability has been severely compromised with 47 per cent of the world's population living in water-stressed regions.
- **Migration**: many of the rural poor who have no alternatives are turning to migration as a path out of poverty. Environmentally displaced people is a major problem in Ethiopia for example where 6.2 million are in need of food assistance as a result of drought.

These changes are taking place in the context of forecast world population growth of 3 billion (to 9 billion) by 2050. The UNEP (2009) estimates that up to 25 per cent of world food production could be lost as a result of climate change, water scarcity, pests and land degradation.

Adaptation is about finding responses that increase the ability of people to manage or cope with the impacts of climate change. At a practical level this means supporting rural communities to find new ways to farm, or different ways to earn a living, and ensuring communities prone to extreme weather are prepared. The EU is working with LDCs and small island developing states to facilitate effective adaptation policies. In the UNFCCC, the EU has tabled ambitious proposals to foster adaptation in a post-2012 global agreement by means of a Framework for Action on Adaptation.[95] The Framework will cover water management, agriculture, biodiversity, forests, desertification, health and disaster risk reduction.

## COP outcome

While nuances exist, all the NGOs responsible for developing countries want the following outcomes:

- An equitable international agreement that will keep global temperatures to as far below 2°C as possible by ensuring rich countries, in the light of their historic responsibility, reduce GHG emissions by 85–95 per cent below 1990 levels by 2050.

- Cognisant of equity and their historic responsibility, rich countries should lead on mitigating the causes of climate change.

- Adequate, accessible and predictable finance for adaptation be provided to developing countries as a form of compensation for damages caused by developed countries and additional to Official Development Assistance.

### Views of Irish NGOs

- Trocaire: Wants rich countries to reduce GHG emissions by 40 per cent by 2020. Adequate, appropriate and additional support should be provided to poor countries to help them adapt to the impacts of climate change.

- Oxfam: Wants the EU to provide €35 billion in new public finance every year to help developing countries cope with the impacts of global warming and this money should be additional to existing aid commitments of 0.7 per cent of national income.

- Friends of the Earth: Getting Ireland to rise to the challenge of climate change and to play its part in preventing climate chaos is their big focus.

- Christian Aid: Wants rich industrialised countries to commit to an 80 per cent reduction in GHG emissions with no offsets by 2050 and to support poorer countries by way of financial support.

NGOs are playing a major part in the global effort to address the climate change and sustainability issues affecting developing countries. The views of global and Irish NGOs will need to inform the discourse on Irish Aid's climate change and sustainability priorities. Trócaire for example is an active advocate that is working on the causes and consequences of climate change both at home and overseas; for instance as regards the introduction of a Climate Change Bill (modelled on what the Joint Oireachtas Committee on Climate Change and Energy Security has recommended). Oxfam is also a keen supporter of global action on climate change. One of their recent cosponsored reports found that 86 per cent of businesses surveyed described responding to climate risks or investing in adaptation as a business opportunity.[96]

*Context*

The UNFCCC secretariat has highlighted the concerns and needs of developing countries in adapting to the effects of climate change.[97] Developing countries are the most vulnerable to climate change impacts as they have fewer resources to adapt; socially, technologically and financially.

Climate change will have far-reaching effects on the sustainable development of developing countries, including their ability to attain the UN's Millennium Development Goals (MDGs) by 2015.

Climate change has a development impact that could bring unprecedented reversals in progress in poverty reduction, nutrition, health and education.[98] As a result, many developing countries' governments have given climate change adaptation action a high, even urgent, priority. Countries have quite different individual circumstances, which typically depend on the climate it experiences as well as geographical, social, cultural, economic and political situations.

Over the next decades, it is predicted that billions of people, particularly those in developing countries, face shortages of water and food and greater risks to health and life as a result of climate change. For example, the IPCC has forecast that by 2020, up to 250 million people in Africa could be exposed to greater risk of water stress; a scenario much worse by a large margin than what is currently unfolding in the Horn of Africa. According to the World Health Organisation, over 2.4 billion people rely on traditional biomass for cooking with indoor air pollution causing 1.4 million deaths annually, and 1.6 billion do not have access to electricity.

The UNFCCC calculates that by 2030 developing countries will need between \$28 and \$67 billion in financing for climate change adaptation projects; this is equivalent to some 0.2 per cent of projected global GDP. Current funding for climate change adaptation is a fraction of this figure and access to these funds is often lengthy and complex.

There is no disagreement internationally that developing countries need assistance to support adaptation in the context of national planning for sustainable development (a term much wider than 'environmental' factors), and more capacity building. This is acknowledged by both the World Bank and the UN in the need to target poverty within an environmental framework. A large amount of work has as a consequence already been carried out on assessing impacts and required actions. These have been translated into National Adaptation Programmes for Action (NAPAs).[99] The Commission sees the need to move beyond NAPAs and towards a programmatic approach to adaptation.

## EU Action

As the world's largest donor of development assistance, the EU is strongly committed to supporting developing countries in the fight against poverty, the achievement of the UN MDGs and the promotion of sustainable development. Combating climate change forms an integral part of this agenda.[100] The EU and its partners in developing countries have many times stressed the importance of finding a durable global solution to the post-Kyoto period. The May 2009 EU–ACP Declaration is one such example.

The Global Climate Change Alliance (GCCA),[101] initiated in 2007 and now active in 18 countries, is designed to deepen dialogue in the context of the post-2012 climate regime to promote cooperation; and, to enhance support on climate change between European and the poorest developing countries. In concrete terms, Member States assist targeted countries to implement priority adaptation and mitigation measures and to integrate climate change issues into their development strategies. The strategy is based on the Bali Action Plan (2007) that emphasises the need for enhanced action on adaptation, with a particular focus on the countries of Africa most affected by drought, desertification and flooding. Current priorities include reducing emissions from deforestation and degradation (REDD), helping implement NAPAs, enhancing participation in the Clean Development Mechanisms (CDM),[102] and mainstreaming climate change policy into poverty reduction development strategies.

The Commission has adopted its Environment and Natural Resources Thematic Programme (ENRTP) for the period 2011–2012, with a budget of some €517 million.[103] The ENRTP addresses several problems that have a profound effect on social and economic development, particularly on the lives of poor people, including climate change, rapidly degrading ecosystems, poor global environmental governance and lack of access to and security of energy supply. Current priorities include: climate change and sustainable energy; environment for development; and, strengthening environment and climate governance. 'Greening' economies is a particular priority measure. The ENRTP is part of the EU's commitment agreed at the Copenhagen COP that more resources are needed to tackle climate change in developing countries. The EU and its Member States have agreed to provide €7.2 billion over three years, including €150 million in additional Commission support over the three-year period 2010–2012.

The EU is also looking at ways to help developing countries (middle income countries being the primary target) put in place National Appropriate Mitigation Actions (NAMAs) and to support the design of low emissions development strategies. However, new projects and policies, eligible to be considered as NAMAs, will only be put in place if adequate financing is provided by developed countries.[104]

In addition to climate change impacts, the EU is involved in helping with the challenge of long-term sustainable management of ecosystems and biodiversity. The growing costs of biodiversity loss and ecosystem degradation risk thwarting development efforts.[105]

Member States are also involved in the Global Energy Efficiency and Renewable Energy Fund (GEEREF); with the Forest Law Enforcement Governance and Trade (FLEGT) Action Plan; SWITCH Programme (Asia); with the EU Energy Initiative (EUEI); the Climate Change Capacity Development project (C3D) (supported by Irish Aid); and the Africa–EU Energy Partnership (which coordinates donor's contributions to climate change). The World Bank and other multilateral partners are also active in the climate change space, in particular through the Climate Investment Funds (CIF) and the Forest Carbon Partnership Facility (FCPF). UNEP is also an important implementing partner as is the UN's Food and Agriculture Organisation.

The Commission has already put in place an approach to promote integration of the environment as a critical cross-cutting theme under main areas of cooperation and is building upon this approach to strengthen consideration of climate change challenges.

## Community-based adaptation (CBA)

One striking example of what seems to be working well in developing countries is the CBA project, which is an approach to increasing the resilience of some of the world's poorest communities to the impacts of climate change. Being community-led it is based on local priorities, needs, knowledge and capabilities. While it is often difficult to distinguish the 'additional' adaptation components, good CBA integrates both scientific and local knowledge into the planning processes, especially where it is underpinned by an active poverty-impact assessment process. Adaptation projects include disaster risk reduction and farmer-led participatory research. Large-scale CBA initiatives are being developed, with the Global Environment Facility and the Small Grants Programme being good examples. The current priority is to scale up the Global Initiative on Community-Based Adaptation.[106]

## Irish aid policy and climate change

The (then) Minister for the Environment, Heritage and Local Government, John Gormley, made some important remarks, as follows, about the impact of climate change on developing countries when he addressed the Oireachtas Joint Committee on Climate Change on 11 November 2010.

- A new treaty will not happen unless it includes a comprehensive financial package to assist developing countries in key areas such as capacity building, mitigation, adaptation, technology and the protection of forests.

- Ireland's contribution to the EU adaptation and mitigation actions may be €180 million by 2020. The total requirement could be €100 billion by 2020, with international public support in the range of €22–50 billion annually, with upwards of €7 billion per year needed between 2010 and 2013.

- Industrialised countries have an obligation to contribute to adaptation to climate change in developing countries and to assisting those countries to mitigate their own GHG emissions.

- Climate change funding is a parallel priority to the MDGs.

The review of the White Paper on Irish Aid announced by Jan O'Sullivan, TD, Minister of State for Trade and Development, in June 2011, will involve an evaluation of progress made in meeting the commitments of the 2006 White Paper and will more significantly set out clear priorities for the future direction of the Irish Aid programme. The review takes place against the backdrop of the changing economic context at home and abroad and the endorsement by the OECD that Ireland's aid programme is 'cutting edge'. The review process is being led by an Expert Group on Irish Aid and involves consultations nationally and internationally over the coming months with a wide range of interests, in Ireland and in the developing world.

The Irish Aid White Paper (2006) clearly states: 'Climate change poses serious threats to development. The increased severity and frequency of droughts, floods and cyclones risk reversing our efforts to improve food security, reduce disease and safeguard livelihoods.' Ireland supports the climate change advocacy work of key international environment and development organisations, such as the International Institute for Environment and Development (IIED), and the World Resources Institute. Irish Aid provides support for the work of the Least Developed Countries Expert Group set up under the UNFCCC (which helps LDCs develop NAPAs). Understandable as the policy was set in 2006, the issue of climate change was not as salient then as it is now; with just six paragraphs devoted to what is now seen as the greatest humanitarian challenge facing mankind today.[107] Coping with current climate change variability and attempting to anticipate future climate change is no longer an option, but a policy imperative.

For Irish Aid one issue must be which elements of the myriad of funding programmes targeted at developing countries best reflects Irish development aid policy priorities and also that represents best value for money having regard to Irish Aid's emerging policy priorities.

Thus it should be expected that climate change and sustainable development will be key issues to be addressed as part of the White Paper review.

## Climate justice

Climate justice lies at the nexus of climate change and human rights and seeks to focus on what impacts climate change has on the most marginalised and disenfranchised in our global community.[108]

'The lens of climate justice brings what can be an abstract or abstruse phenomenon into sharp and immediate focus and illuminates the real human face of suffering and devastation wrought by climate change.' This stark warning from Mary Robinson is designed to modify our collective and individual focus from the mind-set of the developed world away from issues such as competitiveness and short-term impacts, to one that is more people-centred and considers the needs of communities in the LDCs and small island states.

Climate justice incorporates the principle of corrective justice – the idea that the wealthiest nations, who have disproportionately contributed to the rise in emissions through their use of fossil fuel resources have a moral obligation to address the problems of those nations that have, historically, made almost no contribution to the level of these emissions. The 50 least developed nations in the world account for less than 1 per cent of global emissions. The argument goes that this moral obligation must be used to persuade major emitters to make deep and significant absolute reductions in GHG emissions. The Mary Robinson Foundation – Climate Justice (MRFCJ) highlights the IPCC prediction that by 2020 upwards of 250 million people in Africa may be exposed to increased water stress due to climate change, in particular in the arid regions of sub-Saharan Africa and the rangeland systems in parts of eastern Africa. It is also forecast that yields from agriculture in some of the more stressed countries could fall by as much as 50 per cent within a decade.

## Funding an additional effort

One issue of significance for Irish Aid is the decision that the Government will take about what will happen to the revenue from the auctioning of carbon allowances in the post-Kyoto period i.e. from 1 January 2013. The EU's ETS Directive[109] states (Article 11.3) that:

- At least 50 per cent of the revenue from the auctioning of allowances should be used to reduce GHG emissions, including by contributing to the GEEREF and to the Adaptation Fund (as made operational by the Poznan Conference of Climate Change) to adapt to the impacts of climate change.

- These revenues should also be used to avoid deforestation and increased afforestation in developing countries that have ratified the international agreement on climate change, and to transfer technologies and facilitate adaption to the adverse effects of climate change in these countries.

- Member States will be deemed to have fulfilled these provisions if they have in place and implement financial support policies, including in particular in developing countries, which leverage financial support.

Therefore one of the top priorities for Irish Aid is to make the case that a reorientation of Irish Aid policy towards climate change adaptation should be cofinanced from part of Ireland's share of EU auctioning revenue.

## Conclusion

All developed and emerging countries now accept that a solution needs to be found to address the impacts of climate change. They may have different views about the extent to which binding targets should or should not be set or whether the UN is the most appropriate body to conduct the negotiations. But aside from these (significant) differences of opinion they all get the main message: the impacts of climate change are already evident and global action is needed.

The developing countries – typically low GHG emitters – are the most exposed and cannot afford to invest in adaptation or mitigation measures. There are multifaceted initiatives, cofinanced by bilateral and multilateral bodies, all seeking to address the LDC's climate change and sustainability challenges. In the light of the outcome of the Durban COP there appears to be a momentum to set up climate funds to assist these countries.

## Chapter 4

# The economics of climate change

To a first approximation, raising the price of carbon is a necessary and sufficient step for tackling climate change. The rest is largely fluff.

William Nordhaus, 2007

## Introduction

While there is uncertainty about the costs of inaction, it is generally agreed that failing to tackle climate change will have significant implications for the world economy, especially in developing countries. Furthermore, there are risks of unpredictability, potentially large and irreversible, damage worldwide. The Stern Review concluded the economic and welfare costs of policy inaction could equate to as much as a permanent 14.4 per cent loss in average world consumption per capita.[110]

Estimating the impacts of climate change is key to any discussion of mitigation or adaptation policies. In order to decide whether action is needed or not, and to choose the target, policy-makers need to know the cost of inaction and how the cost of mitigation policies weighs against the benefits of acting.[111]

The uncertainties about the impacts of climate change are large and include: GHG emissions projections; the accumulation of emissions in the atmosphere and how the resulting concentration will affect average global temperature; the non-market (physical) impacts of a given temperature increase; the valuation of these impacts in terms of GDP; and the risk of abrupt climate change. These uncertainties are not fully reflected in existing estimates of global impacts in monetary units. For example, the risk that a given level of GHG concentration may lead to exceptionally high increases in temperature or the risk of extreme events with large consequences are seldom integrated into estimates.

Economists see climate change as a wide-ranging market failure. Economic actors – firms and individuals – do not pay for the negative consequences or 'externalities' of their behaviour.[112] GHG emissions arising from fossil fuel consumption, certain types of farming and industrial processes, affect the well-being of others and impose a cost on them, yet emitters are not required to compensate for these costs and are therefore not considered when taking commercial decisions. Emitters consume more of the good, in this case the atmosphere's ability to absorb GHG, than would have been the case had they been forced to account for the true cost.

The market failure that climate change represents goes far beyond other market failures such as pollution or congestion due to the consequences, which involve potentially exorbitant costs and irreversible change for the planet, and also because the problem is more long term, involving complex intergenerational costs and benefits.

Opinions differ about the importance of setting a carbon price. Where low-carbon technology investments can be driven by other policy concerns such as energy security or reduced exposure to rises in oil prices, a carbon price may be important but not essential. For example, the majority of energy-efficiency investments are 'no regrets' measures that do not require a carbon price incentive. Where structural barriers to investment exist, a carbon price is necessary but not sufficient.

## BAU and other scenarios

The business-as-usual (BAU) baseline provides a basis against which the economic implications of climate change mitigation efforts can be assessed. Under this BAU scenario, world GHG emissions, which have roughly doubled since the early 1970s, would nearly double again between 2008 and 2050. As a result, atmospheric concentrations of $CO_2$ and GHGs more broadly would increase to about 650 ppmv by 2050, and continue to rise thereafter with temperatures rising by upwards of 6°C by

2100. There is a significant probability of very large losses under this BAU scenario.[113] It follows that an economically rational response would be to reduce global emissions to levels that ensure a 'low' probability of extreme, irreversible damage from climate change.

Given the magnitude of emission cuts required to reduce world emissions by at least 50 per cent by 2050, it is essential to minimise the costs involved. The OECD estimates that the economic cost (lost GDP) could be relatively modest if there was global pricing of carbon and a longer pathway was used. For instance, if global emissions continued to around 2025 world GDP would be 4 per cent lower in 2050 compared to the BAU baseline scenario.[114] On the other hand, a BAU scenario would see GHG emissions rising by about 70 per cent between now and 2050.

The cost of mitigation policies are expected to be unevenly distributed across countries with those using carbon more intensively and/or exporting fossil fuel facing the largest GDP costs. In general, despite their cheaper emission abatement opportunities, emerging economies and developing countries are more affected than developed countries because the level and growth of their production is more intensive in terms of use of fossil fuels. Likewise, the mitigation efforts in terms of percentage reductions in GHG emissions per capita relative to the BAU scenario is also generally higher in developing countries, in this case owing in part to cheaper abatement opportunities. Again, these estimated mitigation costs are assumed to take place in the context of a global broadly-based carbon market with relatively few distortions or imperfections. Without this precondition, costs would be much higher. In order for such cost-efficient mitigation action to be feasible, a number of policy instruments must be put in place or expanded so as to create the proper incentives to ensure that emissions are reduced first where it is cheapest to do so.

While views differ on the appropriate extent and urgency, there is broad consensus on the need for some action to reduce the high economic risks posed by expected levels of global warming under BAU projections. This can take the following two main forms, with action on both fronts now widely seen as needed:

- Adapting behaviour and investment to reduce the economic and social impact of climate change, for example, by constructing flood defences in response to rising sea levels.

- Mitigating the extent of climate change by reducing GHG emissions, for example through improved energy efficiency; carbon capture and storage; increased reliance on nuclear and renewable energy sources; and reduced deforestation.

While certain policies to address the climate change problem are in place, their scale and coverage need to be increased. The question of quite how much policy intervention would be desirable, however, has generated a lively debate, reflecting the differing assessments of relative costs and benefits of action and inaction, and uncertainty associated with these.

## Macroeconomic and fiscal impacts of climate change[115]

- Direct negative impact on output and productivity from long-term temperature change and more intense and/or frequent extreme weather events, particularly for agriculture, fisheries, and tourism

- Costs from sea-level rise and increased severity of flooding

- Increased risk of widespread migration and conflict, resulting from long-term climate deterioration and greater damage from extreme weather events

- Deteriorating fiscal positions arising from weakening of traditional tax bases and/or increased expenditure on mitigation and adaptation

- Costs arising from efforts to mitigate carbon emissions, including higher energy prices and increased investment

- Balance of payments problems in some countries owing to reduced exports of goods and services or increased need for food and other essential imports. Damage to ports and roads may disrupt trade flows

- Adverse 'non-market' effects associated with the loss of biodiversity and ecological systems, and the effects of climate change on human health and the quality of life.

## Macroeconomic and fiscal impacts

More positively, there is potential revenue to be gained from mitigation schemes – a double dividend – with benefits to the public finances as well as to the environment, from reduced reliance on more distortionary taxes. Depending on how policies are implemented, some low-income regions may in the future also benefit financially from the international trading of GHG emissions rights.

Determining an effective response to climate change requires calibrating the nature, extent, and distribution of these effects. Climate scientists have naturally focused on the uncertainties associated with the climate change process as such. But there are also substantial uncertainties in assessing the associated economic and wider welfare effects. Aggregating effects over time also requires a choice of the discount rate, on which there is wide disagreement in recent debate. Consequently, estimates of the economic impact of climate change vary considerably.

Several studies have addressed these challenges, using models that emphasise different effects and linkages. The Stern Review, for example, projects potential losses rising substantially over time, with the range of the central estimates from 1 to 2 per cent of GDP in 2050, 2 to 8 per cent by 2100, and 5 to 14 per cent by 2200.

## Stern Review on Climate Change

The Stern Review on the economics of climate change discusses the effect of climate change and global warming on the world economy. Although not the first economic report on global warming, it is significant as the largest and most widely known and discussed report of its kind. It is essentially an 800-page synthesis of economists' research on the economics of climate change.

Its main conclusions are that a quantum of investment equivalent to 1 per cent of global GDP per annum is required in order to avoid the worst effects of climate change, and that failure to do so could risk global GDP being up to 20 per cent lower than it otherwise might be.

## Key messages of Stern Review

- Climate change is a result of the externality associated with GHG emissions; it entails costs that are not paid for by those who create the emissions.

- It has a number of features that distinguish it from other externalities, including its long-term and persistent impacts, its global reach, and the risks in the economic impacts are pervasive.

- The impacts of climate change are broad ranging and interact with other market failures and economic dynamics, giving rise to many complex policy problems.

- The breadth, magnitude and nature of impacts imply several ethical perspectives, such as those focusing on welfare, equity and justice, freedoms and rights, are relevant.

- Questions of intra- and inter-generational equity are central.

- Standard externality and cost benefit approaches have their usefulness for analysing climate change but they can be only starting points for further work.

## Economic impacts

- The benefits of strong, early action considerably outweigh the costs.

- Unabated climate change could cost the world at least 5 per cent of GDP each year; if more dramatic predictions come to pass, the cost could be more than 20 per cent of GDP.

- The cost of reducing emissions could be limited to around 1 per cent of global GDP; people could be charged more for carbon-intensive goods.

- Shifting the world onto a low-carbon path could eventually benefit the economy by $2.5 trillion a year.

- By 2050, markets for low-carbon technologies could be worth at least $500 billion.

- What is done now can have only a limited effect on the climate policy over the next 40–50 years, but what is done in the text ten to twenty years can have a profound effect on the climate in the second half of this century.

The Stern Review's conclusions, in summary, were as follows:

- The monetary cost of climate change is now expected to be higher than many earlier studies suggested (because these studies tended not to include some of the most uncertain but potentially most damaging impacts).

- Modelling the overall impact of climate change is a formidable challenge, involving forecasting over a century or more as the effects appear with long lags and are very long-lived; most use 2–3°C warming as a starting point.

- However, BAU temperature increases may exceed these limits by the end of the century and this increases the likelihood of a wider range of impacts than previously considered (such as abrupt climate change) which, in turn, are more difficult to model.

- Using an integrated assessment model (that endeavours to estimate the global and dynamic impact of climate change), the total cost of BAU climate change to equate to an average (minimum) reduction in global per capita consumption of 5 per cent.

- A higher (20 per cent) figure would result if non-market impacts (environment and human health) were included; if the burden fell heavier on the poorer regions of the world; and, due to the existence of amplified feedbacks in the climate system.

The Stern Review has been criticised by some economists on the basis that Stern did not consider costs past 2100; he used an incorrect discount rate in his calculations; he underestimated abatement costs because he ignored the likelihood of government failure; and that stopping or significantly slowing climate change will require deep emissions cuts everywhere. Other economists have supported Stern's approach, or argued that Stern's estimates are reasonable, even if the method by which he reached them is open to criticism.[116]

The central issue in economic debate over the Stern Review concerned the discounting methodology used to evaluate flows of costs and benefits occurring in the future. Because most of the impacts of climate change are expected to occur in the long-term, the social discount rate which measures the importance of welfare of future generations relative to the present strongly shapes the global impact estimate of climate change. There is a widespread and longstanding disagreement among economists about the appropriate level of the Special Drawing Right (SDR) and this discourse came to a head over the proposed discount rate used in the Stern Review.[117] A fundamental obstacle to gaining broad support for mitigation policies, for example, is a lack of consensus on the appropriate discount rate in evaluating alternative outcomes: a low discount rate places a high weight on the benefits of current action, which largely come far in the future, relative to the more immediate costs, thus warranting a high immediate effort.

There are three main reasons commonly proposed for placing a lower value on consumption occurring in the future rather than in the present:

- Consumption levels will be higher in the future, so the marginal utility of additional consumption will be lower.

- Future consumption levels are uncertain.

- Future consumption should be discounted simply because it takes place in the future and people generally prefer the present to the future (inherent discounting).

Debate over the Stern Review initially focused on the third of these points. The difference between Stern's estimates and those of others, such as Yale economist Professor William Nordhaus (one of his main critics), can largely (though not entirely) be explained by the difference in approach regarding discounting. Stern has been accused of consistently picking the most pessimistic scenario for every choice that one can make. His critics claim he double-counts particularly the risks and he underestimates what development and adaptation will do to impacts.[118]

The Stern Review has been the subject of considerable scrutiny. For example, the UK House of Lords Economics Committee was sharply critical, both as regards the scientific basis of global warming and as regards the economics of mitigation policies.

It is instructive to review the debate that surrounded the Stern Review's methodologies as it highlights many of the main points of dissention among economists. Many believe that his review exaggerates the costs of inaction. Criticism has centred on the choice of discount rate used to ascertain the current value of future impacts.[119] Stern uses ethical arguments to justify his choice of a low discount rate of 1.4 per cent, giving greater priority to distant costs, and thereby justifying deeper cuts in current emissions and consumption. Nordhaus and others argue that a discount rate should be chosen to match their interpretation of market data (between 3 and 4 per cent) in accordance with standard economic practice. This approach would value impacts two generations hence at approximately 10 per cent of current impacts.[120] Using a high discount rate is justified with reference to projected global GDP growth: why would the current generation (relatively poor) invest in well-being of future generations (relatively rich)?

Others take the opposite view. Ecological economists argue that the choice of discount rate in fact errs on the high side.[121] They take issue with the assumption of continued global economic growth and argue that as resources continue to be depleted at current rates, a limit to the Earth's capacity to absorb the effects of such growth will be reached and further growth will become impossible. They conclude that future generations could well be poorer than current generations and that a negative discount rate should therefore be chosen. Others argue that a discount rate of zero should be chosen in the long term where there is much uncertainty; Weitzman proposes a zero discount rate for time horizons around 50 years and a negative discount rate for longer time horizons.[122]

Taking account of the critics, the key results regarding climate change and competitiveness can be summarised as follows.

The transition to a low-carbon economy will bring challenges for competitiveness but also opportunities for growth. The costs of mitigation of around 1 per cent of GDP are small relative to the costs and risks of climate change that will be avoided. However, for some countries and some sectors, the costs will be higher. There may be some impacts on the competitiveness of a small number of internationally traded products and processes. Stern warns about overstating the negative competitiveness concerns and states that such concerns can be reduced or eliminated if countries or sectors act together. Nevertheless, there will be a transition to be managed. For the economy as a whole, there will be benefits from innovation that will offset some of these costs. All economies will undergo continuous structural change; the most successful economies will be those that have the flexibility and dynamism to embrace the change.

Stern argues that policies on climate change can also help to achieve other objectives. These co-benefits can significantly reduce the overall cost to the economy of reducing GHG emissions. If climate policy is designed well it can, for example, contribute to reducing ill-health and mortality from air pollution, and to preserving forests that contain a significant proportion of the world's biodiversity. National objectives for energy security can also be pursued alongside climate change objectives. Energy efficiency and diversification of energy sources and supplies support energy security, as do clear long-term policy frameworks for investors in power generation.

While acknowledging the contribution Stern has made to the debate, and accepting the broad thrust of findings, because of the large uncertainty surrounding some of the results of the Stern Review, and the huge variance in its findings compared with most other major, international, peer-reviewed publications on the matter, some care needs to be exercised in interpreting the results of the Stern Review, and other studies should be taken into account when assessing future economic costs of climate change.

Another criticism of the Stern Review is that it does not address the key issue of so-called 'low probability, high-impact' events. Many scientists believe that reaching a tipping point and setting in motion catastrophic climate change needs to be considered as a very real possibility.[123] Even if the probability of this scenario were only found to be of a small order of magnitude, the cost implications would be so great that they would be strong enough to influence current policy. In any event, more sophisticated modelling can better take account of unexpected risks.

Ecological economists further reject the approach employed by Stern in ascribing a monetary value to every incremental rise in temperature. They point out that there remains considerable uncertainty in the relationship between $CO_2$ concentrations in the atmosphere and temperature levels. Even if temperature rises could be accurately predicted, the costs and benefits of impacts arising on ecosystems, costal zones, agriculture, built environment, human health and life are often difficult to predict and monetise, and ascribing value necessarily involves making value judgments.

The economic valuation of climate change impacts and of adaptation and mitigation strategies has shown to be particularly challenging and there has been serious questioning regarding the applicability of standard economic tools and theory.

The IPCC's Fourth Assessment Report summarised much of the cost–benefit literature on the topic and put the cost for stabilisation of emissions at 435–535ppm/$CO_2$e concentrations in the atmosphere at less than 3 per cent of global GDP by 2030; this translates into an annual loss of less than 0.12 per cent of GPD growth.[124]

There is a consensus among economists that it is necessary to take action on mitigating emissions of GHG to correct the global market failure of climate change. According to Nordhaus: '...all economic studies find an economic case for imposing immediate restraints on greenhouse emissions'.[125]

## Creating a global carbon market

There are also significant new opportunities across a wide range of industries and services. Markets for low-carbon energy products are likely to be worth at least $500 billion per year by 2050, and perhaps much more. Individual companies and countries should position themselves to take advantage of these opportunities. Climate change policy can help to root out existing inefficiencies. At the company level, implementing climate policies may draw attention to money-saving opportunities. At the economy-wide level, climate change policy may be a lever for reforming inefficient energy systems and removing distorting energy subsidies, on which governments around the world currently spend around $250 billion a year. Energy economics is also an important driver of investment decisions.

On the premise that the Parties to the global climate change negotiations will not reach a consensus on legally binding GHG reduction commitments for at least four more years, the prospects of having a fully functional global carbon market in the short term are somewhat unrealistic. For a global carbon market to work several steps would have to be taken. First, the high subsidies ($250 billion) paid (mainly in non-OECD countries) to energy production and/or consumption would have to be phased out as they amount to a negative carbon price that keeps fossil fuel consumption, and hence GHG emissions, higher than they would otherwise be. Closing the gap between domestic and international fossil fuel prices could cut GHG emissions drastically in the subsidising countries, perhaps by as much as 30 per cent. Second, the global carbon market would grow if the EU ETS was linked to other ETS, including regional initiatives, provided the CDM (a crediting mechanism that allows GHG emission reduction to be achieved outside the country/region) was scaled up, and if there was regulatory certainly about using domestic carbon offsets for non-ETS compliance purposes.

The OECD concluded that if a fully-fledged global carbon market was developed by 2020, it should be possible to keep temperature increases under 3°C at a cost of just one-tenth of a per cent of average world GDP growth between 2010 and 2050; or a 4 per cent reduction in GDP in 2050 (bearing in mind that GDP is forecast to grow by some 25 per cent in this period).[126]

## Policy instruments

The political appeal of any post-2012 international climate change policy framework will ultimately hinge, to a large extent, on its overall cost-effectiveness and the way costs and benefits are spread across emitters. In turn, cost effectiveness both across and within countries will be determined by the choice and design of the policy instruments that will be selected to reach any particular climate objective.

The ideal set of instruments would meet three broad criteria: equalise marginal abatement costs across all emission sources and sinks in order to fully exploit existing opportunities for low cost GHG emission reductions; foster an efficient level of innovation and diffusion of GHG emission reducing technologies in order to lower future marginal abatement rates; and cope effectively with risks and uncertainties.[127]

There are a variety of policy instruments available for tackling climate change. Each has pros and cons; all must be integrated into a coherent policy response framework. This means policy design should build in adequate incentives for action.

### Policy instruments

- Carbon taxes
- Emissions trading (cap and trade) schemes (ETS)
- Standards (building codes)

- Information (eco-labels)
- Technology support policies and clean technology development.

In principle, putting a price on GHG emissions through price mechanisms such as carbon taxes, ETS, or a hybrid of both can go a long way towards building up a cost-effective climate policy framework. This is the core strategy of the EU and the Australian Government for example. Taxes and ETS give emitters continuing incentives to search for cheaper abatement options through both existing and new technologies. They can also be designed and adjusted to minimise short-term uncertainty about emission abatement costs (for example through the use of banking and borrowing provisions).

However, market mechanisms are unable to deal with all the market imperfections that prevent some emitters from responding to price signals. Furthermore, in some countries it is not possible to use a carbon price for political reasons.

While multiple market failures arguably call for multiple policy instruments, poorly designed policy mixes could result in undesirable overlaps, which would undermine cost-effectiveness and, in some cases, environmental integrity. For example, if a price is put on carbon through the introduction of an ETS, applying other policy tools such as energy efficiency in addition to the carbon price can lead to overlap and might lock-in inefficient technologies. The European Commission is preoccupied about this possibility in the context of changes to the EU ETS. Thus as a general rule the OECD recommends that different instruments should address different market imperfections and/or cover different emission sources.

There is further consensus that, in line with economic theory, pricing the externality – in this case GHG emissions – is the most efficient and effective way to address the problem. There is less consensus surrounding the choice of instrument with which to price carbon and the level at which it should be implemented.

The majority of environmental economists favour the use of carbon taxes as an efficient policy instrument. Others favour the use of an ETS with auctioned permits. Both of these instruments would result in the emitter having to integrate the external costs of their actions into decision-making frameworks. Taxes based on the carbon content of fossil fuels would mean that emitters would have to pay more for the fossil fuels (thus reducing demand); it would also create a revenue stream, which could be used to compensate or cushion the effects on vulnerable sections of society. Emissions trading with auctioned permits would result in a scarcity of permits (if the cap is set low in relation to habitual emissions) that polluters would have to bid for; this would also create a revenue stream. The effects would thus be similar to those of a carbon tax.

A cost-effective international policy framework to reduce GHG emissions should minimise the overall economic cost of achieving any given climate mitigation objective. To that end, alternative policy options may be assessed along three broad criteria: 1) the extent to which they abate existing emissions at least cost, which requires the set of policy instruments to be not only cost effective per se but also provide sufficient polit-ical incentives for wide adoption and compliance: 2) whether they foster an efficient level of innovation and diffusion of GHG emission-reducing technologies; and 3) their ability to cope effectively with uncertainty surrounding both climate change and abatement costs.

The introduction of policy instruments to address climate change is most often based on the precautionary principle and the polluter pays principle.

The 'precautionary principle' is a moral and political princi-ple, which states that if an action or policy might cause severe or irreversible harm to the public, in the absence of a scientific consensus that harm would not ensue, the burden of proof falls on those who would advocate taking the action.

The 'polluter pays' principle is a principle in international environmental law where the polluting party pays for the damage done to the natural environment. It is perhaps more relevant to the funding rather than the design of policies.

The debate on policy and policy options is continued in Part 2.

## Carbon taxation

The rationale behind environmental taxes is that the additional economic cost they impose per additional unit emitted will act as an incentive to the emitters to reduce their emissions and associated environmental impacts.

A corrective tax on the global negative externality associated with GHG emissions is a straightforward instrument available to achieve cost-effective climate mitigation. In the absence of any other market failure a global tax on GHG emissions, or equally a fully harmonised domestic GHG emission tax, would be expected to induce all emitters to equalise marginal abatement costs to the level of the tax, thereby ensuring that the cheaper abatement options are fully exhausted.

At EU level decisions on taxation require unanimity; hence perhaps there is no EU carbon tax. On the other hand, decisions on the EU ETS are taken on qualified majority voting; one of the reasons emissions trading is the cornerstone of EU climate policy.

Environmental tax reform covers three main components:

- A shift in the fiscal burden away from labour costs towards environment and natural resource costs (e.g. carbon tax, $CO_2$-based vehicle road tax)
- An increase in the number of taxes and charges on environmental 'bads' and an adaptation of existing schemes to better internalise external environmental costs and cover the costs of environmental services (e.g. landfill levy, plastic bag tax)
- The removal of tax incentives that give rise to environmental degradation (e.g. tax reliefs for multi-storey car parks, holiday homes, etc.).

There are four main issues for industry regarding environmental taxation:

1. The level/burden of the tax
2. The ability to pass the burden of the tax onto consumers (the incidence versus the imposition of the tax)
3. The nature of exemptions, rebates and ability to hypothecate revenues
4. The time frame for the introduction and implementation of the tax.

Environmental tax measures that are effective in achieving their aim operate where there is an alternative at a lower cost than the tax (e.g. fuel switching to lower carbon fuels) or an alternative to reduce the exposure to the tax (e.g. improving energy efficiency). All other instruments for reducing emissions (e.g. negotiated agreements, regulation, information and awareness programmes) work better when economic instruments for reductions in emissions are also applied. The requirement, therefore, is a taxation and incentives framework that applies across sectors, and is integrated with alternatives, where possible, for decision-makers to reduce emissions.

Taxation measures used in combination with other instruments, in particular ETS, need to be implemented with a high degree of care, and it will be necessary to review the impact of taxation (vis-à-vis cost competitiveness) and possible revenue-recycling measures for those firms participating in the EU ETS. There is a large consensus that exemptions should be provided for enterprises engaged in emissions trading, and potentially also those participating in negotiated agreements, and that at least some of the revenue raised should be recycled to industry to avoid adverse cost-competitiveness impacts.

The evidence from other European countries shows that environmental taxation, of which carbon taxation is one example, can have a positive impact on economic growth and competitiveness. The COMETR research project, funded by the European Commission, found that environmental tax reform implemented in Denmark, Germany, Netherlands, Sweden and Finland had a positive effect on GDP compared to the counterfactual reference case of no environmental tax reform, with a neutral effect in the UK (Figure 8).[128] COMETR provided an ex-post assessment of experiences and competitiveness impacts of using carbon/ energy taxes as an instrument of an environmental tax reform, which shifts the tax burden and helps reduce the carbon emissions that cause global warming. COMETR analysed world market conditions for a set of energy-intensive sectors as a framework for considering competitiveness effects; analysed the effects of environmental tax reform on sector-specific energy usage and carbon emissions in Member States that introduced carbon/energy taxes on industry; presented a macroeconomic analysis of the competitiveness effects of environmental tax reform for individual Member States as well as for the EU as a whole; and finally, reviewed mitigation and compensation mechanisms for energy-intensive industries.

As the European Commission points out, competitiveness is not only an economic but also environmental concern, because

## Figure 8: The effect of environmental tax reform on GDP

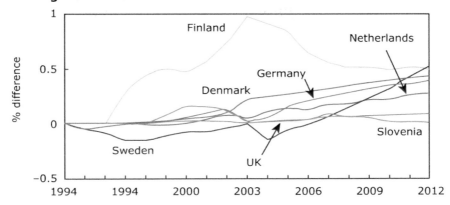

*Source:* NERI, Cambridge Econometrics, ESRI, IEEP, PSI and WIIW (2007), *Competitiveness Effects of Environmental Tax Reforms*, Final Report for the European Commission.

the migration of polluting industries to countries with lower standards would not reduce global emissions. The COMETR research project found that in the six Member States that have carried out green tax reforms, 'carbon leakage' (which describes the displacement of emissions from one geographical area to another as a result of policy, without any reduction in global emissions) has been very small and in some cases negative.

Carbon taxation would indeed have more adverse impacts on individuals and sectors that consume above average amounts of energy or who are very dependent on solid fuels. According to the COMETR project, the most vulnerable sectors to a carbon tax would be basic metal and paper and pulp industries, whereas transport is relatively unaffected. But one of the points of such a tax is to provide a long-term signal that could encourage people, where possible, to make less carbon-intensive lifestyle and investment choices. Another possible disadvantage of carbon taxation is that some sectors – particularly transport – are relatively insensitive to price rises due to low elasticities of demand, potentially leading to increased costs without a reduction in emissions. Even still, a predictable price signal could have an effect on demand in such sectors in the long term, and meanwhile carbon taxation raises revenue that can be invested in mitigation strategies or used for other purposes, such as reducing taxes on employment The generation of additional revenue is a crucial difference between a carbon tax and high energy prices caused by external factors (such as a rise in the price of crude oil). The effectiveness of a carbon tax will depend on carefully planned accompanying measures, especially for areas with high emissions and a low sensitivity to price increases.[129]

## Competitiveness issues

- Carbon taxation should be revenue-neutral to industry and revenue-recycling options should be examined ex ante so that industry is treated fairly and given the opportunity to switch to more low-carbon processes. Given that firms engaged in EU ETS are internalising the costs of carbon, and will do so at an increasing level post-2012 when auctioning of emissions permits becomes the standard allocation methodology, such enterprises should be exempted from carbon taxes or given large rebates.

- The level/burden of the tax is important, and should ideally be set at a rate that results in a proposed abatement target of emissions reductions (e.g. a 3 per cent reduction in $CO_2$), or relative to some benchmark based on international carbon tax levels. Alternatively, it could be set to the estimated market value of carbon, enabling the full (market) cost of carbon to be passed on to consumers (where applicable).

- The ability to pass the burden of the tax or charge onto consumers is important. The more monopoly power there is in a given sector, the more likely the tax or charge will be passed on to consumers. In a perfectly competitive market, some firms may be able to absorb some of the cost themselves through increased process efficiencies, etc., but others may not. In industries where profit margins are tight, some firms may be vulnerable to closure.

- Consideration needs to be given to the nature of exemptions, rebates and the ability to ringfence or hypothecate revenues. Rebates or exemptions outside the EU ETS could be tied to legally binding negotiated agreements.

- In order to facilitate proper planning it would be necessary for governments to signal, well in advance, the definitive start date for the tax and the level for the tax in year one and subsequent years. This is because it is evident that industry cannot change its energy requirements with immediate effect. Firms have made decisions about technologies based on previous tax codes and cannot easily or quickly adjust to an increased tax regime. A definitive approximate starting date for the tax should be announced at least two years in advance, and the rates to be applied in each year should be announced at that time. From the perspectives of public and industry acceptability, the tax should be implemented at a time when oil prices are relatively stable and low.

Only Denmark, Ireland, Finland and Sweden have a carbon tax in place. However, these rates are fixed at different levels and according the European Commission they do not reflect the carbon price under the EU's ETS.

The OECD has concluded that environmental taxation can spur innovation and in the short term can boost efficiency and competitiveness. It deters environmentally damaging activities by making them more costly, while incentivising the creation and diffusion of new technologies. The OECD recommends that the revenue collected should be used to reduce the fiscal burden elsewhere. The European Environment Agency points out that carbon taxation should be part of the policy mix, with renewable energy and energy-efficiency policies having the potential to contribute to emissions reduction.[130]

## EU energy taxation

On 13 April 2011 the European Commission presented its proposals to overhaul the outdated rules on the taxation of energy products in the EU.[131] The new rules, if adopted, by way of the introduction of minimum rates, aim to restructure the way energy products are taxed to remove current imbalances and take account both their $CO_2$ emissions and energy content.

These proposals are intended to replace the (2003) Energy Tax Directive, which sets out common rules on what should be taxed, when and what exemptions are allowed.[132] Minimum rates, based mainly on the volume of energy consumed, are laid down for products used in heating, electricity and motor fuels. This has created unfair competition between fuel sources and what the Commission believe to be unjustifiable tax benefits for certain types of fuel compared to others. For example, coal is the least taxed and ethanol is the most taxed. Renewables face particular discrimination because they are taxed at the same rate as the energy source they are intended to replace; for example bio-diesel is taxed the same as diesel. Above these minimum rates, Member States are free to set their own national rules as they see fit.

Existing energy taxes would be split into two components that, taken together, would determine the overall rate at which a product is taxed. One would be based on $CO_2$ emissions of the energy product and would be fixed at €20 per tonne of $CO_2$. The other would be based on energy content i.e. on the actual energy that a product generates measured in Gigajoules (GJ). The minimum rate would be fixed at €9.6/GJ for motor fuels, and €0.15/GJ for heating fuels i.e. all fuels used for transport and heating. On social grounds, the Commission will allow Member States to exempt energy consumed by some households for their heating, no matter what energy product is used. Bear in mind that households account for 10 per cent of EU GHG emissions. A gradual introduction of EU energy taxation is envisaged from 2013, with long transitional periods proposed for the full alignment of taxation until 2023, which will leave time for industry to adapt to the new taxation structure.

The Commission wants to promote energy efficiency and consumption of more environmentally friendly products and to avoid distortions of competition in the single market. Therefore the proposal favours renewable energy sources and encourages the consumption of energy sources emitting less $CO_2$. At the moment, the most polluting energy sources are, paradoxically, the least taxed. For example, bio-fuels are amongst the most heavily taxed energy sources in spite of the EU's commitment to increase the share of renewable energies in transport. The draft Directive proposes to rectify this by taxing bio-fuels on the basis of their own – generally lower – energy content. If they meet the relevant sustainability criteria they would also be exempt from the $CO_2$ element to better reflect their better performance as regards $CO_2$ emissions.[133]

The intention is that sectors outside the ETS – which account for half of the EU's GHG emissions – will be covered by a carbon price signal.

It will take at least until the end of 2012 before the draft Directive is adopted bearing in mind that a unanimous decision from the 27 Member States is required. However, in publishing its proposals (along with a detailed regulatory impact assessment), the Commission has facilitated governments wishing to redesign their tax policies to reflect the principles of sustainable development, the required switch to renewables and to address how best carbon taxation should be part of the policy mix in reducing GHG emissions.[134]

## Subsidies

A feed-in tariff ('REFIT' or 'FIT') or a feed-in premium are policy mechanisms designed to accelerate investment in renewable energy technologies. It achieves this by offering long-term contracts to renewable energy producers, typically based on the cost of generation of each technology. The goal of feed-in tariffs is to offer cost-based compensation to renewable energy producers, providing the price certainty and long-term contracts that help finance renewable energy investments.

The European Commission has concluded that 'well adapted feed-in tariff regimes are generally the most efficient and effective support scheme for promoting renewable electricity'.[135]

REFITs typically include three key provisions:

• Guaranteed grid access
• Long-term contracts for the electricity produced
• Purchase prices based on the cost of generation.

Under a REFIT, eligible renewable electricity generators (which can include homeowners, business owners, farmers, as well as private investors) are generally paid a cost-based price for the renewable electricity they produce. This enables a diversity of technologies (wind, solar, biogas, etc.) to be developed, providing investors with a reasonable return on their investments.

This principle is explained well in Germany's 2000 Renewable Energy Source Act:

The compensation rates...have been determined by means of scientific studies, subject to the provision that the rates identified should make it possible for an installation – when managed efficiently – to be operated cost-effectively, based on the use of state-of-the-art technology and depending on the renewable energy sources naturally available in a given geographical environment.

Basically this means that if you build out your installation at an appropriate cost, and run it efficiently to produce your energy at the appropriate cost, you will make an acceptable return. The tariff (or rate) may differ to enable various technologies to be profitably developed. This can include different tariffs for projects in different locations (e.g. rooftop or ground-mounted for solar PV projects), of different sizes (residential or commercial scale), and sometimes for different geographic regions. The tariffs may also be designed to ratchet downward over time to both track, and encourage, technological change. The fact that the payment levels are performance-based puts the incentive on producers to maximise the overall output and efficiency of their project.

REFITs typically offer a guaranteed purchase agreement for electricity generated from renewable energy sources. These agreements are generally framed within long-term (15–25-year) contracts. As of 2011, feed-in tariff policies have been enacted in over 50 countries.

Subsidies via REFITs are therefore a commonly applied economic instrument by governments to attempt to secure a particular outcome by incentivising favoured technologies or practices. Carefully designed subsidies can succeed in reducing GHG emissions if this is the intended outcome, but there are examples of perverse subsidies such as the requirement to produce electricity from burning peat (one of the most carbon-intensive methods of electricity generation).

In general, renewable energy projects are capital intensive, and therefore they require project finance. Essentially projects must be in a bankable state before banks and financing companies become involved in funding them. For example, Deutsche Bank's perspective is that:

...as investors, we are primarily interested in assessing policy regimes that encourage technology innovation, development, demonstration, deployment and diffusion in terms of their investability. In this light, we look for a number of clear ideas. To be effective, policies must:

- Be transparent, long-term and exhibit certainty through consistent, secure and predictable, payment mechanisms;

- Introduce incentives that decrease over time as technologies move towards market competitiveness;

- Eliminate non-economic barriers (grid access, administrative obstacles, lack of information, social acceptance);
- Provide fair and open access to distribution channels (e.g. transmission grid); and
- Be enforceable.[136]

Deutsche Bank believe that most successful feed-in tariff regimes also require utilities to connect all eligible renewable energy generation, up to a specified limit per year, guaranteeing that renewable power producers will be able to feed their energy onto the grid. They also have a track record of successfully scaling up renewable-generating capacity.

Transparency, longevity and certainty drive investment decisions. Deutsche Bank make the case that REFITs can stimulate investment on a large scale while containing and maintaining transparency, longevity and certainty.[137] A critical feature of a successful REFIT regime is periodic reviews, conducted in a transparent manner, of its progress and effectiveness. Such reviews can respond to changing market conditions in renewable technologies so that a fair return is established for investors. Ultimately appropriate REFITs create transparency and certainty, which incentivises scale-up, and reduces the cost of capital. These tariffs also should be market responsive. Problems with the implementation of feed-in tariffs have tended to arise when a government may set the price for renewables too high, which can lead to inefficiencies and budgetary issues.

## Competitiveness and carbon leakage

Climate change poses considerable challenges for the EU's competitiveness position in three main ways. First, the policies to which the EU is a signatory that aim to mitigate and adapt to the impacts of climate change are costly to the enterprise sector, and these pose some concerns to the business community struggling to keep costs competitive in an increasingly globalised economy. Second, the effects of climate change itself may have impacts on competitiveness; coastal erosion, land loss and flooding are for instance major concerns with palpable impacts for agriculture and tourism. Third, countries that are seen to be less proactive in terms of prioritising sustainable development and climate change policy may suffer from reduced levels of foreign direct investment in the environmental and eco-innovation sectors; the converse is also true, of course.

From the outset, the Kyoto Protocol and the UNFCCC has had to contend with tension between effective action to slow climate change, and maintenance of competitiveness. Competitiveness concerns were the explicit prime motivation for the withdrawal of the US and (at the time) Australia from the Kyoto process. They believed that mitigating $CO_2$, in the absence of emissions caps for rapidly developing nations such as China, India and Brazil, would be too costly and ineffective. The exclusion of the US and Australia exacerbated the competitiveness problem for nations who had signed the Kyoto Protocol and who would need to cut emissions to meet their target: namely, the original EU-15, Canada and Japan. Competitiveness concerns have since plagued Canada, the largest trading partner of the US and the bearer of relatively difficult emissions targets.[138] Such concerns have also been articulated in the climate-related policy debates in the EU and have continued to dog the elaboration and implementation of the EU's ETS.[139]

It is important in any discussion on mitigating the effects of climate change that both the negative and positive impacts on enterprise are considered. In setting out the potential costs to enterprise resulting from implementing policies to tackle climate change it is important to identify the opportunities that will arise.

Many Member States feared their sectors would lose competitiveness if they took on ambitious action to reduce emissions without similar efforts by other countries outside the EU. To protect their energy-intensive industries, in the EU-ETS to 2012, a number exempted these industries from emissions reductions, provided them with low targets, or allocated emissions permits to them for free. Exempting energy-intensive industries from carbon pricing, however, could raise the cost of achieving global emissions target significantly. For example, the OECD estimates that exempting energy-intensive industries would raise the costs of action by 50 per cent in 2050.[140]

One of the important considerations in EU climate policy is avoiding carbon leakage. This concerns the risk that in the absence of sufficient global effort, domestic action leads to a shift in market share towards less efficient installations elsewhere, thereby resulting in increased emissions globally. There are, of course, many reasons for competitive advantages and disadvantages other than the costs of carbon, but the more competitor countries sign up to comparable levels of effort to cut emissions, the less the risk of carbon leakage. The EU's climate and energy package recognised that the risk of carbon leakage had to be monitored and put in place measures to counter it.

The fact that the carbon price has been lower than originally foreseen has consequences for the carbon leakage debate. In addition, due to the fall in emissions, energy-intensive sectors already in the ETS before 2013 are likely to end up with a very considerable number of unused freely allocated allowances at the end of the second period of the ETS in 2012, which can be carried over into phase three (2013–2020). This will put them into a comparatively better position when facing international competition compared with 2008 estimations. Impacts of EU's 20 per cent target are estimated to be less than 1 per cent, with the organic chemicals, inorganic chemicals and fertiliser sectors hardest hit with production losses of respectively 0.5 per cent, 0.6 per cent and 0.7 per cent. Only the sector 'other chemicals' has an even higher impact of 2.4 per cent. Compared to the EU's unilateral implementation of the 20 per cent target, some EU energy-intensive sectors would actually be in a slightly better position, while for other sectors it would make no difference at all. Given the uncertainties related to the actual implementation of the Copenhagen Accord, the Commission considers that the measures already agreed to help energy-intensive industries – free allocation and access to international credits – remain justified at present. On the other hand, it could be argued that fears about competitiveness losses should not be exaggerated. For example, if the EU acted alone to reduce GHG emissions (by 50 per cent in 2050), almost 12 per cent of their emission reductions would be offset by emission increases in other countries. However, if all industrialised countries were to act, this leakage rate would be reduced to below 2 per cent.[141]

Addressing carbon leakage with border tax adjustments (applying taxes on imports of goods manufactured in non-carbon restricting countries) has been mooted as a potential solution, but given WTO rules this is unlikely to happen for political (never mind economic) reasons.[142]

There are cases where carbon leakage can have effects other than loss of competitiveness. For some Member States at the periphery of the EU with easy interconnection to countries outside the EU, there could be an impact on energy security.

For example, this is the case for the Baltic states, given the unique situation of the Baltic electricity markets. This is one of the reasons why the ETS already provides for an optional and partial exemption from full auctioning for these countries. However, the main issue for carbon leakage is the competitive difference between the EU and third countries. There are, therefore, broadly three ways in which carbon leakage, if it can be demonstrated, could be tackled: by giving further support to energy-intensive industries through continued free allowances; by adding to the costs of imports to compensate for the advantage of avoiding low-carbon policies (i.e. border taxes); or by taking measures to bring the rest of the world closer to EU levels of effort.

The most obvious way to provide further help to level the playing field by action inside the EU is to maintain the free allocation of allowances. As set out in the current legislation, there would also be an option of including imports into the ETS. Specific proposals have been formulated along these lines according to which international aviation activities has been included in the ETS. That would imply that allowances would have to be bought on the market to cover for the emissions of certain imported goods. This raises broader issues about the EU's trade policy and its overall interest in an open trade system: a number of emerging economies have already signalled their concerns related to this issue and any system would have to recognise that developed and developing country mitigation efforts will not run at the same pace. Also the impact of increased costs of imported inputs for EU manufacturers needs to be considered. Such a measure could also potentially be circumvented by EU imports being delivered by the 'cleanest' third country producers, while keeping 'dirtier' production for their own domestic use.

The inclusion of imports per se in the ETS would need to be very carefully designed to ensure that it is fully compatible with WTO requirements. First, it could be hard to implement a system that sought to define in detail the carbon content of each individual category of goods, but such precision might be required: this suggests that the system could at best only be envisaged for a limited number of standardised commodities, such as steel or cement. Second, for each category of goods an average EU carbon content would have to be defined. This could become an administrative burden, and require agreement on what constitutes such an average; this is likely to be a difficult and protracted process. Third, it would seem challenging to verify the performance of individual installations in third countries without a highly sophisticated monitoring and reporting system in place at installation level.

Ultimately, there are three key variables that together serve as a useful screen for assessing competitiveness impacts in any given sector:

- Energy intensity
- Ability to pass on increased costs to consumer
- Opportunities for abatement.

**Energy intensity**: The more energy a sector or firm uses in its production process, the more it will be vulnerable to price increases through either carbon taxes or through auctioned permits in the EU ETS. Under any ETS implementation scenario, energy prices are likely to increase as permits have to be bought (rather than given for free). In the aluminium, cement and the co-op (food) sectors, for instance, where energy can comprise more than 30 per cent of the cost of production, the potential exposure is high.

**Ability to pass on costs to consumers**: This ability depends on the availability of substitutes, either other goods that satisfy the same needs, or production from foreign firms in the same sector. Transport costs are an important factor here. If these are high, costs are likely to increase as ETS is rolled out further to include aviation and perhaps shipping. The global nature of the product's market is also an important factor in assessing the competitiveness impacts of ETS. If the product is 'perfectly' global, then firms located in ETS-participating countries will face higher production costs. At the firm level, the degree of domestic competition is important. The more monopoly power, the better able a firm is to pass on cost increases to consumers in the form of increased prices. The nature of the product in question also matters. Is it a luxury good that consumers will buy more of when prices fall, or is it a staple that will be bought in steady volumes regardless of price?

**Abatement opportunities**: Firms and sectors where there are unexploited low-cost opportunities for abatement have advantages over those where there is no 'low-hanging fruit' (either because it has already been harvested, or because the state of technology is not well advanced).

There are different ways in which action by the EU could help to bring low-carbon measures in other countries closer to EU levels, closing the competitive gap for energy-intensive industries. These would help to remove any 'free rider' effect or unfair competition from third countries.

For example, the EU could consider applying a more targeted approach to the nature and recognition of international credits in the ETS. Options are to reinforce efforts to move towards sectoral crediting based on ambitious crediting thresholds (except for the LDCs), and to restrict the use of CDM credits generated in energy-intensive sectors (e.g. steel, cement and aluminium) in third countries other than the LDCs. Consideration could also be given to enhance the environmental integrity of CDM credits from countries that are not participating adequately in international climate efforts. One promising option for such an enhancement would be to apply a multiplier, for instance requiring two CDM credits to be surrendered per tonne emitted in the ETS. These ideas, being canvassed by the Commission, could be embodied in bilateral agreements on sectoral crediting between the EU and a number of third countries. For example, the EU could engage in supporting a pilot for an EU/China sectoral crediting agreement on steel.

Other approaches would see more positive efforts by the EU to help partners to meet EU levels of climate action and close any potential competitive gap. For developing and emerging economies, this could include technology transfer. For more developed partners, the rapid development of an international carbon market covering, in the first place, the most energy-intensive sectors across the world, would remove the need for special measures to be taken.

## Carbon price

The provisions of the Kyoto Protocol and the EU ETS already allow for national abatement challenges to be met, to some extent, through the purchase of carbon credits. For each credit purchased, 1 tonne of carbon is reduced elsewhere in Europe or in the developing world. From an economic perspective, it is the relationship between the marginal abatement cost of various domestic measures and the costs of carbon credits on the open market that will influence government strategy in achieving its abatement objectives. As the price of carbon credits rises, cost–benefit analysis will force governments to consider increasingly costly domestic policy alternatives. If the cost of permits falls, however, it becomes increasingly attractive to purchase credits.

The price of carbon is generally set, like any market, by the balance of supply and demand. Overall demand is determined by the amount of emissions through the year. Demand is specifically influenced by fundamentals such as weather and fuel prices; and other variables such as government policy. Supply in the emissions trading sector is determined by the overall allocation of allowances and carbon credits available to the market. The actions of electricity generators are critical determinants of price.

As the EU accounts for about 10 per cent of global emissions, the price of carbon will to an increasing extent be predicated on how large non-EU developed and developing economies approach the issue of climate change at political level in the context of the negotiations on a new Kyoto Protocol. This assumes of course that a global carbon market will eventually emerge.

Early predictions of the price of carbon for the trading period 2008–2012 varied from between €17[143] and €39/t $CO_2$e, with many analysts forecasting a price of between €20 to €25/t $CO_2$e for 2012.[144] ABN-AMRO estimated that a steady demand for CERs and rising emissions should result in a price of €15 per tonne in the Kyoto period; but higher if the appropriate regulatory decisions were made. There are many forecasts for the long-term price of carbon. Some studies point to a price of between €20–25/t $CO_2$e. Others analysts believe that as the options for cheap emissions reductions are used up, prices are more likely to be determined by the cost of carbon capture and storage technology. Bank of Ireland Global Markets predicted a price of €50–60/t $CO_2$e[145] and the European Commission's POLES projections forecast carbon prices to reach €37 per tonne by 2020 and €64 per tonne by 2030.[146]

The reality has been somewhat different. At peak (June 2011), EUAs were priced at €16.34/tonne, but the price fell to €9.72/tonne by November 2011 and to just €7/tonne in March 2012.[147] The balance between the price of the carbon allowance and its fundamentals has been quite different between the first and second EU ETS periods (i.e. before and after 2008), and is characterised by the increasing role played by the fundamentals during Phase II. According to CDC Climat Research, allowance prices have tended to be undervalued almost systematically since the end of 2009, and by up to 30 per cent in late 2010. One of the reasons is that non-energy sectors were particularly affected by the slowdown in economic activity, which increases the allowance supply for the same level of demand, and leads to imbalance close to the one observed at the beginning of Phase 1. Other factors affecting the price include the uncertainty regarding the exact market operation rules for the period between now and 2020 and to an even greater extent in relation to the post-2020 period. The implications of the carry-over of surplus AAUs from the first to the second commitment period is also impacting on the carbon price. Incidences of fraud have not helped matters as this had the effect of causing a lack of confidence among market players. Supply–demand balances were made even more difficult to anticipate due to the potential use of Kyoto credits (CDMs and JI credits), which contributed to an increase in the supply of carbon assets. A certain degree of uncertainty also remains regarding the transition to a mostly auction-based scheme during the EU ETS phase 3 (2013–2020).[148]

The market for CERs and ERUs post-2012 is another piece of the jigsaw as CERs will remain a viable compliance instrument for ETS operators.[149]

In assessing the policy options in relation to the EU moving towards a minus 30 per cent emission-reduction target, the Commission concluded carbon prices could reach €72/tonne; €44.5/tonne in the event of a move to a 'gradual' carbon market; and €22/tonne should a 'perfect' global carbon market emerge.[150] More recent analysis suggests the ETS price through to 2020 will be closer to €16.50/tonne. The Commission's analysis also suggests that a uniform non-ETS carbon price of €5/tonne will be sufficient across the EU to enable Member States to meet their obligations under the Emissions Sharing Directive (see below).[151]

Although predictions differ for the post-2012 period, what market analysts believe is that carbon prices are not on a significant upward trajectory, with the forecast EUA price now at €10.50/tonne for 2013 and €14.20/tonne over phase 3. The CER price is now estimated at €8.20/tonne for 2013 and €9.70/tonne over phase 3.[152]

Despite the fact that the ETS market is working well there have been calls for the Commission to better manage the carbon price in the light of the (low) price of allowances. On the other hand, a recent survey found that the carbon price is a less decisive factor in investment decisions than had previously been assumed.[153] One suggestion is that there should be an immediate tightening of the market by setting aside allowances in phase 3.[154] Another proposal is that the EU should set legally binding targets for the ETS and non-ETS sectors for 2030, 2040 and 2050.[155] Matters came to a head at the informal meeting of EU environment ministers held in Horsens (18-19 April 2012). The Danish Presidency's briefing note drew attention to on-going concerns about the decline in the carbon price. Having listened to the ministers' view, Connie Hedegaard, the European Commissioner responsible for climate change, announced that proposals will be submitted to the Climate Change Committee for decision this year.

The voluntary (non-compliance) market plays a part in the carbon market dynamics. In 2010, some 131 Mt were transacted to a value of $424 million – up almost a third on 2009. Forecast volumes for 2011 are in the region of some 200 Mt. This market segment is a key focus of Ireland's Green IFSC project where efforts are ongoing to develop an international carbon standard and an associated Dublin Voluntary Offset Registry.

## Distributional issues

The choice of discount rate, as already discussed, has implications for the distribution of costs between current and future taxpayers. On a global level, the adoption of targets for temperature rises, stabilisation, or emissions reductions, is constantly dogged by debates within the developed and developing world about who should foot the cost. The choice between various domestic policy measures will also have implications for small and large business, households, taxpayers and consumers. Likewise, the choice between domestic measures in general and the purchase of carbon credits on the market will also have implications for taxpayers and consumers. It is clear that substantial revenues will accrue from mechanisms that put a price on carbon emissions, be they auctioned permits or carbon taxes. These revenues present positive options for their use, including reducing other taxes, investing the funds in energy conservation measures and protecting the living standards of those on lower incomes, each of which has implications for competitiveness and social equity. Governments will thus be presented with a number of choices.

## The marginal abatement cost curve

Determining the correct mix of policies and measures to be adopted, and which sectors to be targeted to reduce emissions, can be done with reference to a comprehensive MACC for a particular country or the global economy as a whole. An example of a global MACC is given below (Figure 9).

### Figure 9: Global MAC curve

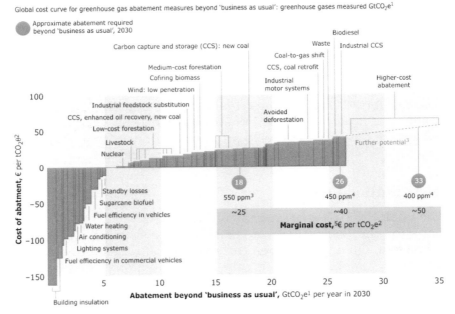

*Source:* Enkvist, P.A., Nauclér, T. and Rosander, J. (2007), 'A Cost Curve for Greenhouse Gas Reduction', *McKinsey Quarterly Review*, 1.

The MACC is a technology-specific but policy-neutral snapshot of one future year. It deliberately ignores behavioural change as a policy option. It identifies the costs of the principal measures that have the potential to reduce or significantly offset GHG emissions. The determination of the cost of mitigation is less problematic than the determination of the cost of emitting. The MACC is a measure of the cost of reducing emissions by a tonne of $CO_2$. Some abatement measures are very cheap. The $CO_2$ emissions avoided by, for example, insulating a hot water tank can be achieved at negative cost. When a price is set for emitting, then all emission-reduction options costing up to the price will be pursued, especially if the price looks like being a stable one.

The abatement potential of each technological option is represented by the horizontal widths of the bars.[156] The options are ranked in ascending order of cost and the cheapest appear below the zero cost line, in the left-hand side, indicating the negative cost options.[157] As advances in technology occur, some of the costs will become lower.

Developing national MACCs helps to show where the cheapest abatement options arise domestically. These curves also offer an insight into what level the price of a carbon would need to be for stabilisation to occur at a particular level globally.

In theory, society should be willing to pay to mitigate all emissions costing less than or equal to the social cost of carbon, or in economic terms, where the MACC equals the social cost of carbon (SCC). Thus the optimal stabilisation goal for the world would be where the MACC is equal to the SCC.[158]

## Conclusions

The Government has signalled a gradual shift of the tax base away from taxing what we want more of, such as investment and work, towards taxing what we want less of, such as pollution. Carbon taxation is a central plank of Ireland's new environmental tax reform framework. In line with best practice, ETS operators are exempt from the carbon tax.

The Government is likely from budget 2013 to take account of the negotiations at EU level on the adoption of an EU Energy Tax.

Ireland has also completed a country-specific MACC that will help define priorities in the post-2012 National Climate Change Strategy.

Critical working assumptions will have to be made about carbon pricing and trends in the context of national climate policy and an optimal low-carbon strategy best suited for Ireland's circumstances.

## Chapter 5

# The EU's 20–20–20 package

The EU's climate change package, one of the most radical sets of proposals to come out of Brussels, is on par with monetary union.

Dieter Helm, January 2008

## Introduction

EU Member States have varying degrees of commitment to climate change policy and have had differing levels of success in controlling emissions. The European Commission has, however, been consistent in offering leadership among Member States on the issue; this has resulted in an overall ambitious level of commitment in the EU to emissions reductions. This internal commitment has, in turn, allowed the EU to take a leadership role in international climate change negotiations.

Launching the EU's climate change and energy policy package, Commission President Barroso described the initiative as:

...part of the solution both to the climate crisis and to the current economic and financial crisis. It represents a green 'new deal' which will enhance the competitiveness of EU industry in an increasingly carbon constrained world. Moving to a low-carbon economy will encourage innovation, provide new business opportunities and create new green jobs.

A primary driver for investment is compliance with the EU's climate change and renewable energy strategies. This chapter provides a brief background to the EU's climate change policy and explains what is called the 20–20–20 package: a comprehensive set of binding rules about climate change targets and the greater penetration of renewable energy in Europe by 2020.

This part of the book is all about policy and, in particular, its influence on investment decisions. If policy is of limited interest to you, skip to Part 2 which sets out the green economy business opportunities that may arise as a direct consequences of policy already decided at European level.

## Climate change policy in the EU – principles, rules and actors

The central tenet of EU climate change policy is the goal dating from 1996 of limiting global mean temperature rises to +2°C compared to pre-industrial level,[159] reaffirmed at the March European Council of 2007 and other meetings subsequently.[160] This target is based on the Kyoto Protocol principle (grounded in the 1992 UNFCCC) of avoiding dangerous anthropogenic interference with the climate system. The scientific modelling suggests that stabilisation at 450 ppm $CO_2e$ would yield a 50 per cent probability of staying within this target. Global average mean temperature rises above this threshold could increase the risk of non-linear and potentially catastrophic events being triggered.

Whether it is achievable at a politically acceptable cost is questionable given that current GHG concentrations in the atmosphere are approaching levels at which a 2°C temperature rise would appear inevitable.[161] A cost–benefit analysis undertaken by the European Commission found that the impact of stabilisation at +2°C would have only minimal impacts on global GDP.[162] The IPCC's Fourth Assessment Report produced similar findings.[163] The Stern Review, however, concluded that it would be very costly to stabilise at a level of concentrations considered by the Commission.[164] The Stern Review (which it is recalled is based on the work of many researchers) estimated that the cost of stabilisation at a level of GHG concentrations that would likely equate to a 2.4–2.8°C rise in global average mean temperature would be 1 per cent of GDP.[165]

It has been argued that the possibility of temporarily over-shooting the emissions trajectory needed for stabilisation below +2°C and compensating with more severe emissions reductions at a later date might reduce the costs of stabilisation.[166] The basic idea is that GHG concentrations could be reduced in the long term after exceeding a 'safe' level in the coming two to three decades. This approach could allow more room to manoeuvre in staying within +2°C, and would reduce the cost. Either way, the opportunity to stabilise at +2°C is slipping away fast.

EU Directives and Regulations relating to climate change policy-making fall under the environment chapter of the EC Treaty (Articles 174–176). Under the Environmental Title, quali-fied majority voting in the Council and the codecision procedure with the European Parliament is used for the adoption of legis-lative acts.[167] However, several exceptions to the use of qualified majority voting exist, meaning that decisions taken in these areas must be taken unanimously. Proposals with fiscal impli-cations require unanimity – a proposal on an EU-wide carbon tax in 1992 was opposed by the UK, Ireland, France, Spain and Portugal and failed to garner the unanimous support it required – as did measures affecting Member States' energy taxation. In practice, agreement is needed by a high proportion of partici-pants across the EU institutions for climate change policy to be adopted.

The Lisbon Treaty includes a number of significant new pro-visions on climate change. Article 171.1 commits the EU to promoting measures at international level to deal with regional or worldwide environmental problems, 'and in particular com-bating climate change'. For the first time combating climate change is explicitly stated as an EU treaty objective. Although this reference to combating climate change is limited to the inter-national level, it is possible that a proactive European Court of Justice could take a maximalist approach and use this article to challenge other EU laws. Several aspects of the new Energy Title could also have implications for EU climate change policy. For instance, Article 176A, which refers to the establishment of an internal market for energy, references the need to preserve and improve the environment in so doing and goes on to commit EU policy 'to promote energy efficiency and energy savings and the development of new and renewable forms of energy'.[168] Although arguably EU policy is already committed to, for example, the promotion of renewables and energy efficiency, these articles offer a clear legal basis outside the political agreements at European Councils for these policies.

International environmental policy-making is described as an area of mixed competences.[169] This means that individual Member States have competences to negotiate in international bodies and to conclude international agreements (a right enshrined in Article 174.4 of the EC Treaty).[170] Positions adopted prior to UNFCCC negotiations must therefore be based on consensus. Positions are prepared by the EU's working party on International Environmental Issues (IEI) and the Council of Environment Ministers or the European Council adopts final positions, where necessary. The EU's presidency has responsibility for drafting the EU's position and representing the EU at negotiations as part of the troika.[171] Given the requirement for consensus, the presidency plays an important role in moving negotiations forward at EU coordination meetings – attended by climate change delegations and representatives of the Commission – which take place during UNFCCC negotiations on a daily basis.

Since February 2010, the Directorate General for Climate Action of the European Commission (DG CLIMA) is responsible for drafting legislation and coordinating negotiations on climate change.

## Deciding targets

At a meeting of energy and environment ministers in October 1990, the EU agreed for the first time to stabilise emissions. At Kyoto, the EU agreed to an 8 per cent emissions reduction by 2012 based on 1990 levels; this aggregate target was then divided among Member States as in Table 2 on page 117.

The 'rich and green' group of countries (Germany, the Netherlands, Finland, Denmark and Austria) took on ambitious reduction targets, with Germany's reduction target (facilitated by the process of reunification) accounting for more emissions reductions than the rest of the other Member States combined.[172] The 'cohesion countries' – Portugal, Ireland, Greece and Spain (the 'PIGS') – were allowed to increase their emissions in order to allow for different economic development patterns.

As the EU's provisions and commitments expire at the end of the Kyoto Protocol period (December 2012), the EU had to adopt a (much) revised policy framework for the forthcoming period.

**Table 2: EU-15 Kyoto burden sharing agreement**

| Country | Kyoto Target - 2012 % 1990 |
|---|---|
| Portugal | +27 |
| Greece | +25 |
| Spain | +15 |
| Ireland | +13 |
| Sweden | +4 |
| Finland | 0 |
| France | 0 |
| Netherlands | -6 |
| Italy | -6.5 |
| Belgium | -7.5 |
| UK | -12.5 |
| Austria | -13 |
| Denmark | -21 |
| Germany | -21 |
| Luxembourg | -28 |
| **EU** | **-8** |

*Source:* European Environmental Agency (2005), *The European Environment, State and Outlook.*

## The 20–20–20 package

In its energy and climate change package, published in January 2007, which was later endorsed by European leaders at the Spring European Council in March 2007, the EU committed itself to a 30 per cent emission-reduction target by 2020 compared to 1990 levels provided other developed countries commit themselves to comparable emissions reductions. The EU heads of state and government (the European Council) set a series of demanding climate and energy targets (known as the '20–20–20' targets) to be met by 2020. These are:

* A reduction in GHG of at least 20 per cent below 1990 levels

* 20 per cent of energy consumption to come from renewable resources

* A 20 per cent reduction in primary energy use compared with projected levels to be achieved by energy efficiency.

On 23 January 2008, the European Commission published a package of proposals made up of seven papers:

- A proposal on revision of the EU emissions trading scheme (ETS) for the post-2012 period
- A proposal on effort sharing the 20–30 per cent binding emission-reduction target (on 1990 levels by 2020) between Member States
- A proposal to establish a legally binding target for renew-ables of 20 per cent of EU energy consumption by 2020, binding national targets and a 10 per cent target for bio-fuels in transport for all Member States
- New guidelines on state aids for environmental protection
- A communication on carbon capture and storage (clean coal)
- An assessment of energy-efficiency action plans.

The package was adopted on 23 April 2009, with the European Parliament playing an important role as part of the co-decision procedure with the Council of Ministers.

## The 20–20–20 package

A revision and strengthening of the EU's ETS, the EU's key tool for cutting emissions cost-effectively. A single EU-wide cap on emission allowances will apply from 2013 and will be cut annu-ally, reducing the number of allowances available to businesses to 21 per cent below the 2005 level in 2020. The free allocation of allowances will be progressively replaced by auctioning, and the sectors and gases covered by the system will be somewhat expanded.

An 'effort-sharing' Decision governing emissions from sectors not covered by the EU ETS, such as transport, housing, agri-culture and waste. Under the Decision each Member State has agreed to a binding national emissions limitation target for 2020 that reflects its relative wealth. The targets range from an emis-sions reduction of 20 per cent by the richest Member States to an increase in emissions of 20 per cent by the poorest. These national targets will cut the EU's overall emissions from the non-ETS sectors by 10 per cent by 2020 compared with 2005 levels.

Binding national targets for renewable energy which collectively will lift the average renewable share across the EU to 20 per cent by 2020 (more than double the 2006 level of 9.2 per cent). The targets will contribute to decreasing the EU's dependence on imported energy and to reducing GHG emissions.

## Effort- (burden-) sharing of emissions

The effort-sharing of emissions reductions between Member States will no longer apply to the sectors and installations covered by the EU ETS. As the trading (i.e. ETS) sector no longer remains under national jurisdictions, the effort-sharing in the non-trading (i.e. non-ETS) sectors applies to approximately 60 per cent of GHG emissions across the EU.

### Main features of the effort-sharing Decision175

- At EU level there will be a 10 per cent reduction in non-ETS emissions by 2020 using a 2005 baseline. Taken together with the ETS GHG reduction targets, there will be a 14 per cent reduction in GHG emissions by 2020; or 20 per cent using a 1990 baseline. The year 2005 was chosen as verified ETS emissions data was to hand for that year.

- It is envisaged that emissions from the non-trading sector will decrease after 2020 in the context of the EU's commitment to de-carbonise the European economy by 2050.

- Member States have individual targets that were determined using GDP/per capita as the main criterion. Thus countries with a low GDP will be allowed to emit more than they did in 2005 by upwards of 20 per cent. Ireland as well as two other Member States was set a 20 per cent emission-reduction target.

- It will be left to Member States to define and implement policies and measures in the sectors covered (transport, agriculture, waste, buildings, services, small industrial installations).

- A number of EU initiatives will assist Member States to define their strategy, including new efficiency standards for boilers and water heaters, eco-labeling, and the implementation of the Landfill Directive.

- Member States can use credits from CDM and JI projects to meet their national targets up to a limit of 3 per cent of 2005 emissions subject to certain conditions. For example, CDM credits are non-bankable and not transferable. In the event of a global agreement on climate change this threshold may be adjusted.

- Also in the event of a global agreement being reached, the Commission will bring forward proposals to address land use, land use change and forestry (LULUCF) and higher national targets to be met by 2020.

- Several flexibilities have been built in, including banking and borrowing of emissions subject to a 5 per cent maximum; the transfer of over-achieved emission reductions between Member States; and the option of investing in projects in other Member States (i.e. a non-Irish investor could invest in a domestic project that delivers a quantum of verifiable emission reductions as an offset and vice versa).

- If a Member State fails to meet its linear reduction target it must take corrective action and in the event of a persistent failure to meet its targets, the Commission is allowed to launch infringement proceedings before the European Court of Justice.

- Member States are required to make an annual report on steps being taken to reduce what are legally binding GHG emission-reduction targets.

- A Climate Change Committee comprising the Commission and Member States will supervise the implementation of the effort-sharing Directive. It will decide, for example, on detailed rules for transfer, and guidelines for reporting etc.

The Commission has clarified that the Member States with the highest emission-reduction targets, such as Ireland, cannot meet these targets solely by domestic measures as this would not be economically efficient. Setting differentiated targets and using flexible instruments would provide a mechanism for redistribution of money to the poorer Member States (the cohesion countries) who (prior to the current economic recession) could cost-effectively over-achieve their share of the reduction effort.

## Effort sharing – assessment

Ireland has implemented the Decision as such instruments have direct effect i.e. they do not require primary or secondary legislation.

To meet the EU's binding GHG reduction targets will require Government policies and measures to reduce non-trading GHG emissions by some 7/8 Mt by 2020 or to purchase compliance from other Member States if it is cost effective to do so. The Government's review of national climate change policy points out that the least cost route to 2020 may not be the best option as it may become more expensive to reduce carbon emissions in the medium to long term.[176]

As there is no indication about the nature of the optimal mix of proposed initiatives in the non-trading sector it is difficult to draw conclusions.

However, there are some key messages. Given the require-ment to increase agriculture production to meet the Food Harvest 2020 targets, reducing agriculture emissions will con-tribute but a fraction of the required effort. In one of the report's background papers, the Department of Agriculture, Food and the Marine notes that agriculture emissions will have fallen in 2012 by 8.5 per cent compared to 1990 and that at 37 per cent of non-ETS emissions, agriculture in Ireland faces one of the most challenging targets given the high contribution of the sector to the national economy. However, in the knowledge that much work is being done on emerging technologies the Department has stated that the scope of agriculture's abatement-reduction potential is no more than 4 per cent.[177]

Despite the publication of the SmarterTravel strategy, and its 49 actions, there is no budget available to deliver the proposed measures in the transport sector.[178] Indeed the document does not set a measurable target for the reduction of transport emis-sions between 2005 and 2020. Several policy options including the electrification of the public transport system and a more ambitious electric vehicles programme are not mentioned.[179]

The main pillar of the Government's strategy appears to be a reliance on an accelerated afforestation programme that could result in some 4.8 Mt in sequestered carbon being used to offset the Government's target. There are two problems with this. First, offsetting forestry carbon is not allowed under EU rules and will require Member States to adopt a Directive (on foot of a Commission proposal) to allow for carbon offsets. An EU pro-posal, which will take at least two years to adopt, will address the baseline and verification, monitoring and accounting issues, all of which are quite complex. Second, even if a doubling of afforestation got underway this year the carbon sequestered at the level needed will not happen until well after 2020.

Mitigation in the non-ETS side of the economy is our biggest challenge given Ireland's unusual national emissions profile. The EPA has warned that the difficulty in actually achieving the 2020 target (regardless of which set of assumptions are made) should not be underestimated. Even if the measures in the more ambitious scenario are fully delivered, the 'distance to target' (i.e. how short Ireland will be on its legal GHG emission-re-duction commitments) could be some 4 Mt by 2020. There is a recognition – given the absence of emission reduction pro-grammes of scale – that a purely compliance-focused approach will result in an embedded and substantial requirement for very deep emission cuts and/or the purchase of (cheap) carbon credits beyond 2020.[180] The Government's low-carbon strategy will identify GHG emission-reduction scenarios after 2020. If by 2020 Ireland is struggling to meet the overall target set for the non-ETS sector this would not augur well for meeting a higher target after that period.

There may be grounds, in the context of Ireland's low-carbon strategy towards 2050 (as envisaged in the review of climate change policy), given the projected price of allowances through to 2020 (which inter alia reflect a degree of over-compliance in some Member States) and a sharp fall in Ireland's GDP over the past four years, to recalibrate the profile of Ireland's domestic efforts. Affordable and feasible sector specific mitigation strate-gies are clearly required.

Two of the most important (and deliverable) measures – although of limited benefit to the non-trading sector – are likely to be in the areas of renewable energy and energy efficiency; see below.

## Renewables (RES) target

The main features of the RES Directive area as follows:[181]

- A common framework for the production and promotion of energy from renewable sources is established.

- All Member States have been given a target calculated according to the share of energy from renewable sources in its gross final consumption for 2020. In Ireland's case this is 16 per cent; the rate of penetration was just 3.1 per cent in 2005. In addition, the share of energy from renewable sources in the transport sector must amount to at least 10 per cent of final energy consumption in the sector by 2020.

- It is possible for Member States to exchange an amount of energy from renewable sources using a statistical transfer, and to set up joint projects concerning the production of electricity and heating from renewable sources. Subject to some conditions, cooperation with third countries is also possible.

- Each Member State must be able to guarantee the origin of electricity, heating and cooling from RES sources. Common rules for these 'guarantees of origin' will apply.

- Technical specifications must be defined for renewable energy equipment and systems in order to benefit from support schemes. In addition, it is a requirement that national building regulations and codes are adapted to increase the share of all kinds of energy from RES sources in the building sector. From 1 January 2012, new public buildings and existing public buildings that are subject to renovation must respect the provisions of the RES Directive.

- The Commission is required to submit additional proposals, for example as regards the amount of electricity originating from renewable sources used to power EVs.

- It is a requirement that Member States take steps to develop transmission and distribution grid infrastructure, intelligent networks, storage facilities and the electricity system in order to allow the secure operation of the electricity system as it accommodates the further development of electricity production from RES sources, including interconnectors.

- In an attempt to allay mounting fears on the effectiveness of bio-fuels in reducing emissions and to counter the unintended consequences of the target on, for example, food production and food prices, several environmental criteria were set. The GHG emissions savings accruing from use of bio-fuels must be 35 per cent or more (measured against the product they displace) and must not be sourced from areas designated for nature protection, bio-diverse grasslands, wetlands or forests. The Commission will report on a sustainability scheme for energy use of biomass by 31 December 2012. It is hoped that with these criteria, the manner in which first generation bio-fuels are developed to meet the target would ensure environmentally positive outcomes. In the medium to long term, it is expected that second (and third) generation bio-fuels will play an increasingly important role.

- If a Member States fails to meet its indicative trajectory, a revised NREAP must be submitted for the Commission's approval that indicates how the RES target will be met with additional measures. The Commission is authorised to propose corrective action where this is considered appropriate.

- From 31 December 2011 and every two years thereafter, Member States are required to submit a report to the Commission on the implementation of the Directive. In turn, the Commission will issue a report on the EU-wide situation.

- A Committee on Renewable Energy Sources comprising Member States will assist the Commission in relation to all matters covered by the RES Directive. A separate Committee on the Sustainability of bio-fuels and bio-liquids has also been set up.

The Commission has assessed the requirements for a sustainability scheme for energy uses of solid and gaseous biomass sources in electricity, heating and cooling.[183] The Directive has been partly transposed into Irish law.[184]

## RES – assessment

While this comprehensive Directive has been almost universally welcomed on the grounds that it introduces an integrated approach to promoting the use of renewable energy sources in heat, transport, and electricity service provision in the EU, Member States are continuing to adopt quite different approaches as regards the types and levels of subsidies and financial supports for renewable energy projects.[185]

It is arguable that in the light of the tensions in the emerging energy landscape and the mounting evidence of climate change, and with due consideration of competitiveness effects, the level of ambition and the time frame for achievement of the targets proposed are appropriate. An emerging problem is the low price of carbon and the likelihood (as explained earlier) that prices may stay low for the foreseeable future.

The EU's bio-fuel targets are challenging for Ireland and considerable care and attention to detail, as well as technical innovation, will be required if progress towards the 10 per cent target is to be sustainable with respect to the economic, social and environmental constraints and realities.

The Directive should enable each Member State to optimise its own indigenous production of energy from renewable sources by sector while having recourse to meeting its full obligation by means of cross-border trading arrangements with supporting guarantees of origin.

Notwithstanding the apparent limited ambition of the 20 per cent target, the time-bound nature of the commitment entails implications for investment in infrastructure, grid operating systems research, processing plant, and equipment procurement logistics, which are significant at the EU and national levels. High levels of investor confidence will be essential and therefore the policy path and roadmap will need to be evidently robust to mitigate risk and secure the finance necessary.

The Commission's oversight arrangements are such as to ensure that the whole sustainable energy project is guided at an appropriate pace and with a balance that ensures that the short- and medium-term concerns of the European citizen are fully addressed i.e. the pass-through costs are kept at an affordable level.

Ireland's NREAP envisages that the overall 16 per cent target will be achieved with around 40 per cent consumption in the electricity sector being from renewable sources (75 MW wave and tidal; 153 MW of biomass generation; 234 MW of hydro; and 4,649 of wind – 4,094 MW onshore and 555 MW offshore);[186] 10 per cent in the transport sector (RES-T); and 12 per cent from heat (RES-H).[187] There is no evidence to hand that suggests the RES-T and RES-H targets will be met.

Since the NREAP was submitted in draft form to the Commission there have been further falls in projected demand for electricity. Eirgrid's All Island Generation Capacity Statement (2011–2020) concludes Ireland will need some 300 MW less wind capacity by 2020. Given what is installed, approved, but awaiting connection and in the pipeline (Gate 3), Ireland should easily meet its RES-E target.

Finally, the Commission's evaluation of Ireland's NREAP has identified long lead times for grid connections as a particular weakness. The Meath-Tyrone 400kV interconnector is a case in point.

## Energy efficiency

Energy efficiency is essentially about achieving the same level of energy service with less energy, be it space heating, hot water, lighting, driving or powering the workplace. The potential is huge. For example, energy savings of 6 million tonnes of oil equivalent (Mtoe) would mean that 17 coal-fired stations or 9,000 wind turbines would not need to be built in the EU.

The first important EU initiative in this field was the (2006) Energy Efficiency Action Plan, which contained 85 policy measures together aimed at reducing energy consumption by 14 per cent by 2020. In addition, the Cogeneration Directive (2004) and the Energy Services Directive were adopted (2006), as were a revision of the Energy Labelling Directive (2010), and the Energy Performance in Buildings Directive (2010). A new Energy Efficiency Plan was adopted in March 2011.[188]

Reducing energy consumption and eliminating energy waste are among the main goals of the EU. Thus as part of the 20–20–20 package Member States are committed to reduce annual consumption of primary energy by 2020. As current estimates show the EU is not on track to achieve this target with forecast savings of 9 per cent only, the Commission has proposed a new Directive on energy efficiency.[189]

### Main features of draft Energy Efficiency Directive

- There will be a legal obligation on Member States to set up energy-saving measures (but not targets).

- Energy distributors or retail energy sales companies will be obliged to save 1.5 per cent of their annual sales by volume.

- The public sector is to lead by example, for instance in relation to renovating buildings to meet higher energy-efficiency standards; across the EU public buildings account for some 12 per cent of the total stock.

- There are incentives for SMEs to complete energy audits.

- Setting up of national heat and cooling plans for developing the potential for the application of high-efficiency cogeneration (CHP) and efficient district heating and cooling.
- Energy service companies (ESCOs) will be encouraged to provide upfront investment; the potential for ESCOs in the EU is some €25 billion.

The Commission emphasised in its impact statement that the payback period for investment in energy efficiency is short and positive.

Member States and the Commission will meet in the Council's Energy Working Group with a view to adopting the Directive (taking account of the comments of the European Parliament where over 1,800 amendments have been submitted). Aspects of the draft Directive are controversial and are being hotly debated. For example, Ireland is concerned that the pay and you save scheme currently under consideration and the associated Public Service Obligation (PSO) could be inadvertently undermined by the proposal.

Ireland's NEEAP was published in May 2009 and sets a 20 per cent energy-efficiency target. This involves, should all measures be implemented fully, a reduction of 23 Gwh of energy saving by 2020 (a 15 per cent saving on the baseline period), GHG emission reductions of some 5.7 Mt and avoided energy costs valued at €1.6 billion. The proposed measures are consistent with the White Paper *Delivering a Sustainable Energy Future for Ireland – the Energy Policy Framework for 2007–2020*.

The main features of the 90 actions listed in the NEEAP include:

- A national insulation programme targeted at one million homeowners to assist them reduce their energy bills
- Supports for businesses, such as tax allowances for energy-efficiency technologies
- The introduction of an energy demand reduction target (of 8,000 GWh by 2020)
- Green procurement to cut energy usage in the public sector by 33 per cent

- The roll-out of an electric vehicles development strategy that may see some 10 per cent of the fleet being electrically powered by 2020.

Ireland's second NEEAP, which has been submitted to the Commission contains 34 measures, most of which are based on NEEAP 1.

In addition, following a public consultation, the Better Energy – the National Upgrade Programme was launched in May 2011 as part of the Government's jobs initiative. One of the underpinning principles is a move to place the building energy rating scale at the centre of energy-saving calculations. With an additional budget of €31 million approved for 2011, SEAI (the implementation body) hopes to retrofit 20,000 buildings and attract a further €30 million in private investment. *Better Energy* will replace the Home Energy Saving Scheme, the Warmer Homes Scheme and the Greener Home Scheme.[191]

## Energy efficiency – assessment

Energy security and GHG abatement targets are equally well served whenever energy service needs are effectively met with better use of energy resources. In general, all targets will be achieved at least cost to the consumer when the economic potential of energy efficiency is fully realised.

*Better Energy* has the potential to achieve significant energy savings, as once the enabling legislation is adopted the sellers of energy now have formal targets to deliver energy-efficiency upgrades, the size of their target being linked to their share of the market. Some 25 suppliers of 75 Gwh of energy are engaged with the process.

Critical will be the preferred model for funding the desired energy-efficiency measures for householders and businesses. Innovative financing proposals are under active consideration, such as the 'pay as you save' formula whereby utilities lend money to consumers with repayments linked to the savings achieved. Despite the fact the work has been ongoing for over two years, it is not now expected that a scheme will be launched before 2014. An IIEA report points to the challenges that can only be met if attractive financing options are made available to consumers.[192] If fully implemented, this 1.7 Mt GHG emission-reduction programme will not have much impact on targets facing residential and commercial properties in the non-ETS side of the economy.

SEAI is clearly on top of this agenda, is open to fresh thinking and has demonstrated itself as a facilitator of eco-innovation.

## Moving the EU's target beyond 20 per cent 193

When the EU decided in 2008 to cut its GHG emissions, it showed its commitment to tackling the climate change threat and to lead the world in demonstrating how this could be done. The agreed cut of 20 per cent from 1990 levels by 2020, together with a 20 per cent renewables target, was a crucial step for the EU's sustainable development and a clear signal to the rest of the world that the EU was ready to take the action required. The EU will meet its Kyoto Protocol target and has a strong track record in climate action. But it has always been clear that action by the EU alone will not be enough to combat climate change and also that a 20 per cent cut by the EU to deliver the goal of keeping global temperature increase below 2°C compared to pre-industrial levels is not the end of the story. EU action alone is not enough. All countries will need to make an additional effort, including cuts of 80–95 per cent by 2050 by developed countries.

That was why the EU matched its 20 per cent unilateral commitment with a commitment to move to 30 per cent, as part of a genuine global effort.[194] This remains EU policy today. Since the EU policy was agreed, circumstances have been changing rapidly. We have seen an economic crisis of unprecedented scale. It has put huge pressure on businesses and communities across Europe, as well as causing huge stress on public finances. But at the same time, it has confirmed that there are opportunities for Europe in building a resource-efficient society.

We have also had the Copenhagen, Cancún and Durban COP meetings. Despite the disappointment of failing to achieve the goal of a full, binding international agreement to tackle climate change, the most positive result was that 55 countries accounting for some 80 per cent of emissions made pledges to cut emissions, even though these will be insufficient to meet the 2°C target.[195]

The purpose of the Commission's Communication was not to decide now to move to a 30 per cent target: the conditions set are clearly not met. Instead, to facilitate a more informed debate on the implications of the different levels of ambition, this Communication sets out the result of analysis into the implications of the 20 per cent and 30 per cent targets as seen from today's perspective.

The baseline for assessing what the 30 per cent target might mean must be to analyse what the 20 per cent target implies today. Not surprisingly, the economic crisis has had a major impact on the assumptions made when the 20 per cent was agreed. But its impact has worked in different ways. Between 2005 and 2008, the EU cut its emissions from 7 per cent to 10 per cent below 1990 levels.[196] So when the crisis hit, stepped up climate action and high energy prices had already led to an acceleration in EU emission reductions. The crisis brought an immediate further reduction. Verified emissions in the ETS in 2009 were 11.6 per cent below 2008 emissions. Carbon prices fell correspondingly, with a drop in early 2009 from some €25 to €7 per tonne of $CO_2$ (January 2012). But the fall in carbon prices has shown how the impact of the ETS on companies and consumers can also adapt to changing economic circumstances.

This one-off reduction in emissions meant that in 2009, the EU emitted around 14 per cent less GHG than 1990. But, of course, as production recovers in energy-intensive industries like steel, this rate of reduction cannot be simply extrapolated into the future. However, the absolute costs of meeting the 20 per cent target have fallen. In the analysis presented in 2008 underpinning the climate-energy package, based on the expectation of continued economic growth, the costs of reaching the target were estimated as at least €70 billion per annum in the year 2020.[197] The Commission's recent analysis also takes account of the recession.[198] The price tag is now estimated at €48 billion (0.32 per cent of GDP in 2020). This represents a reduction of some €22 billion, or 30 per cent less than expected two years ago. Nevertheless, this reduction in absolute costs comes in the context of a crisis that has left businesses with much less capacity to find the investment needed to modernise in the short run, and great uncertainty over how long it will take to recover.

The lower cost of the climate and energy package today is due to the interplay of several factors. First, lower economic growth has effectively reduced the stringency of the 20 per cent target. Second, the rise in oil prices proved an incentive to improve energy efficiency: energy demand has fallen. Third, the carbon price is likely to remain lower as allowances not used in the recession are carried forward into the future.

The flexible architecture of the ETS means that the impact of the crisis will have consequences lasting several years. With many allowances unused during the crisis, companies will be able to carry over some 5–8 per cent of their allowances from the 2008–2012 period into the third phase of the ETS (2013–2020). In addition, the achievement of renewable energy targets and efficiency measures reduce emissions further. The result will be a carbon price well below the projections made in 2008.[199]

At the same time, the crisis has put heavy pressure on the EU economy. Businesses today are squeezed by depressed demand and the challenge of finding sources of funding. With a lower carbon price, government revenue from auctioning could also be halved, adding to pressure on public finances and reducing another potential source of public funds available for climate purposes. The requirement has not gone away to find the investment needed in areas like electricity, heating, and transport to reach the agreed 20 per cent renewable energy target.

To reach the goal of staying under a 2°C temperature increase requires reductions of 80–95 per cent by 2050 for developed countries, compared to 1990.[200] Even if some of this could be accounted for by EU efforts outside its borders, an initial estimate indicates the EU's own domestic emissions would have to fall to roughly 70 per cent. The trajectory agreed in 2008 would bring the EU's domestic emissions down to -20 per cent by 2020 and, if continued unchanged, up to -25 per cent in 2030. This is not enough to take the EU to its 2050 level of ambition at optimal cost. If action is delayed, the EU, as well as its global partners, would have to catch up after 2020. For example, the International Energy Agency has estimated that at the global level, every year of delayed investment on more low-carbon energy sources adds €300–400 billion to the price tag.[201] There is a risk that, with the 20 per cent target by 2020 now driving change less strongly than expected in 2008, the task for the EU after 2020 will become more difficult and more expensive.

## An analysis of the 30 per cent target

The changing circumstances that have had such an impact on the 20 per cent target also underline the need for a careful

analysis of the mooted 30 per cent target. The economic consequences of the 30 per cent target for the EU must be clear. Going
beyond 20 per cent would in all probability entail increasing
the stringency of existing policies or introducing new policies.
The question arises, therefore, what these new policies might
be, which existing policies might be made more stringent, and
how this stringency might be increased. The options below are
among those that could be considered by the EU if and when
the decision is taken to step up to the 30 per cent target.

As the primary tool to drive emission reductions, the Commission argues that ETS should be the starting point for options
for going beyond 20 per cent. For example, the ETS could be
recalibrated by 'setting aside' a share of the allowances planned
for auction. Should a political decision be taken to increase the
emission-reduction target, the ETS could make its main contribution to a stepped-up target through a gradual reduction
of the allowances auctioned. A tighter ETS cap would raise the
level of environmental achievement and would have the effect of
strengthening the incentive effect of the carbon market. Reducing auctioning rights by some 15 per cent over the whole period
2013–2020, representing some 1.4 billion allowances, could be
sufficient according to the Commission. Projections suggest that
auctioning revenue might increase by around a third, because
carbon prices are expected to increase by more than the reduction of allowances auctioned.

How Member States use the new revenue from auctioning
will be important in terms of investing in low-carbon solutions
for the future. One point of view is that fast movers that invest
in top performing technologies should be rewarded. The benchmarking system provides an opportunity to identify those who
make rapid progress in improving performance and to reward
them with extra unallocated free allowances. This would be a
way to release extra finance to companies ready to innovate.
Any attempt to hypothecate auctioning revenue will be opposed
by others who believe it is not the Government's job to pick
winners. The revenue could instead be used to reduce business
costs (employers' PRSI for example).

Regulation can contribute to reaching more ambitious climate
targets, particularly by encouraging energy and resource efficiency. This can come through product standards, such as the
measures taken under the Eco-design Directive and limits of
$CO_2$ emissions from vehicles, and implementation of the EU's

digital agenda.[202] Smart grids can help change consumer behaviour, increase energy efficiency and enable a higher penetration of renewable energy.

The Commission will continue to encourage Member States, regions and cities to step up low-carbon investment by directing a greater volume of cohesion policy funding towards green investments. This would accelerate the existing trend to use cohesion funds more effectively to boost renewable energy, energy efficiency, and the promotion of public transport. It would also provide an alternative to the use of surplus AAUs as a source of funding, which undermines the environmental integrity of the carbon market. Significant energy-saving possibilities remain unused due to many market and regulatory barriers. An enhanced energy-efficiency policy framework would make an important contribution to move beyond the 20 per cent.

Land use, land use change and forestry (LULUCF) activities were not included in the 2008 climate and energy package, but have potential for additional emission reductions. Also maintaining and restoring natural carbon sinks is necessary to avoid further emission increases. Today, uncertainties in calculation and volatility make short-term predictability of LULUCF activities – and their contribution to EU targets – difficult to assess. However, as the work continues to establish effective rules to govern these activities, they could over time provide a growing contribution to the mitigation effort through improved cultivation methods and forestry management. The Common Agricultural Policy post-2013 could incentivise farmers and foresters to move towards more sustainable practices and make a greater contribution to emission reductions over time.

The EU was first in recognising that efforts made outside its borders can stimulate private sector action. The CDM has led to several thousand projects worldwide, often making very cost-effective reductions. One way to improve the leverage of EU action would be to substitute part of the demand for CDM credits with new sectoral credits.[203] This would redirect carbon market finance towards actions with a greater potential for carbon reduction (e.g. in the power sector in advanced developing economies), and could be linked to schemes like a multiplier for conventional CDM credits (e.g. industrial gas projects).[204] This could deliver significant additional emission reductions in developing countries to contribute to the overall EU effort, while leaving at the same time greater room for continued CDM in the LDCs.

On maritime emissions, the EU will continue to pursue an international agreement through the International Maritime Organisation and the UNFCCC. As agreed under the climate and energy package, the EU will take steps to move forward if no such agreement has been agreed by 31 December 2011.

The fact that the 20 per cent is now more in reach than was assumed in 2008 has an obvious knock-on effect on the challenge of meeting a 30 per cent target. In absolute terms, the €70 billion price tag in 2020 as estimated in early 2008, would be sufficient today to take the EU more than half way towards stepping up from 20 per cent to 30 per cent, although in a situation where the EU economy is more constrained.

The additional total costs for the EU to step up from the current 20 per cent to 30 per cent are estimated to be around €33 billion in the year 2020, or 0.2 per cent of GDP. In order to achieve this 30 per cent reduction, it is estimated that the carbon price in the EU ETS would need to be some €30 per tonne of $CO_2$, which is similar to the level estimated to be necessary to meet the 20 per cent reduction target in 2008. Domestic emissions would reduce to -25 per cent compared to 1990 with the remaining being covered by banked allowances and international credits. The total cost of a 30 per cent reduction, including the costs to go to 20 per cent, is now estimated at €81 billion, or 0.54 per cent of GDP.[205] Therefore, going to the 30 per cent reduction target represents an increase of €11 billion compared to the absolute costs of the climate and energy package in 2020 as projected in 2008. But while costs clearly have decreased, the reduced profitability of companies, spending power of consumers, and access to bank loans has reduced the ability of the EU economy to invest in low-carbon technologies: a legacy of the crisis that can only be offset by the return of economic growth and proactive policies to prioritise growth in these sectors.

In terms of sectors, the Commission's analysis suggests that the greatest potential for emissions reductions comes from the electricity sector through a combination of improved demand-side efficiency and a reduction of carbon-intensive supply-side investments. A significant amount of ageing electricity-generating capacity needs to be replaced in the coming decade, and doing this by low-carbon solutions represents an important opportunity to reduce emissions. As for industrial sectors in the

ETS, some have a significant cost-effective potential (e.g. refineries). In the effort-sharing sectors, households and services are potential sources to reduce $CO_2$ emissions, mainly from heating. In the agricultural sector, according to the Commission, experience in some Member States suggests that there may be further potential for reducing methane and nitrous oxide emissions in intensive farming.

The analysis further highlights that in relative terms the cost-effective split between efforts in the ETS and non-ETS sectors in the case of a 30 per cent reduction target remains largely the same as for the 20 per cent target. In the case of moving to a 30 per cent target, in 2020, the ETS cap would be 34 per cent rather than the current 21 per cent below 2005 emissions, while the overall target for sectors not covered by the ETS would be 16 per cent, rather than the current 10 per cent below 2005 emissions. A potential move to 30 per cent would require a decision on a specific mix of options on how to share the additional reductions.

## Latest analysis

In October 2010, EU environment ministers asked the Commission to assess the consequence at Member State level in relation to the possible move to a 30 per cent emission-reduction target. The Commission used this opportunity to bring forward new analysis about the revised costs and benefits of the climate and energy package.[206]

### 20–20–20 package – updated analysis

- Many Member States are projecting they will overachieve their target in the sectors outside the ETS.
- As a consequence of the economic recession, emissions have fallen and many operators have built up a large buffer of banked allowances and unused international emission-reduction credits in the EU ETS; some 2.4 billion allowances by 2020.
- This surplus is having a depressing effect on the price of allowances.
- There is now a risk of Europe getting locked into too high carbon investments.

- In 2010, EU-27 GHG emissions (including aviation) were 14 per cent below the 1990 level.

- There will be much less auctioning revenue to distribute as a result of lower carbon prices. However, if a 30 per cent target were introduced revenues could rise by €7 billion to €28.5 billion by 2020. If these happened Ireland's share (0.9 per cent of the total) would rise to €256 million by 2020.

- Revenues from potential transfers of national emissions allowances between Member States under the Effort Sharing Directive are expected to be significantly lower.

- Achieving 25 per cent out of the 30 per cent reductions domestically by 2020 is now estimated to cost €70 billion in terms of the direct net impact on energy consumers.

- Moving to a 25 per cent emission-reduction target would require an additional investment of €18 billion annually (2016–2020) in electricity grids, power plants and energy-efficiency measures.

- The extra cost of reducing GHG emissions by 30 per cent (instead of 20 per cent) is around €33 billion (0.2 per cent of EU GDP).

The Commission also clarified that it wished to increase the share of the EU's budget spent on advancing Europe's transition to a low-carbon and climate-resilient society to €200 billion over the period 2014–2020. It needs to be emphasised that the greatest portion of EU cofinancing will go to Member States that have a much lower GDP per capita than Ireland.

To recap, if the Commission's proposals had political support the emission-reduction target for the EU ETS sector would rise from 21 per cent to 34 per cent and to 16 per cent (from 10 per cent) in the non-trading sector.

## Conclusion

Since the EU took its historic decisions on combating climate change in 2008, the economic crisis has brought some fundamental changes to the political and economic landscape of the EU's climate policy. The pressure on the EU economy is intense. The EU, however, remains committed to action on climate change. The EU has led the way in showing how concrete, effective measures can be taken to reverse the trend of increasing greenhouse gas emissions without adversely affecting economic growth. It will stay in the vanguard of global efforts with the implementation of the climate and energy package.

The implementation of policies to cut GHG emissions is one of the key drivers for the modernisation of the EU economy, directing investment and innovation to sectors with huge potential for growth and employment in the future. As set out in the *Europe 2020* strategy, it is one of the core themes in any credible strategy to build sustainable prosperity for the future.[207] For many Member States, but not in Ireland's case, the full implementation of their NREAPs and NEEAPs will help them meet their domestic targets.

The Commission has set out how changed global circumstances have impacted on the targets set in 2008. While the absolute costs of meeting a 20 per cent target have been reduced, representing a welcome relief for businesses facing the uphill battle of recovery, it also represents a risk that the effectiveness of the 20 per cent target as a motor for change diminishes somewhat. This all comes at a time of severe economic constraint, both for governments and businesses.

Therefore, it is important for Ireland to analyse the consequences of a possible move to a 30 per cent target. At present the conditions set at EU level for stepping up to such a target have not been met i.e. a global post-Kyoto agreement. Even if the Commission were mindful to bring forward more ambitious proposals, quite a number of Member States would not welcome such an initiative in the current economic climate.

The Government's low-carbon strategy will have to consider, for example, the cost-effectiveness of meeting part of our compliance shortfall by purchasing transfers from those Member States who will over-achieve in meeting their non-ETS emission-reduction targets. Given the price of allowances and the trend line this may well become a financially attractive proposition. The cost–benefit of relying on a greater share of carbon offsetting will be central to the policy mix that will determine the elements of the post-2012 National Climate Change and Low Carbon Strategy.

What the Government could do is to set an indicative trajectory not to 2020 but to 2030 (or indeed to 2050), which is perhaps a more realistic deadline given the conclusions of the Durban COP. Determining the optimal short-, medium- and long-term mix of domestic mitigation and offsetting by means of carbon allowance purchases is the policy conundrum. Sector policies will inevitably have to be developed. For example, if for strategic reasons the Government decides to allow an increase in agriculture emissions it can only do this provided there are counterpart (and equitable) measures in place elsewhere in the non-ETS economy; this is easier said than done.

## Chapter 6

# The EU emissions trading system

First, I worry about climate change. It's the only thing
I believe has the power to fundamentally end the
march of civilisation as we know it, and make a lot
of the other efforts that we're making irrelevant and
impossible.

Bill Clinton, 2006

## Introduction

Emissions trading is an alternative market-based approach
to a carbon tax, although the two policies are not mutually
exclusive. The benefit of emissions trading is that overall emissions are reduced, in theory, at minimum cost to the economy
because each firm can choose whether to reduce its emissions
or purchase additional permits, depending on the price. In a cap
and trade scheme a cap is set across the economy or economic
sector, permits are allocated to participating firms according to
a division of the overall cap, and firms are obliged to restrain
their emissions to their allocated permits or else purchase additional permits. In this way the regulator creates a scarcity that
in turn creates a carbon price depending on demand.

There are many design options that affect the performance of
an ETS, including the method of allocation (e.g. by auctioning
or grandfathering), the penalties for non-compliance, the definition of participating entities, and the point at which emissions
are controlled. The EU Emissions Trading System (EU ETS)

for example controls emissions at a mid-point of the economy; at installations either operating in certain specified sectors or combusting fuel above a certain power rating.

The EU ETS is a cornerstone of the EU's policy to combat climate change and its key tool for reducing industrial GHG emissions cost-effectively. Being the first and biggest international scheme for the trading of GHG emission allowances, the EU ETS covers (2010) some 11,000 power stations and industrial plants.

The ambition is for the EU ETS to serve as a model for other countries considering similar national or regional schemes, and to link these to the EU ETS over time.

## EU ETS (to end 2012)

The legal basis for the EU ETS is Directive 2003/87/EC.[208] In January 2005, the EU ETS commenced operation as the largest multi-country, multi-sector GHG emission trading scheme. The first phase ran from 2005 to 2007 and the second phase runs until the end of 2012 to coincide with the first Kyoto commitment period. Its main features are as follows:

### *Basic principle*

The scheme works on a 'cap and trade' basis. Each Member State is required to set an emission cap covering energy activities, production and processing of ferrous metals, mineral and pulp, paper and board activities. Together with international aviation these industries form the 'trading sector'.[209] This means there is a 'cap', or limit, on the total amount of certain GHGs that can be emitted by the factories, power plants and other installations in the system. Within this cap, companies receive emission allowances that they can sell to or buy from one another as needed. The limit on the total number of allowances available ensures that they have a value. At the end of each year each company must surrender enough allowances to cover all its emissions, otherwise heavy fines are imposed. If a company reduces its emissions, it can keep the spare allowances to cover its future needs or else sell them to another company that is short of allowances. The flexibility that trading brings ensures that emissions are cut where it costs least to do so.

## NAPs

The proposed aggregate number of allowances allocated to each installation for the period is set down by each Member State in a national allocation plan (NAP). The current suite of NAPs set out the total quantity of GHG emission allowances that Member States grant to their companies in the second (2008–2012) trading period. Before the start of the first and the second trading periods, each Member State had to decide how many allowances to allocate in total for a trading period and how many each installation covered by the ETS would receive. The NAP also includes emissions projections for sectors not covered by the scheme and the combined total of projected emissions from the 'trading' and 'non-trading' sectors that must be consistent with the Member State's Kyoto target. The Commission may reject a NAP if it is not consistent with the criteria for the NAP set out in the Directive, or more likely suggest changes. The assessment of the NAPs is done by the European Commission based on criteria set in Annex 3 of the EU ETS Directive. For example, the proposed total quantity of allowances must be in line with a Member State's target within the framework of the Kyoto Protocol. This means that a Member State should make sure that the allocations granted to their installations are consistent with meeting its overall Kyoto target.

## EU cap

The EU ETS cap is the total amount of emission allowances to be issued for a given year. Since each allowance represents the right to emit 1 tonne of $CO_2$ – or an amount of another GHG giving the same contribution to global warming as 1 tonne of $CO_2$ – the total number of allowances, i.e. the 'cap', determines the maximum amount of emissions possible under the EU ETS. The EU-wide average annual cap for 2008–2012 amounts to some 2 billion allowances per year; 10.5 per cent lower than what was initially proposed in Member States' NAPs. Annual emissions per installation are now 8.3 per cent below 2005 levels. In the past three years, on aggregate, operators surrendered mostly allowances (EUAs) (95 per cent) to cover their emissions. The remaining 5 per cent of their surrender obligations were met by CERs and/or ERUs.

## Coverage

The EU ETS now operates in 30 countries (the 27 EU Member States plus Iceland, Liechtenstein and Norway). It covers $CO_2$ emissions from installations such as power stations, combustion plants, oil refineries and iron and steel works, as well as factories making cement, glass, lime, bricks, ceramics, pulp, paper and board as well as international aviation. Nitrous oxide emissions from certain processes are also covered. Between them, the installations currently in the scheme account for almost half of the EU's $CO_2$ emissions and 40 per cent of its total GHG emissions. The EU ETS will be further expanded to the petrochemicals, ammonia and aluminium industries and to additional gases in 2013, when the third trading period starts.

## Flexible instruments

The EU ETS Directive recognises that credits from project-based mechanisms, such as the CDM and JI, would increase the cost-effectiveness of reaching emission-reduction targets. They would also result in technology transfer to transition and developing countries, thus assisting these countries in achieving their sustainable development goals. In October 2004, it was therefore decided to link the Kyoto mechanisms with the EU ETS.[210] As a result, from 2008, Member States were allowed to purchase Kyoto ERUs and to permit installations to use ERUs to fulfil their emissions reductions commitments as well as the CERs of the ETS, within certain limits. These limits are defined by the principle of 'supplementarity'. This is interpreted by the Commission to mean that 'use by operations may not lead to a situation where more than half the (emissions reductions) efforts undertaken by a Member State, taking into account government purchases (of emissions permits), is made through Kyoto flexible mechanisms'.[211]

## Auctioning

While auctioning of carbon allowances is limited during the first and second trading period, it will be the main allocation method as of 2013. During the first trading period (2005–2007), Member States auctioned only very limited quantities of carbon allowances, and also during the second trading period (2008–2012) the lion's share of carbon allowances was still allocated for free.

## Registries

The registries system comprises the EU ETS registries and the Community Independent Transaction Log (CITL) is at the core of the EU ETS. Operational since January 2005, the registries system ensures the accurate accounting of all allowances issued under the EU ETS and keeps track of the ownership of allowances in the same way as a banking system keeps track of the ownership of money. Those allowances are held in accounts in electronic registries administered by Member States (the EU ETS registries). Each Member State and Norway, Iceland and Liechtenstein has a national ETS registry. These registries are online databases that record:

- NAPs indicating the allowances assigned to each Member State
- Accounts (held by a company or a physical person) to which those allowances have been allocated
- Transfers of allowances ('transactions') performed by the account holders
- Annual verified $CO_2$ emissions from installations
- Annual reconciliation of allowances and verified emissions, where each company must have surrendered enough allowances to cover all its emissions.

The EU ETS registries also provide public information and reports on the participants and the performance of the trading scheme. To participate in the EU ETS, a company or a physical person must open an account in one of the registries of the relevant Member State. The CITL records and authorises all transactions that take place between accounts in the EU ETS registries. This verification is done automatically and ensures that any transfer of allowances from one account to another is consistent with the ETS rules. The national registries are connected to the CITL through a central hub operated by the Secretariat of the UNs Framework Convention on Climate Change called the International Transaction Log (ITL).

## ETS to date – assessment

The revised EU ETS Directive will, once implemented, radically alter climate change policy-making of the EU and its Member States in the post-2012 period as cap setting for emissions from Member States' tradable sectors will be determined by the Commission from 2013, and permits allocated accordingly. Member States currently have control over the allocation of emissions among installations operating within their borders. In the NAPs produced at the beginning of each trading period, Member State agencies (the EPA in Ireland's case) allocated the available permits among the installations operating under the tradable sector. This process led to a lack of uniformity in allocation rules between Member States, intense lobbying by industry and differing approaches to cap-setting across the EU. For example, several Member States took the precaution of allocating more permits than there had actually been emissions for the previous year.

These factors created an uneven playing field for industry across the EU and, initially, a collapse in the price of permits. Although the price stabilised in the second trading period, the process was considered cumbersome and lead to a constant tension between Member States and the Commission. The Commission argued that an EU-wide cap-setting process would lead to greater predictability in the price of permits and greater emissions reductions.

As a consequence the Commission proposed that emissions from the tradable sector be reduced by 21 per cent on 2005 levels by 2020, or 1.74 per cent per annum.[212] This would equate to an emissions cap of 1,720 Mt by 2020 for the EU ETS sector. This sector will thereby be required to shoulder a large share of the emissions reduction burden – it currently makes up about 41 per cent of overall emissions but will be required to contribute 60 per cent of total abatement. As the greater share of cost-effective abatement options exists in the trading sector, particularly in power generation, this move was widely anticipated. The Commission indicated that it would consider protecting energy-intensive industries via a requirement on international competitors operating under a liberal

144

carbon regime (read the US and China) to surrender allowances when exporting goods to Europe. This proposal elicited a sharp response from US trade representative, Susan Schwab, among others, when first announced.

There have been several assessments of the operation of the EU ETS.[213]

## Post-2012 ETS

Following a comprehensive review of the EU ETS focusing on its functioning and scope, the Commission proposed a number of comprehensive modifications to the scheme, which become operational in 2013.[214] They build on the main lessons learned to date, for example that greater harmonisation is needed as Member States tended to interpret some key provisions differently for examples as regards the allocation of allowances; more detailed rules are also needed about monitoring, verification and reporting requirements; and the cap on national emissions during the second commitment period has resulted in emission reductions.

The key features of the revised EU ETS Directive include the following:

### NAPs

From 2013 there will be a single EU-wide cap with allowances allocated on the basis of the harmonised rules set out in the EU ETS Directive. NAPs will therefore not be needed any more.

### Trading period

This has been increased from five years (2007–2012) to eight (2013–2020).

### Target

ETS emissions across the EU will be reduced by 21 per cent in 2020 with reference to verified 2005 baseline data.

### Cap

An EU-wide cap will be set. The cap will decrease each year by 1.74 per cent of the average annual total quantity of allowances issued by the Member States in 2008–2012. The cap for 2013 has been determined at just under 2.04 billion allowances. This annual reduction will continue beyond 2020 but may be subject to revision not later than 2025.

## Allowances

Free allocations to installations will be based on harmonised rules known as the Community-wide implementation measures (CIMs). No allowances will be allocated free of charge for electricity production, with only limited and temporary options to derogate from this rule. For industry and heating sectors, allowances will be allocated for free based on ambitious (GHG performance-based) benchmarks. Installations that meet the benchmarks (and thus are among the most efficient installations in the EU) will in principle receive all allowances they need. Installations that do not meet the benchmark will have a shortage of allowances and the option to either lower their emissions (e.g. through engaging in abatement) or to purchase additional allowances to cover their excess emissions. In contrast to the allocation methods in force since 2005 and until 2012, this new system will no longer have the perverse effect of providing more free allocation to the highest-emitting installations. The benchmarks are also very important for the achievement of a low-carbon economy. They provide a strong signal for what is possible in terms of low-carbon production and are a milestone to show that the EU is pressing ahead with the implementation of its ambitious climate agenda and that it is serious in striving to become a low-carbon economy. The benchmarks are to be developed per product, to the extent feasible. Generally speaking a product benchmark is based on a value reflecting the average GHG performance of the 10 per cent best-performing installations in the EU producing that product. The benchmarks were established on the basis of the principle 'one product = one benchmark', which means that the benchmark methodology does not differentiate by technology or fuel used, nor the size of an installation or its geographical location. On 14 April 2011 the Climate Change Committee approved the content of guidance documents and templates to facilitate the application of the harmonised allocation rules.

## Auctioning

The volume of allowances as well as the arrangements for such auctioning is governed by the Commission's Auctioning Regulation.[215]

Auctioning of allowances will become the rule from 2013 rather than the exception (as it was during the second commitment period) for electricity generators. From the start of the third trading period in 2013 at least 30 per cent of the allowances to other operators are expected to be auctioned. The level of auctioning for non-exposed sub-sectors will increase in a linear manner so that by 2020 some 70 per cent of allowances will be auctioned; the quantum will rise to 100 per cent by 2027. Sectors and sub-sectors found to be exposed to a significant risk of carbon leakage will receive allowances for free based on ambitious benchmarks, but for non-exposed industry such allocations will be phased out.

Auctions will be conducted in an open, transparent, harmonised and non-discriminatory manner and the process will be predictable. Auctions will be designed to ensure full, fair and equitable access for small and medium-sized enterprises covered by the EU ETS and small emitters. All participants will have access to the same information at the same time and an appropriate legal framework will be in place to minimise any risk of money laundering, terrorist financing, financial crime, insider dealing and market manipulation. The organisation and participation in auctions will be cost-efficient and undue administrative cost will be avoided. The Commission's Auctioning Regulation seeks to ensure these objectives. The Auctioning Regulation also provides for the Member States and the Commission to procure jointly a common platform to auction emission allowances on behalf of the Member States. On 23 November 2011, two joint procurement agreements (JPA) entered into force. The first JPA concerns the procurement of common auction platforms that will be used by 24 Member States (accounting for some 60 per cent of EU ETS emissions); Germany, the UK and Poland opted out. The second JPA concerns the monitoring of the auctions conducted on all auction platforms. The Commission considers that a common platform best ensures respect of the principles of non-discrimination, transparency and simplicity, provides the best guarantees for full, fair and equitable access to small and medium sized enterprises covered by the EU ETS, and best minimises the risk of market abuse. The Member States that wish to appoint an auction platform of their own are allowed to do so, since the Regulation provides for rules as to the functioning of such auction platforms and the coordination with the common auction platform. A total of 88 per cent of allowances to be auctioned by each Member State will be distributed on the basis of the Member State's share of historic emissions under the ETS.

## New entrants reserve

Some 5 per cent of the total quantity of allowances will be put into a reserve for new installations that join the ETS. Thus new investors sourced by IDA Ireland could avail of this provision.

## Auctioning revenue

Ireland – along with several Member States – disagree with the binding nature of the Directive's provisions about the allocation of auctioning revenue to assist climate change adaptation and mitigation projects; with at least 50 per cent of revenues to tackle climate change both in the EU and in developing countries. The proceeds of auctioning 300 million allowances from the new entrants reserve will be used to support up to twelve CCS demonstration projects and projects demonstrating innovative renewable energy technologies. Several terms and conditions will have to be met by prospective project promoters. It is difficult to estimate the potential revenue that will be generated by auctioning as the price and quantity are not known. One study predicted EU-wide revenues of €64 billion between 2013 and 2020.[216] The latest Commission estimate is that a 30 per cent emission-reduction target would cause auctioning revenue to rise to some €7 billion by 2020; or around a third higher than with the current 20 per cent target. Ireland's share (0.9 per cent of the EU-27 total) is forecast to be €224 million by 2020; well below previous estimates.[217]

## Expansion of the coverage of the ETS

From 2013, the scope of the ETS will be extended to include other sectors and GHGs. Inter alia, more $CO_2$ emissions from installations producing bulk organic chemicals, hydrogen, ammonia and aluminium will be included, as will nitrous oxide emissions from the production of nitric, adipic and glyocalic acid production and perfluorocarbons from the aluminium sector. Installations performing activities that result in these emissions will be included.

## Price of allowances

Supply and demand will determine the price of allowances. The price will reflect therefore fundamental factors such as economic growth, fuel prices, rainfall and wind (as it affects wind energy) and temperature (as it affects heating and cooling). The EU ETS provides a stable and predictable regulatory framework that is vital for market stability. The banking of allowances from the second period is not expected to have any impact on the price. If, for more than six consecutive months, the allowance price is more than three times the average price of allowances during the two preceding years in the European market, the Commission is required to convene Member States to discuss the issue. If it is found that the price evolution does not correspond to market fundamentals, the Commission may either allow Member States to bring forward the auctioning of a part of the quantity to be auctioned, or allow them to auction up to 25 per cent of the remaining allowances in the new entrants' reserve.

## LULUCF

As the EU's rules stand at present, it is not possible to use credits from carbon sinks like forests. This policy blockage is obviously a key issue for Coillte and private investors in Irish afforestation; assuming that the issue of the property rights of the carbon are addressed by way of amending legislation. The Commission may change its mind should a comprehensive global deal emerge from the COP negotiations. But for the present, their view is that part of the proceeds from auctioning allowances should be used for investments in LULUCF activities both inside and outside the EU and, with this in mind, the Commission has proposed the setting up of the Global Forest Carbon Mechanism – a performance-based system for financing reductions in deforestation levels in developing countries.[218]

## Other credits

It is possible for projects in Member State which reduce GHG emissions not covered by the ETS to issue credits provided no double counting arises and that (yet to be adopted) common EU provisions apply.

## Emission credits from third countries

The current provisions about the use of credits generated by emission-saving projects undertaken in third countries to cover part of their emissions (in the same way as they use ETS allowances) will be extended. For example, the use of such credits (which may amount to some 1.6 billion allowances) will be increased to 50 per cent of the EU-wide reductions over the period 2008–2020. The precise percentages to be applied have yet to be determined. These projects will have to be officially recognised under the JI or CDM arrangements.

## Small installations

The EU ETS applies from 2013 to installations (where they carry out combustion activities and have a thermal input below 35 MW) reporting emissions over a three-year period in excess of 25,000 tonnes of $CO_2$ e; the current threshold is 10,000 tonnes. Installations operated by hospitals may be excluded. If excluded from the EU ETS small-scale operators will instead be covered by the arrangements decided for the non-ETS sector, including carbon tax.

## Community registry

The revised ETS Directive provides for the centralisation of the ETS operations into a single Community registry. This new registry will be operated by the Commission and will replace all EU ETS registries currently hosted in the Member States. The registry will be used by more than 25,000 end-users (e.g. operators, traders). All transactions taking place in the registry will be subject to the approval of the European Union Transaction Log (EUTL), the successor of the CITL.

## Expanding the ETS

The EU has set out a vision for the development of an international carbon market: the market is expected to develop through bottom-up linking of compatible domestic cap and trade systems. The ambition (perhaps optimistically) is that an OECD-wide carbon market will be operational by 2015, which would be extended to include economically more advanced developing countries by 2020. New sectoral crediting mechanisms would be a stepping stone to cap and trade for these developing countries. Currently, domestic cap and trade systems are being implemented or discussed in the US, Japan, Australia, South Korea, New Zealand and Switzerland, among others. The European Commission is also a founding member of the International Carbon Action Partnership (ICAP). The partnership is made up of countries and regions that are actively pursuing the development of carbon markets through implementation of mandatory cap and trade systems. The partnership provides a forum to share experiences and knowledge. The EU ETS will be able to mutually recognise allowances issued by any country or administrative entity (such a group of states under a federal system).

## Oversight framework

On 21 December 2010 the Commission published a Communication on carbon market oversight, which provides a first assessment of the current level of protection of the carbon market from market abuse and similar problems. It concluded that a major part of the carbon market is subject to appropriate oversight, but that more may be needed in the spot market. On the basis of this stock-taking, the Commission consulted stakeholders during the first half of 2011 and asked advice on how best to enhance the level of market oversight and ensure the continued integrity of the carbon market. If necessary, the Commission will come forward with a legislative proposal.

## Ireland's ETS

At present, the only ETS for GHG in Ireland is the EU ETS, which began operating in 2005 and controls emissions from large-scale fixed-source emitters, such as large industrial units and power-generating stations. It covers about 40 per cent of national $CO_2$ emissions (or 29 per cent of total Irish GHG emissions) but omits major emitting sectors like transport and agriculture. The current trading scheme runs until 2012. Thereafter the ETS becomes a common EU competence. Ireland's NAP (2008–2012) was developed in consultation with a National Allocation Advisory Group and was informed in its decisions by consultants ICF/Byrne Ó Cléirigh. There was extensive stakeholder consultation on what is a strategically important document for the installations covered by the ETS.

**Figure 10: Meeting the Kyoto Protocol targets**

■ Kyoto Protocol Limit – 13% above 1990 baseline value
   ■ Assigned amount - 314.2 Mtonnes of $CO_2e$ for the period 2008 – 2012
   ■ Equates to on average 62.8 Mtonnes of $CO_2e$ per annum

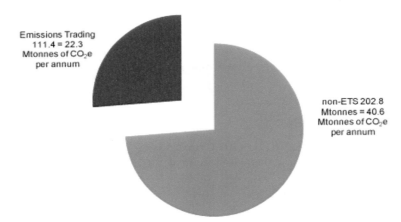

*Source:* EPA, presentation to the Oireachtas Joint Committee on Climate Change and Energy Security (2011).

The EPA has published a review of the first six years of the operation of the ETS in Ireland.[219] The main finding is that some companies have received far more allowances than their emissions subsequently proved to be, resulting in many companies receiving windfall gains.

The main conclusions of the regulatory impact statement on the implementation by Ireland of the revised EU ETS Directive are as follows:[220]

**Table 3: Ireland's largest emitters and over-allocations (2008–2010)**

| | | | |
|---|---|---|---|
| ESB Moneypoint | 3,769,179 tonnes | Synergen | 774,735 tonnes |
| CRH plc Platin | 1,496,902 tonnes | Tynagh Energy | 746,094 tonnes |
| Limerick Alumina Refining | 1,146,694 tonnes | Hunstown Power | 727,124 tonnes |
| ESB Tarbert | 1,009,580 tonnes | ESB Shannonbridge | 709, 660 tonnes |
| Quinn Cement | 1,006,753 tonnes | Edenderry Power | 632,319 tonnes |
| ESB Poolbeg | 901,446 tonnes | ESB Aghada | 530,318 tonnes |
| CRH plc Limerick | 854,357 tonnes | ESB Lough Ree | 516,190 tonnes |
| Viridian Power | 813,085 tonnes | Lagan Cement | 509,225 tonnes |

*Source:* EPA (2011), *Verified Emissions 2008–2010.*

- Over 100 installations will be covered.

- The EPA will continue to have an important role in relation to the operation of the ETS.

- The share of total EU auctioning rights to accrue to Ireland is about 0.92 per cent.

- There is no case for excluding any installation or hospital from the EU ETS.

The RIA failed to determine the cost to consumers arising from the Directive's implementation and did not attempt to estimate the potential revenue that could be generated as a result of auctioning revenue.

The Directive has been partially implemented in Ireland.[221] A decision has yet to be taken about the implementation of the provisions on the use of auctioning revenue.

## Aviation

As air travel becomes cheaper, EU emissions from aviation (which account for 3 per cent of global emissions) are increasing fast. Someone flying from London to New York and back generates roughly the same level of emissions as the average person in the EU does by heating their home for a whole year. In order to mitigate the climate impacts of aviation, the EU decided to impose a cap on $CO_2$ emissions from all international flights – from or to anywhere in the world – that arrive at or depart from an EU airport.

After undertaking a wide-ranging consultation of stakeholders and the public and analysing several types of market-based solutions, the Commission – supported by the Member States

– concluded that bringing aviation into the EU ETS would be the most cost-efficient and environmentally effective option for controlling aviation emissions.[222]

A number of US and Canadian airlines and airline associations contested the measures transposing the Aviation ETS Directive in the UK. The European Court of Justice ruling of 21 December 2011 confirmed 'that the application of the ETS to aviation infringes neither the principles of customary international law at issue nor the Open Skies Agreement'.

Compared with alternatives such as a fuel tax, bringing aviation into the EU ETS will provide the same environmental benefit at a lower cost to society – or a higher environmental benefit for the same cost. In other words the impact on ticket prices, airline companies and the overall economy will be smaller for a given environmental improvement. The inclusion of aviation within the ETS is expected to accelerate technology and fuel innovations and bring about more efficient air traffic control management.

Like industrial installations, airlines will receive tradable allowances covering a certain level of $CO_2$ emissions from their flights per year. After each year operators must surrender a number of allowances equal to their actual emissions in that year. Some 208 Mt of emissions are expected to be issued in 2013. A 2004–2006 baseline figure was used in calculating these figures. Some 82 per cent of the allowances will be allocated free to aircraft operators and 15 per cent are allocated by auctioning with 3 per cent kept for fast growing airlines and new market entrants.

From 1 January 2012, emissions from all domestic and international flights that arrive at or depart from an EU airport are covered by the EU ETS. In addition to the 27 Member States, the EU ETS for aviation covers three EEA–EFTA states (Iceland, Liechtenstein and Norway) and will extend to Croatia by 1 January 2014 due to the country's planned accession to the EU on 1 July 2013.

The airline industry is not at all happy with the inclusion of aviation emissions within the ETS.

Ryanair (with projected emissions of 8 Mt/year) has taken issue with the Directive. Ryanair in common with all airlines using EU airports has to pay for only 15 per cent of the GHG it emits. In that respect the company is no different from the 11,000 other heavy energy users in the EU who have a legal obligation to reduce their emissions. Ryanair announced in October 2011 that the compliance cost of meeting their emissions trading obligations was €16 million a year; this figure was based on buying carbon allowances at €10.75 a tonne. The price of these allowances has fallen by a third (January 2012) to €7.22 so the company's compliance costs must have fallen? Ryanair may have to buy 1.2 Mt of carbon allowance (15 per cent of the 8 Mt emitted) in 2012 and multiplied by €7.22 their compliance cost equals €8.7 million. Ryanair carried some 76.4 million passengers in 2011 and assuming a similar number fly next year then the per capita cost of compliance being passed onto passengers should be just 11 cents and not 25 cents.[223] No doubt the Commission for Aviation Regulation will have something to say about Ryanair's decision.

The total cost to EU-based airlines is forecast in the region of €3–3.5 billion/year.[224] It is expected that airlines will pass on the net cost of compliance to passengers. Compared to airport charges and taxes and surcharges on fuel, it remains to be seen if the compliance costs will affect travel patterns and demand.

It also remains to be seen if airlines will encourage passengers to offset the carbon footprint of their flights by a more systematic use of voluntary carbon credits.[225]

## ETS post-2013 – assessment

The EU ETS post-2013 will remove the allocation for the entire traded sector from Member States' influence (and interference) and establish it at a Community level. As a consequence, emissions reductions in the traded sector will no longer be part of Ireland's GHG emissions inventory. As an EU cap will be set and as fully harmonised rules will be fixed regarding the allocation of allowances it will not be necessary for Ireland to prepare a further NAP. Emissions trading is less important to Ireland compared to other Member States as our non-traded sector will account for 64 per cent of national emissions by 2012, well in excess of the 50 per cent EU average. It is, therefore, crucial that Ireland has policies for all sectors of society other than the traded sector. A 21 per cent reduction in emissions from Ireland's ETS operators is the equivalent to a baseline of some 17.6 Mt by 2020. However, a 21 per cent reduction by Irish ETS operators is only a theoretical concept as there is no requirement on Irish ETS operators per se. The 21 per cent reduction can be achieved anywhere within the EU.

Auctioning is now accepted as a method that will create the greatest incentive for investments in low-carbon technology. Auctioning will generate significant revenues for the Exchequer. For example, in 2015 if EU or Irish powergen companies purchase 10 million allowances from the Irish Government at a price of €25 per tonne, this would generate €250 million for the Exchequer. If the price is lower obviously the revenue will be less. In a scenario where there is 100 per cent auctioning by 2020, and on the basis of the current volume of emissions indentified in the NAP, the Irish Exchequer could receive €800 million per annum; assuming a high price for carbon. Revenues from auctioning and from a proposed carbon tax will be very significant so careful consideration will need to be given as to how best to use this resource to assist in the implementation of the measures in the National Climate Change Strategy post-2012 and in providing subsidies to help certain cohorts of society offset the projected increases in electricity and fuel prices. The economic literature shows that the macro-economic impact of auctioning largely depends on how revenues are recycled back into the economy. For example, revenues could be ringfenced and targeted at particular low-carbon technologies; or used to reduce employer PRSI thereby making employment creation a more attractive proposition; or used to offset compliance costs associated with the implementation of the Directive.

Energy-intensive firms and sectors in countries that did not sign up to the Kyoto Protocol enjoy an advantage as they are not subject to an ETS or other measures. The Commission has recognised this competitiveness issue. Companies within the ETS who are exposed to international competition will not have to move to full auctioning on the grounds that they are at significant risk from 'carbon leakage' i.e. they could be forced by global competitive pressures to relocate production to countries outside the EU that did not impose comparable constraints. The transfer of cement production outside the EU would be one such example. Several Irish operators will benefit from this flexible approach. In general, the intra-EU competitive effect should, broadly speaking, be neutral. Industries that are exposed to extra-EU competition will continue to receive free allocations of permits under EU guidelines that have yet to be clarified; there is the danger that they will face unfair competition

156

from industries based outside the EU not subject to stringent emission-reductions measures. There are thus considerable competitiveness implications that much be addressed.

The price of electricity will be increased by a factor that has not been determined as a direct result of the new EU ETS post-2012 and this will affect all households and the cost of doing business in Ireland.[226]

It would be useful if the Department of Finance estimated approximately how much revenue the Irish Exchequer might receive over the period 2013–2020 as a result of the auctioning of EU ETS allowances and the most cost-effective way to allocate some of this funding to assist climate change mitigation and adaptation projects by leveraging private investment.

What is important to recognise is that the ETS is now embedded at EU level and Ireland's traded sector will have no option but to work within its rules post-2012. On the other hand, given the significant concerns about the low carbon price it is possible that the Commission will bring forward proposals that may seek to tighten the cap for Europe's powengen sector.

## Recent developments

Before the end of 2012, some twenty new legal acts and documents have to be in place in order to ensure the proper functioning of the EU ETS. Among the key instruments are Commission Decision 2010/634/EU on the revised EU ETS cap [227] and Commission Decision 2011/278/EU determining transitional EU-wide rules for harmonised free allocation of emission allowances.[228] Much progress has been made to this end. The EU ETS cap for 2013–2020 has been updated taking into account the extended scope of the EU ETS post-2012. Enhancements of the integrity and security of the registries system underpinning the EU ETS have been prepared. The Commission has proposed to amend the list of sectors and sub-sectors (e.g. bricks, tiles) that are deemed to be exposed to a significant risk of carbon leakage. Agreement has been reached on a proposal to start auctioning of up to 120 million allowances in the form of futures or forwards in 2012. Its aim is to ensure a smooth transition from the second to the third trading period. Regulations will be published on the verification of emission reports and the accreditation and supervision of verifiers.

## Chapter 7

# Ireland's greenhouse gas emissions

Our foot is stuck on the accelerator and we are heading towards an abyss.

Ban Ki-moon, UN Secretary General,
8 September 2009

## Introduction

The National Climate Change Strategy (NCCS) designated the EPA with responsibility for developing annual national emission projections for GHGs for all key sectors of the economy, in collaboration with relevant state and other bodies.[229] These emission projections serve to inform national policy initiatives and to allow Ireland to comply with EU reporting obligations.[230]

The EPA produces GHG emission projections annually, which allows the most recent environmental and other policy developments to be taken into account as well as updates to key assumptions (such as revisions to anticipated economic growth).

On 16 April 2012, the EPA released figures for projected emissions of Ireland's GHG emissions from 2012 to 2020 that take account of SEAI's (December 2010) energy forecasts,[231] which are based on the *World Recovery* scenario from the ESRI's 2008 Medium-Term Review (which assumes a recovery in economic growth from 2011).[232] The projections are heavily influenced by assumptions about the successful implementation of existing GHG emission reduction policies and planned programmes, in particular the promotion of renewable energy and energy efficiency and the inclusion of forest sinks as an eligible carbon offset.

GHG emissions are projected to be substantially lower than historical emissions, which peaked in 2001 at 70.2 Mt of $CO_2$e.

The projections indicate a total 'distance to target' for the Kyoto Protocol period, i.e. to end 2012, of 4.1–5.1 Mt. This compares to a total distance to target of 12.7–15 Mt in the EPA's April 2010 projections. In estimating Ireland's distance to target under the Kyoto Protocol, the impact of forest sinks is included as allowed for under Article 3.3 of the Protocol. Purchases already made by the Carbon Fund managed by the National Treasury Management Agency on behalf of government, as well as unused allowances from the EU ETS new entrants reserve (some 6 Mt), means that Ireland will comply with its Kyoto obligations without any further purchases.[233]

A second and different set of legally binding targets applies under the EU Commission's 'Energy and Climate Package', which was agreed by the European Parliament and Council in December 2008 and became law in June 2009. Under this package, Ireland is required to deliver a 20 per cent reduction in non-ETS GHG emissions by 2020 (relative to 2005 levels). The non-ETS sectors cover those that are outside the EU ETS and include agriculture, transport, residential and waste. The projections indicate that total non-ETS emissions will be 4.1–7.8 Mt above the 2020 target. This compares to a projection of 7.6–12.4 Mt above the 2020 target in the EPA's April 2010 projections. In addition, the projections indicate that Ireland will exceed its binding annual limit in 2015–2017 and will exceed its obligation by as much as 20.6 Mt over the period 2013–2020.

## GHG emission inventory/projections

A GHG **emission inventory** is a compilation of historical GHG emissions from sources, such as transport, power generation, industry and agriculture, from 1990 to the most recent year for which data is available. The inventory, which provides details for all sectors, covers the time period 1990–2009 (Figure 11).

A GHG **emission projection** is an estimate of what emission levels are likely to be in the future based on key assumptions such as economic growth, fuel price and government policy. Emissions projections serve to inform national policy initiatives,

**Figure 11: Ireland's GHG emissions 1990–2010**

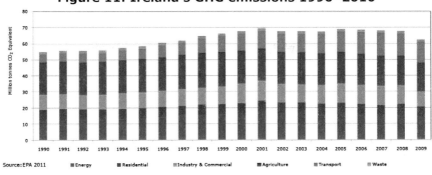

*Source:* EPA (2012), *Ireland's Greenhouse Gas Emissions Projections 2011–2020*.

such as the carbon budget, and allow Ireland to comply with EU reporting obligations on projections. The EPA publishes GHG emissions projections on an annual basis and submits emissions projections to the European Commission. Projected emissions are classified into the following six IPCC sectors: energy, industrial processes, solvent and other product use, agriculture, land-use land change and forestry waste. Projected GHG emissions are depicted graphically in the chart below under two scenarios; *With Measures* (existing policies and measures) and *With Additional Measures* (existing and planned policies and measure) (Figure 12).

**Figure 12: Ireland's projected GHG emissions to 2020**

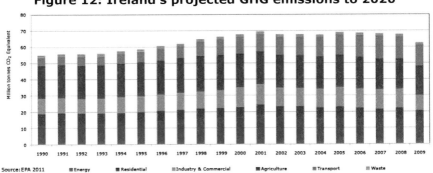

*Source:* EPA (2012), *Ireland's Greenhouse Gas Emissions Projections 2011–2020*.

## Input data and key assumptions

The GHG emission projections are based on data provided by a range of state agencies and organisations, most notably SEAI for energy forecasts and Teagasc for forecast animal numbers, crop statistics and nitrogen fertiliser use. Energy-related emissions projections are based on energy forecasts published by SEAI in December 2010. These energy forecasts are based on *ESRI's Low Growth* scenario published in *Recovery Scenarios for Ireland: An Update*. In this publication, the ESRI produced a number of scenarios that indicate that economic output could be 15 per cent to 20 per cent below where it would have been without the current economic crisis. The *Low Growth* scenario was used by SEAI as a basis for its energy forecasts and therefore underpins the emission projections presented here.

Agriculture emissions projections are based on data from Teagasc's FAPRI-Ireland model which were provided to the EPA in December 2011. The FAPRI-Ireland model is a dynamic, partial equilibrium model that is linked both to the FAPRI-EU and world modelling systems. The scenario underpinning the agriculture emissions projections assumes full achievement of the Food Harvest 2020 targets.[234] These targets are projected to lead inter alia to an increase in the share of dairy cows and a decrease in the share of suckler cows in the bovine population.

Table 4 outlines the key macroeconomic assumptions that underpin the projections.

**Table 4: Key macroeconomic assumptions underlying the GHG emission reduction projections**

| | Average Annual % Growth | |
|---|---|---|
| | 2011–2015 | 2016–2020 |
| GDP | 3.0% | 3.3% |
| GNP | 2.3% | 3.6% |
| Personal Consumption | 0.2% | 2.9% |

| | 2010 | 2011 | 2015 | 2020 |
|---|---|---|---|---|
| Housing Completions ('000) | 15 | 10 | 32 | 33 |
| Stock of cars ('000) | 1,917 | 1,819 | 1,891 | 2,032 |
| Population ('000) | 4,428 | 4,427 | 4,484 | 4,603 |
| ETS Carbon $C_{2009}/tCO_2$ | - | 14.50 | 25.00 | 33.00 |
| Carbon tax $C_{2009}/tCO_2$ | - | 15.83 | 25.00 | 33.00 |
| Coal $\$_{2009}$/tonne | - | 97 | 98 | 106 |
| Oil $\$_{2009}$/barrel | - | 106 | 108 | 110 |
| Gas $\$_{2009}$/MBtu | - | 10 | 11 | 12 |
| Peat $\$_{2009}$/MWh | - | 15 | 15 | 15 |

*Source:* EPA (2012), *Ireland's Greenhouse Gas Emissions Projections 2011–2020.*

## Description of emissions scenarios

Two emissions projections are presented that show two potential outlooks to 2020 depending on policy development and implementation.

**Figure 13: Ireland's GHG emissions projections *With Measures (WM)/With Additional Measures (WAM)***

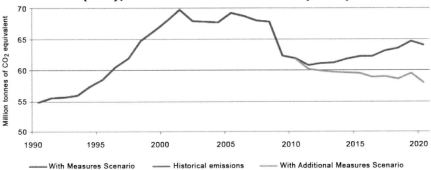

*Source:* EPA (2011), *National Emissions Projections.*

**Table 5: Description of projection scenarios**

| With Measures Scenario | **Energy-related emissions projections**<br>• Based on SEAI *Baseline* energy forecast. These energy forecasts are based on a set of macroeconomic projections for Ireland produced by the ESRI in September 2011.<br>**Agriculture emission projections**<br>• Based on forecasts of animal numbers, crop statistics and nitrogen fertiliser use produced by Teagasc in December 2011 which assume achievement of "Food Harvest 2020" targets.<br>**Waste**<br>• Assumes that the Landfill Directive targets (Directive 1999/31/EC) will be reached in 2013 and 2016.<br>**Forestry**<br>• Projections of the future impact of forest sinks were provided by Department of Agriculture, Food and the Marine. Estimates of forest cover are based on maintaining planting rates of 8,000 hectares per year into the future. |
|---|---|
| With Additional Measures Scenario | **Energy-related emissions projections**<br>• Based on SEAI *NEEAP/NREAP* energy forecast. The *NEEAP/NREAP* energy forecast builds on the *Baseline* energy forecast with additional assumptions to account for Ireland's National Energy Efficiency Action Plan and National Renewable Energy Action Plan. This includes measures such as 20% improvement in energy efficiency across all sectors, 40% renewable electricity (RES-E) share and 10% renewable transport (RES-T) share (including 10% electric vehicles penetration target).<br>**Agriculture emission projections/Waste/Forestry**<br>• As above |

*Source:* EPA (2012), *Ireland's Greenhouse Gas Emissions Projections 2011–2020.*

The *With Measures* scenario is based primarily on SEAI's baseline energy forecast, which incorporates the anticipated impact of policies and measures that were in place (and legislatively provided for) by end of 2010.

The *With Additional Measures* scenario is based on SEAI's NEEAP/NREAP energy forecast. Under this more optimistic policy scenario, the targets set out in government policy documents such as Ireland's National Energy Efficiency Action Plan (NEEAP)[235] and the National Renewable Energy Action Plan (NREAP)[236] are assumed to be met in full.

GHG projections under both scenarios are shown in Figure 13.

The two scenarios are summarised in Table 5.

## Compliance with the Kyoto Protocol

By 2010, the EU-27 had succeeded in cutting emissions by 15.5 per cent since 1990 (the figure for the EU-15 is 10.7 per cent), while the European economy grew by 41 per cent over the same period.[237] The strong performance of the UK and Germany, which account for a third of total emissions, strongly influenced the overall picture. GHG emissions fell for six consecutive years up to and including 2010. Between 2008 and 2009, emissions fell by 7.1 per cent in the EU-27, much more than the 4 per cent contraction in GDP. However, in 2010 emissions rose by 2.4 per cent. Thus the EU-15 is on target to meet if not over-achieve its 8 per cent emission reduction target. Taking into account the planned use of Kyoto flexible mechanisms, use of unused allowances from the EU ETS new entrants reserve and carbon sinks, only Austria, Italy and Luxembourg, in the Commission's assessment, might face difficulties with meeting their targets. Under the Kyoto Protocol, Ireland is required to limit total national GHG emissions to 314.2 Mt over the five-year period 2008–2012, which is equivalent to an average of 62.8 Mt of $CO_2$e per annum. The Kyoto Protocol limit was calculated as 13 per cent above Ireland's 1990 baseline value, which was established and fixed at 55.61 Mt following an in-depth review of Ireland's 2006 GHG inventory submission to the UNFCCC.

In the country report for Ireland, the European Environmental Agency noted that average 2008–2010 emissions were 14.4 per cent higher than the base year level of minus 13 per cent. In the non-traded sector emissions were significantly higher than their respective target, by an amount equivalent to 5.2 per cent of Ireland's base year emissions. LULUCF activities are expected to decrease net emissions by an annual amount equivalent to 5 per cent of base year level emissions. Ireland intends to acquire Kyoto units equivalent to 3 per cent of base year emissions. Taking all these effects into account, average emissions in the non-traded sector were below their target level by a gap representing 2.8 per cent of base year emissions. The EEA concluded that Ireland was on track towards its burden-sharing target by the end of 2010.

The latest data from the EPA confirms this assessment, with GHG emissions falling by 0.43 Mt (0.7 per cent) in 2010 to 61.31 Mt. Emissions from companies covered by the EU ETS fell sharply in 2011; by 1.6 Mt to 15.8 Mt. The reduction was largely due to a decline in emissions from the cement industry (down 12 per cent) and from power generators (decrease of 11 per cent). In fact, the over-allocation of allowances to the cement sector is some 7 Mt; a significant windfall.

Figure 14 shows emissions for the period 1990–2020 for both *With Measures* and *With Additional Measures* scenarios and compares with the Kyoto Protocol limit for the 2008–2012 period. Projected emissions for the Kyoto period include the impact of forest sinks.

**Figure 14: Historical and projected GHG emissions (including forest sinks for the 2008–2012 period) for each scenario and the Kyoto Protocol target**

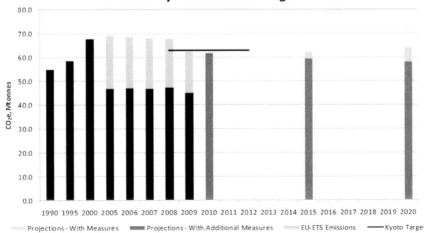

*Source:* EPA (2012), *Ireland's Greenhouse Gas Emissions Projections 2011–2020.*

To determine compliance with the Kyoto Protocol, it is necessary to consider the relative contributions of the ETS and non-ETS sector emissions. The second NAP allocates 22.3 Mt to those installations covered by the EU ETS (Table 6). The remainder (i.e. 40.6 Mt) is compared with projected non-ETS sector emissions (including the impact of forest sinks) to assess the Government's purchasing requirement and/or need for additional domestic action.[238]

**Table 6: Estimation of distance above Kyoto limit after first two years of Kyoto Protocol period**

| | Mt CO2eq | | | |
| --- | --- | --- | --- | --- |
| | 2008 | 2009 | 2010 | 2008–2010 |
| Total National Emissions | 67.57 | 61.74 | 61.31 | 190.62 |
| Less Verified Emissions for ETS | 20.38 | 17.22 | 17.36 | 54.96 |
| Total Non-ETS Emissions | 47.19 | 44.52 | 43.95 | 135.66 |
| | | | | |
| Kyoto Limit | 62.84 | 62.84 | 62.84 | 188.51 |
| Less ETS Allocation | 22.28 | 22.28 | 22.28 | 66.84 |
| Total Non-ETS Limit[1] | 40.56 | 40.56 | 40.56 | 121.67* |
| | | | | |
| Distance above Kyoto limit after first three years of Kyoto Protocol period (excluding forest sinks) | 6.63 | 3.96 | 3.40 | 135.66-121.67 = 13.99 |
| | | | | |
| Forest sinks | -2.68 | -2.82 | -3.01 | -8.51 |
| Distance above Kyoto limit after first three years of Kyoto Protocol period (including forest sinks) | 3.95* | 1.14 | 0.39 | 5.48 |

[1] It is important to note that not all of 22.28 Mt $CO_2$ was allocated to ETS sectors in 2008, 2009 and 2010. The remainder is mainly reserved for New Entrants over the 5 year period 2008-2012 and if not fully utilised will revert to the national account. It is currently estimated that this will amount to around 6 million tonnes of $CO_2$ over the five year Kyoto period. The actual allocation to installations was 19.97 Mt $CO_2$ in 2008, 20.03 Mt $CO_2$ in 2009 and 20.96 Mt $CO_2$ in 2010, which compares to verified emissions of 20.38 Mt in 2008, 17.22 Mt $CO_2$ in 2009 and 17.36 Mt $CO_2$ in 2010.

*Source:* EPA (2012), *Ireland's Greenhouse Gas Emissions Projections 2011–2020.*

While the national mitigation Kyoto target is an average of 62.8 Mt per annum, the target for the non-ETS sector is 40.6 Mt, which results in a distance to target of between 0.8 Mt/a to 1 Mt/a using the *With Measures* and *With Additional Measures scenarios* respectively. While the reduction in the distance to target (compared to earlier forecasts) is a positive outcome in terms of compliance, its occurrence is primarily a direct result of the current economic recession and the economic outlook in the short term.

## Implications for Government purchasing requirement

When the NCCS was published in 2007 the estimated amount of carbon allowances or credits to be acquired by the state in the 2008–2012 period was 18 million units.[239] However, given the sharp fall in national emissions the revised purchasing requirement for compliance purposes for the five-year period 2008–2012 will be in the range 4.1–5.1 million units. Based on these projections, and the purchase of 8.3 Mt of allowances to date, there will be a surplus of upwards of 4.2 Mt above Ireland's Kyoto Protocol commitment..

Furthermore, under the NAP 2008–2012, the EPA established a new entrant set-aside whereby allowances were set aside for new entrants coming into the EU ETS and for the expansion of existing installations over the 2008–2012 period. In addition, where an installation is closed in the years 2008–2012, the allowances in respect of future years are withheld and added to the new entrant set-aside. It was stated in the NAP that any allowances remaining unused in the new entrant set-aside at the end of the 2008–2012 period will be retired for Kyoto compliance. It is currently estimated that there will be around 6 million allowances remaining in the new entrant set-aside at the end of the Kyoto period.

If the Government is in possession of excess Kyoto units (i.e. AAUs, CERs and ERUs) following compliance assessment under the Kyoto Protocol, these can be carried over in the next commitment period (if one is agreed) i.e. post 2012 subject to certain rules and limitations. Furthermore, the EU effort-sharing Decision allows Member States to make limited use of credits over the period 2013–2020. This may provide some use for the surplus credits purchased by Ireland's Carbon Fund.

## Compliance with EU 2020 target for the non-ETS sector emissions

It is recalled that the target for Ireland's non-ETS sectors is to reduce emissions by 20 per cent in 2020 relative to 2005 levels; the limit has been provisionally calculated by the EPA as 37.5 Mt.[240]

Figure 15 shows projected emission levels for the *With Measures* and *With Additional Measures* scenarios, without forest sinks. It is projected that in 2020 Ireland will be 4.1–8.8 Mt over the 2020 limit, which is 1–11 per cent below 2005 levels in 2020. The *With Additional Measures* scenario assumes that all targets in government policy documents such as the NEEAP and NREAP are met. The difficulties associated with meeting these targets should not, however, be underestimated. Failure to meet these targets will result in higher emissions levels than those projected under this scenario.

**Figure 15: WM and WAM GHG emissions projections and comparison with the linear reduction pathway required between 2013 and 2020**

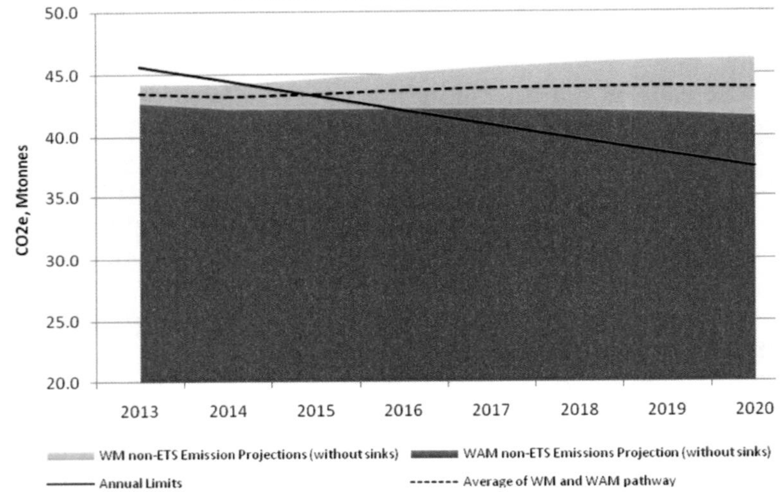

*Source:* EPA (2012), *Ireland's Greenhouse Gas Emissions Projections 2011–2020.*

Under the effort-sharing Decision, Member States are permitted to meet their annual targets through a number of mechanisms, which include carry forward from the following year of a quantity of its annual emission allocation, use of statistical transfers from other Member States who may transfer part of their annual emission allocation and the use of credits from project activities as long as certain criteria are met.

## Statistical transfers

Member States are strongly encouraged (and effectively obliged) to purchase statistical transfers from other Member States who have met their effort-sharing targets. Thus if Estonia had surplus credits these could be acquired (for arguments sake using the Carbon Fund), allowing Ireland to meet its legally binding annual targets. Work on the methodology and protocols for these statistical transfers has yet to begin but will be informed by a similar arrangement for renewables – the Renewable Energy Guarantee of Origin Certificate – that is being developed by the European Commission. As the cost of these statistical transfers may be below the carbon price it may prove very attractive and cost effective for Ireland to make extensive use of this instrument to offset, for example, the distance to target in respect of agriculture emissions. In fact, the cost to Ireland in bridging its projected 9.4 Mt shortfall by 2020 could be as low as €155 million using this valuable flexibility mechanism.[241]

The 2011 emissions projections indicate that cumulative non-ETS sector emissions would be 4.5–30.1 Mt over the 2013–2020 targets. This reduction in the distance to target compared with the previous year's projection is primarily as a result of the economic downturn. This projected decline in transport sector emissions relative to last year's projections plays a significant role in improving the picture for Ireland in terms of meeting our 2020 non-ETS sector emissions target.

GHG emissions and removals related to LULUCF are currently not included in the EU's 2020 target. However, the Climate and Energy Package require the Commission to assess ways of counting LULUCF towards the EU's reduction commitment and, depending on its findings, to make a legislative proposal. The Commission will assess whether emissions and removals of GHG related to LULUCF should be covered by the EU's target of cutting GHG emissions to 20 per cent, or, if the conditions are right, to 30 per cent below 1990 levels by 2020. The LULUCF sector comprises, for example, trees, other living biomass and organic soil carbon, all of which can either absorb $CO_2$ from the atmosphere or emit it to a varying extent, depending on how they are managed and other factors. In Ireland, forest sinks are projected to provide a removal of 4.6 Mt in 2020 (relative to 1990) and 32 Mt over the period 2013–2020, which illustrates the important role that LULUCF could play in developing mitigation strategies for Ireland if there was an EU legal framework in place. It is important to note that if LULUCF are included in the EU 2020 target, the ambition level of 2020 targets could be substantially increased e.g. as part of a step-up to 30 per cent, which could offset some of the gains delivered through the inclusion of LULUCF.

## National and sectoral trends

The trend in total emissions (i.e. both ETS and non-ETS sector emissions) from 1990 to 2009, with projected trends for the *With Additional Measures* scenario is shown in Figure 16. Forest sinks are only calculated and reported for the Kyoto period.

**Figure 16: Historical and projected trends in GHG emissions for the WAM scenario 1990–2020**

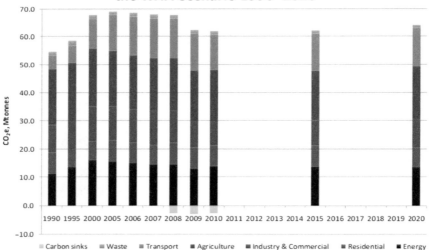

*Source:* EPA (2012), *Ireland's Greenhouse Gas Emissions Projections 2011–2020*.

The *With Measures* scenario is based on SEAI's baseline energy forecast and projects emissions under a scenario where only existing policies and measures (i.e. those that are currently agreed and implemented) are taken into consideration. Under the *With Measures* scenario, total GHG emissions in Ireland for 2020 are projected to be 0.9 per cent higher than 2009 levels.

The *With Additional Measures* scenario is based on SEAI's energy forecasts and assumes existing and additional policies and measures are taken into consideration. Additional policies and measures are defined as those that are currently committed to in government policy documents, such as the NEEAP and the NREAP but are not yet fully implemented. Under the *With Additional Measures* emission projection, GHG emissions in Ireland are projected to decrease by 8.1 per cent between 2009 and 2020, which implies an annual average reduction of 0.8 per cent. This returns GHG emissions in 2020 to 1993 levels.

## Emissions trading sectors

*   Under both *With Measures* and *With Additional Measures* emissions projections, combined emissions from all ETS sectors in the period 2008 to 2012 are projected to be below the annual allocation of allowances that operators received under the second NAP. This is as a result of the projected slow-down in economic growth over the short term and, in addition, a projected increase in electricity generated from renewables.

## Transport

*   Under the *With Measures* scenario, transport emissions (the third largest source accounting for 18.9 per cent of total emissions) are projected to increase by 7.7 per cent over the period 2009–2020 to 12.5 Mt. The *With Measures* scenario includes the impact of VRT and motor tax changes (introduced in 2008), improved fuel economy of private cars and renewable penetration of 3 per cent by 2020.

*   While transport sector emissions were 0.92 Mt lower in 2010 than in 2009 (a decrease of 7.3 per cent) they have increased by 127 per cent since 1990. Transport emissions are projected to be almost 1.1Mt lower in 2020 compared with last year's projection. The ESRI attribute this reduced energy demand from the transport sector to more conservative assumptions on economic growth relative to 2010 which particularly impacts freight transport. In addition, high levels

of emigration in car-owning age groups results in a stabilisation of car ownership levels out to 2020.

- Under the *With Additional Measures* scenario, transport
  emissions are projected to decrease by 1.4 per cent over the
  period 2009–2020 to 11.4 Mt. In this scenario, it is assumed
  that renewable energy penetration is 10 per cent (the RES-T
  target), which includes 200,000 electric vehicles by 2020
  (1 per cent of the target) with bio-fuels contributing 9 per cent.
  In addition, policies and measures such as transport mobility
  management and travel plans, e-work-ing, sustainable transport fleets and efficient driving methods are included.

- The Government's policy approach is set out in *Smarter
  Travel – Sustainable Transport Future*, which lists 49 possible actions.[242] Its implementation will be informed by the
  EU White Paper on Transport, which has set an emission-
  reduction target of 60 per cent by 2050, including the phasing
  out of fossil-fuelled cars in cities and a 40 per cent use of
  sustainable low-carbon fuels in aviation.[243]

## Energy

- Energy sector emissions comprise emissions from power
  generation, oil refining, peat briquetting and fugitive emissions and account for 21.8 per cent of total GHG emissions.
  Emissions from power generation accounted for 96 per cent
  of energy sector emissions in 2009 and are responsible for
  a similar share of emissions over the projection period. In
  2010, emissions relating to energy (principally electricity
  generation) were 0.25 Mt higher than in 2009 (a 1.9 percent
  increase) reflecting a drop in the share of renewables in gross
  electricity consumption from 14.3 per cent to 12.9 per cent.

- Under the revised *With Measures* scenario, total energy sector
  emissions are projected to decrease by 8.7 per cent over the
  period 2010 to 2020 to 12.2 Mt. The decrease in emissions
  is caused by a displacement of gas by renewables which are
  projected to reach 27 per cent penetration in 2020. This is in
  sharp contrast to last year's forecast of an increase in emissions by some 3.4 per cent.

- Under the *With Additional Measures* scenario, total energy
  sector emissions are projected to decrease by 19.8 per cent

over the period 2010–2020 to 12.6 Mt. In this scenario, it is assumed (unrealistically) that for 2020 there is a 40 per cent share of renewable energy in electricity generation with the largest contribution coming from wind (supported by the Gate 3 process). In addition, expansion of biomass electricity generation capacity through the expansion of biomass electricity generation to 270 MW, construction of two waste-to-energy units and at least 75 MW of wave energy, the continued development of landfill gas electricity generation and small-scale biomass CHP, all contribute to renewable electricity generation.

## Agriculture

- Agriculture emissions in Ireland account for some 30 per cent of total GHG emissions; way above the EU-27 average of 9 per cent. Hence this sector has particular challenges. Some 12.8 million head of livestock account for the bulk of the emissions.

- Emission projections for enteric fermentation, manure management and nitrogen application to soils are based on forecast animal numbers, crop areas and projected nitrogen fertiliser application to soils produced by Teagasc in February 2011. These estimates take into account the targets set out in *Food Harvest 2020* published by the Department of Agriculture, Fisheries and the Marine in 2010. The main targets set out in this document are: 1) increasing the value of primary output in the agriculture, fisheries and forestry sector by €1.5 billion by 2020, 2) increasing the value added in the agri-food, fisheries and wood products sector by €3 billion by 2020, and 3) achieving an export target of €12 billion for the sector by 2020.

- Enteric fermentation, manure management and nitrogen application to agricultural soils account for on average 46 per cent, 28 per cent and 22 per cent, respectively of total emissions from agriculture. Emissions from the combustion of fossil fuels accounts for on average 4 per cent of total emissions from agriculture.

- Total emissions from agriculture are projected to increase by 1.1 Mt (6.9 per cent) over the period 2010–2020 to 20 Mt with the lifting of the EU milk quota regime from 2015 (which imposes a production limit on milk output).

- The Government is attaching a high importance on the outcome of the negotiations on the reform of the CAP post-2013 (to 2020) and specifically to EU cofinancing measures that will help farmers use more sustainable and 'green' production methods.

## *Residential*

- Under the *With Measures* scenario, emissions from the residential sector are projected to decrease by 12 per cent to 76.9 Mt between 2010 and 2020. These emissions account for 12.7 per cent of total GHG emissions; 7.82 Mt. The following measures are included in the *With Measures* emission projection: SEAI's Home Energy Saving Scheme; Lighting Efficiency Standard; Efficient Boiler Standard; and the 2008 Building Regulations. Emissions in 2010 increased by 0.40 Mt (5.3 per cent) from the previous year reflecting an increase in fossil fuel use from households due to a considerably colder and longer heating season.

- Under the *With Additional Measures* scenario, emissions are projected to decrease by 33.8 per cent between 20010 and 2020 to 5.2 Mt. Under this scenario, the impacts of the following measures are included: the National Retrofit Scheme, which aims to improve the energy performance of up to 1 million dwellings by 2020; implementation of the Building Regulations; increased impact of the Lighting Efficiency Standard and Efficient Boiler Standard (above those in the *With Measures* scenario); and unspecified measures, yet to be identified, that are required to meet the targets set out in the NEEAP. In addition, increased penetration of renewables is assumed in line with meeting the national RES-H target i.e. 12 per cent thermal heat from renewables by 2020.

## *Industry and commercial services*

- Under the *With Measures* scenario, emissions from the industry and commercial services sector are projected to increase by 4.1 per cent to 9.3 Mt between 2010 and 2020.

These emissions account for 14.6 per cent of total GHG emissions; some 8.97 Mt. The significant downturn in the cement industry, as a result of the downturn in the economy, is included in this emission projection as is a substantial increase in emissions from the alumina industry. In addition, the impact of the Accelerated Capital Allowance Scheme and SEAI energy agreements such as the Large Industry Network and small business supports are taken into account.

- Under the *With Additional Measures* scenario, emissions from the industry and commercial services sector are projected to decrease by 10.6 per cent to 8 Mt between 2010 and 2020. In this scenario, energy demand from industrial and commercial services sectors decreases relative to the *With Measures* scenario as energy-efficiency policies and measures are assumed to be adopted and implemented. These include the implementation of 2010 Building Regulations, the public and commercial sector components of the National Retrofit Scheme and additional measures (as yet unspecified) that are required to meet energy-efficiency targets set down in the NEEAP. In addition, increased penetration of renewables is assumed in the *With Additional Measures* scenario in line with meeting the national RES-H target, which will be driven by the new REFIT tariffs for biomass CHP.

## Waste

- There is only one scenario for waste sector emission projections that account for 1.4 per cent of total GHG emissions; 0.89 Mt. GHG emissions from the waste sector are projected to increase by 15.3 per cent between 2010 and 2020 to 1 Mt. In 2010, the EPA was forecasting 15.3 per cent decrease. It is assumed that the Landfill Directive targets, for the diversion of biodegrad able waste from landfill, are met progressively between 2013 and 2016. This is assumed on the basis of measures and initiatives designed to divert biode gradable waste from landfill. These include guidance published by the EPA for EPA landfill licence holders in relation to biodegradable waste diversion obligations and the introduction of the Waste Management (Food Waste) Regulations 2009, which came into force on 1 January 2010 and are designed to require commercial operations (e.g. restaurants, workplace canteens etc.) to provide for the source separation and collection for recycling of food waste.[244, 245]

- It is assumed that methane capture increases from 71 per cent in 2010 to 75 per cent in 2020.

- In relation to incineration, emissions from the waste-to-energy plant at Car-ranstown (opened in October 2011) and the Poolbeg waste incinerator (due to open in 2015) are taken into account. $CO_2e$ emissions from incineration are projected to be 32 per cent of total waste sector emissions in 2020.

## Overall sectoral contribution

In terms of sectoral contributions to total national emissions over the Kyoto period, Figure 17 shows the share from each of the sectors over the period 2008 to 2012. Agriculture and transport sector emissions account for 50 per cent of emissions. In terms of the sectoral contribution to total non-ETS sector emissions, Figure 18 shows the projected contributions for the *With Additional Measures* scenario in 2020. Under this scenario, agriculture and transport sector emissions account for 75 per cent of total non-ETS emissions. This illustrates the important

**Figure 17: Projected sectoral share of total GHG emissions over the period 2008–2012 for the WM and WAM scenarios**

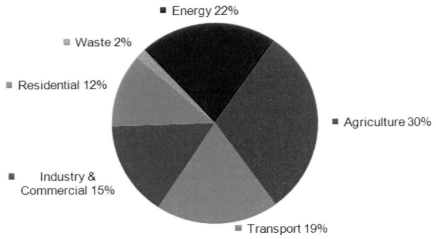

*Source:* EPA (2012), *Ireland's Greenhouse Gas Emissions Projections 2011–2020.*

**Figure 18: Projected sectoral share of non-ETS GHG emissions in 2020 for the WAM scenario**

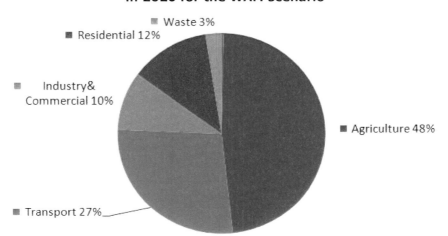

*Source:* EPA (2012), *Ireland's Greenhouse Gas Emissions Projections 2011–2020.*

role that both transport and agriculture will play in developing mitigation options for achieving the 2020 targets in relation to non-ETS sector emissions.

## Comparison between *With Measures* and *With Additional Measures*

The difference between the *With Measures* and *With Additional Measures* scenario shows the impact of additional policies and measures and renewables penetration assumed to meet NEEAP and NREAP targets. The total impact of additional policies and measures and renewables penetration is projected to be 2.46 Mt in 2015 and 5.5 Mt in 2020. Table 7 shows the sectors where the additional measures are assumed to take place.

It should be noted that the SEAI energy forecast and therefore the *With Additional Measures* scenario assumes that targets in the NEEAP and NREAP are met in full. The difficulties associated with meeting these targets should, however, not be underestimated. Failure to meet these targets will mean that the savings outlined above will not be delivered and emissions levels will be higher than those projected.

**Table 7: CO2eq savings from additional policies and measures by sector**

| CO$_2$eq, Mtonnes | 2011–2012 | 2015 | 2020 |
|---|---|---|---|
| Energy | 0.11 | 0.47 | 1.47 |
| Industry | 0.08 | 0.32 | 0.62 |
| Services | 0.11 | 0.36 | 0.69 |
| Residential | 0.31 | 0.88 | 1.70 |
| Transport | 0.07 | 0.42 | 1.05 |
| Total | **0.68** | **2.46** | **5.54** |

*Source:* EPA (2012), *Ireland's Greenhouse Gas Emissions Projections 2011–2020.*

## Comparison with 2010 EPA GHG emissions projections

Since the EPA published its GHG emissions projections in April 2010 there have been significant developments in terms of economic forecasts and policy formulation. It is instructive to compare the emissions projections presented for 2011 with previous work to understand the degree of variability in projecting emissions and where key differences occur. Figure 19 shows

**Figure 19: Comparison with 2011 EPA Greenhouse Gas Emissions Projections**

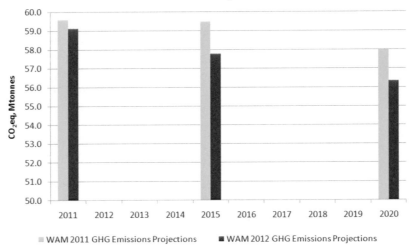

*Source:* EPA (2011), *Ireland's Greenhouse Gas Emissions Projections 2010–2020.*

178

a comparison between the projections presented in April 2011 GHG and those published last year under the *With Additional Measures* scenario.

The emissions projections developed in 2011 are based on GDP growth rates of 3.2 per cent per cent between 2010 and 2015 and 2.1 per cent between 2016 and 2020.

Overall for the Kyoto period, total national emissions are projected to be 0.9 per cent lower compared with last year's projection. The most marked differences in sectoral emissions projections are in the energy sector (3 per cent lower), industry and commercial (4.4 per cent higher) and transport (7.8 per cent lower). For all three sectors reduced energy demand in the context of a projected deeper recession plays a significant impact. For 2020, emissions are projected to be 2.8 per cent lower compared with last year's projection. In the period 2013–2020 there are a number of significant differences compared with last year, particularly in the energy sector (14.6 per cent lower), agriculture (5.6 per cent higher), transport (4.8 per cent lower).

For the energy sector, a higher power generation is assumed over the period 2013–2020 due to a higher level of exports compared with last year's projection. SEAI has indicated that there are several variables interacting to drive the exports in the model, which include relative generation capacity margins in the UK market and in the single electricity market, the expansion of renewable electricity capacity out to 2020, which further depresses the price in the single electricity market relative to the UK market, and differing demand growth in both jurisdictions to 2020.

Agriculture emissions projections for 2020 will be some 5.6 per cent higher because of inclusion of the Food Harvest 2020 targets, which assumes a higher output from the agriculture sector and therefore higher emissions.

For the transport sector, emissions were projected to be almost 4 Mt lower in 2020 compared with the 2009 projection. However, the 2011 forecast changes this to a 0.6 Mt decrease. The ESRI attribute this reduced energy demand from the transport sector to reduced economic growth, which particularly impacts freight transport. In addition, high levels of emigration in car-owning age groups results in a stabilisation of car ownership levels out to 2020.

The impact of the national retrofit scheme, which was announced in 2010, is evident in the residential sector where the scheme seeks to improve the energy performance of up to 1 million dwellings by 2020. This scheme was not included in last year's projections. Slower economic growth relative to last year is primarily responsible for lower emissions from commercial services and industry.

## Energy demand patterns

The latest authoritative analysis of energy use and supply trends from 1990 to 2010, with a particular emphasis on patterns in 2010, clearly illustrates how the economy's performance and the weather affect energy demand. The highlights of SEAI's *Energy in Ireland 1990–2010* are as follows:[246]

**Table 8: Highlights of energy trends in Ireland (2010)**

**The Year 2010**
- Overall energy use fell by 0.3%; the economy contracted by 0.4%.
- At 42Mt energy related $CO_2$ emissions were 1% lower than 2009; 34% above 1990 levels.
- Oil consumption reduced by 4.8%; accounts for 61% of final energy demand; and 2.8% of electricity generation.
- Natural gas consumption rose by 9.2%; accounts for 32% of overall energy supply; and 61% of electricity generation.
- Electricity accounted for less than a fifth of final energy demand; its GHG emissions increased by 2.9%

**Economic Recession and Energy**
- Since 2007, energy-related emissions have fallen by 12% (to 2000 levels) reflecting a 9& fall in energy demand.
- Transport energy demand in 2010 was 18% lower than 2007, with a 42& reduction in energy used for freight.
- Industrial energy demand is down 23% over the past four years even though industrial output is up 13%.
- Coal consumption is down 24% since 2007.
- Energy in buildings grew by 9% since 2007.

**Progress Towards Targets**
- Gross final energy use from renewable energy was 5.5% (2010); the EU target is 16% by 2020.
- Electricity generated from renewable energy (RES-E) was 14.8% (just below the national target of 15%).
- Renewable energy in transport (RES-T) was 2.4%; Ireland's target is 10% by 2020.
- Renewable energy contribution to thermal energy (RES-H) was 4.4%; just below the 2010 target of 5%; the EU's 2020 target is 10%.
- Energy-related CO2 emissions in the non-ETS sectors were 5.4% below 2005 levels.

**Sectoral Highlights**
- Industrial energy use fell by 2.4% while output rose by 11%.
- Transport energy demand fell by 7.9%; aviation grew 2.6%.
- Energy use in buildings increased by 7%.
- Residential energy use increased by 5.9%.
- Energy use in the services sector increased by 9.4%.

*Source:* SEAI (2011), *Energy in Ireland 1990–2010.*

Energy demand growth has been linked to economic growth for many years. SEAI's report, *Energy in Ireland 1990–2008*, shows that in the first period of economic downturn certain types of energy use did decline (Figure 20).[247] This is masked by 2008 being considerably colder than 2007. The 2009 data confirmed a softening of demand in some of the key energy-using areas.

**Figure 20: Sector emission trends 1990–2010**

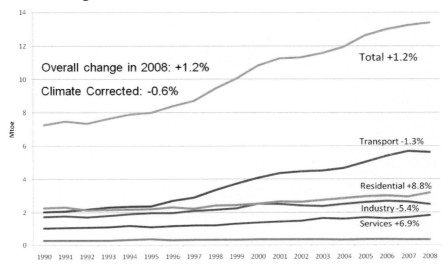

*Source:* EPA (2012), presentation by Laura Burke, Director General, IIEA Carbon Day.

Our dependence on imported sources of energy remains a concern, strengthening the case for diversification into indigenous renewable resources. It is worth noting that the statistical analysis of energy prices across Europe, *Understanding Electricity and Gas Prices in Ireland*, demonstrates clearly that those countries that are most dependent on fossil fuels in electricity generation tend to have the highest electricity prices.

## Latest forecasts

The latest forecasts, based on the figures provided in the appendix to the 2011 carbon budget statement and in the review of *National Climate Change Policy*, are as follows.[248]

These figures differ in some important respects from the UNFCCC report (24 November 2009) on Ireland's emissions, which puts 2007 gross emissions at 69.2 Mt. The UNFCCC report notes that at 46 Mt, the energy sector accounts for 67 per cent of total GHG emissions; and energy emissions increased by 46.8 per cent since 1990, with road transport the principal contributor to the rise.[249]

## Table 9: Ireland's emissions 1990–2020

| Sector (Mt Co2e) | 1990 | 2009 | 2008–2012 Average WM | 2008–2012 average WAM | 2020 forecast | Share 2008–2012 | Change (1990–08) Mt Co2e | % |
|---|---|---|---|---|---|---|---|---|
| Energy | 11.4 | 13.1 | 13.9 | 13.9 | 10.1 | 19.8% | 3.31 | + 29 |
| Transport | 5.2 | 13.1 | 13 | 12.9 | 15.6 | 21.6% | 9.1 | + 176 |
| Residential | 7.5 | 7.5 | 7.3 | 7.2 | 5.8 | 11% | 0.11 | + 0.2 |
| Industry/Services | 9.6 | 9.2 | 9.2 | 9 | 9.4 | 15.9% | 1.82 | + 19 |
| Agriculture | 19.9 | 18.1 | 18.1 | 18.1 | 17.5 | 28.5% | -1.53 | -7.8 |
| Waste | 1.3 | 1.2 | 1.2 | | 1 | 3.2% | - 0.2 | - 15.4 |
| **Gross Emissions** | 54.8 | 62.3 | 62.8 | 62.4 | 54.6 | | 9.27 | + 16.9 |
| Carbon Sinks | | -2.3 | -2.83 | -2.83 | -4.8 | | | |
| Net Emissions | 54.81 | 65.34 | 59.98 | 59.6 | | | | |
| Kyoto Target | | 62.84 | 62.84 | 62.84 | | | | |

*Source:* Appendix to the 2011 Carbon Budget Statement presented by the Minister for the Environment, Heritage and Local Government to the Oireachtas (December 2010).

## Conclusions

The key conclusions of the EPA's forecasts are, in summary, as follows:

• As a consequence of the economic recession GHG emissions have fallen sharply in the past three years and are now at a level of some 61 Mt.

• A full third of the required measures to reduce non-ETS emissions by 2020 have yet to be implemented. These include inter alia a 20 per cent improvement in energy efficiency across the entire economy within less than ten years.

• The most critical issue is the degree of confidence that all the measures in the current NCCS – and its yet-to-be-published successor – are not only adopted but implemented in full, and that they generate the emissions reductions predicted. Under the *With Measures* scenario, Ireland's non-ETS GHG emissions will be some 8 Mt higher in 2020 than our target for that year.

• The Carbon Fund has purchased enough allowances to ensure that Ireland will comply with its Kyoto limits for the period 2008–2012. After 2013 Ireland will be able to meet some of its requirements by the use of statistical transfers.

• In the absence of enabling EU legislation it will not be possible to use carbon sinks as an offset in the non-ETS sector.

This is a significant issue as by 2020 forests could sequester 5 Mt or 60 per cent of Ireland's distance to target. The Council for Forest Research and Development (COFORD) has made the case – having regard to a recent fall in afforestation rates – that much higher levels of afforestation are needed to grow biomass crops and new forests for carbon sequestration.

- Another critical assumption is a significant slowdown in transport emissions (which accounts for almost 30 per cent of non-ETS emissions). However, no details are provided in support of this projection. Nor is there any quantification of the impact that Transport 21 spending will have on transport emissions.

- Agriculture emissions (accounting for 20 Mt by 2020) are forecast to increase by 7 per cent over the period 2009–2020 reflecting the projected increase in output.

- The EPA assumes that the Poolbeg incinerator will be at full capacity by 2017; emissions from incineration are projected to be 3 per cent of total waste emissions by 2020.

- The EPA's emissions projections do not include Irish aviation emissions.

While the reduction in the distance to target for both the Kyoto Protocol period and the 2020 target is a positive outcome in terms of compliance, its occurrence is, primarily, a direct result of the current economic recession and economic outlook in the short term.

According to the EPA, Ireland cannot rely on a recession and needs to develop a low-carbon strategy going forward.

## Chapter 8

# Ireland's policy framework

Nationally, at European level and globally, climate change is one of the most demanding and urgent concerns that humanity faces.

An Taoiseach Brian Cowen, 2008

## Introduction

Irish climate change policy must be considered within the context of international and EU political developments, which in turn are informed by the emerging scientific consensus on climate change. Although countries such as Ireland have a measure of control over their own emissions policies, overall mitigation targets are determined at international negotiations under the auspices of the UNFCCC. As a member of the EU, Ireland's position at these negotiations is determined by decisions taken at the Council of Ministers, and modified by consensus throughout. Its specific target for GHG emissions reductions is negotiated as a share of the EU aggregate target with other Member States.

While Ireland is the second highest emitter per capita of GHGs in the EU, per capita emissions have fallen from 15.6 tonnes $CO_2$e in 1990 to 13.6 tonnes in 2010. The EEA noted that average 2008–2010 emissions in Ireland were 14.4 per cent higher than the base year level. Emissions were significantly higher than target in the non-ETS sectors. On the other hand, LULUCF activities are expected to decrease net emissions by an annual amount equivalent to 5 per cent of base year emissions per year. The EEA predict that Ireland was on track towards its burden-sharing target by the end of 2010.[250]

Ireland's climate change policy is bound by international agreements into which it has entered and by climate legislation implemented at EU level. At Kyoto the EU agreed to reduce emissions by 8 per cent on 1990 levels by 2012. Under the EU's burden-sharing agreement, Ireland's emissions are currently limited to a 13 per cent increase on 1990 levels by 2012.

Under the EU ETS, Ireland is required to produce a National Allocation Plan (NAP) at the beginning of each trading period, which sets the allocation of emissions among installations operating under the ETS in line with Ireland's Kyoto target and outlines how the country will meet its Kyoto commitments. Ireland's second NAP for the period 2008–2012 was submitted to the European Commission in July 2006 and was conditionally accepted in July 2007. The European Commission accepted Ireland's NAP on 5 February 2008 and the EPA took the final allocation decision on the plan.[251]

## Institutional arrangements

The Department for the Environment, Community and Local Government has overall responsibility for climate change policy in Ireland. Its officials (with those from the EPA, the SEAI and the Department of Agriculture, Food and the Marine) represent Ireland at the UNFCCC/COP negotiations as well at meetings at EU level. The Department is also responsible for climate change legislation, including the Climate Change Bill, preparation of a national adaptation strategy and for coordinating the implementation of the current National Climate Change Strategy (NCCS) (2007–2012) and for drawing up the post-2012 NCCS.

The Energy Division within the Department of Communications, Energy and Natural Resources (DCENR) is responsible for oversight of the implementation of the EU legislation on energy and renewables and for setting policy in this area.

A cross-departmental senior officials group, chaired by the Department of the Taoiseach, has a remit to address cross-cutting issues and overall strategy. It reports to a Cabinet Committee on Climate Change and the Green Economy chaired by the Taoiseach, which it should be noted has met infrequently. The preparation of a comprehensive strategy/plan to map out a

GHG emissions reduction pathway to 2020, which will ensure a cost-effective achievement of Ireland's 2020 target under the EU effort-sharing Directive is a top priority.

Parliamentary scrutiny is the responsibility of the Joint Committee on Environment, Transport, Culture and the Gaeltacht. Perhaps indicating the current political priority attached to climate change in Ireland, the Government decided not to reconstitute the Oireachtas Joint Committee on Climate Change and Energy Security, which produced several significant reports over the past years.

The EPA is responsible as the national competent authority for monitoring and verifying Ireland's GHG emissions (through the National Emissions Trading Registry), for developing annual national emission projections for GHGs, and for the implementation of the EU's ETS, including the implementation of Ireland's NAP (2008–2012). The EPA also provides policy advice on climate change to government and manages a climate change research programme.

The SEAI, Ireland's national energy authority, has a remit to transform Ireland into a society based on sustainable energy structures, technologies and practices, and a vision of making Ireland a recognised global leader in sustainable energy.[252]

The Commission for Energy Regulation is the independent body responsible for protecting customers' interests by ensuring safe, secure and sustainable and affordable energy supply. The CER also oversees the liberalisation of Ireland's energy sector and, as a consequence, has an important role to play in relation to promoting the use of renewable energy (but not in relation to the setting of targets), which are defined in its legislation as wind, hydro, biomass, waste including waste heat, bio-fuel, geothermal, fuel cells, tidal, solar and wave.

## National Climate Change Strategy (2007–2012)

Ireland's Kyoto compliant limit of GHG emissions is 62.8 Mt, or 13 per cent above the 1990 baseline estimate, with 22.3 Mt attributable to the ETS sector and 40.6 Mt in the non-ETS sector (agriculture, transport, residential, etc.). The EPA forecasts, under the *With Measures* scenario, that total national emissions will be some 60 Mt on average per annum over the period to 2012. The shortfall (the 'gap') of some 1.6 Mt will be met by the purchase of carbon credits and/or additional domestic action.

This figure falls to 1.3 Mt under the *With Additional Measures* scenario.

The NCCS for 2007–2012 sets out in detail how Ireland will meet its commitments to reduce GHG emissions under the Kyoto Protocol. It includes measures put in place on foot of the first NCCS (2000–2006), and takes account of Ireland's NAP (2008–2012), the National Development Plan (NDP) (2007–2013), Transport 21, the Energy White Paper and the Bio-energy Action Plan. The NCCS also announced the setting up of a Carbon Fund to administer and manage purchases of Kyoto units on behalf of the Irish Government. The NCCS acknowledged that Ireland 'will be expected to achieve further significant reductions in GHGs in the post-2012 period' and that this would necessitate 'radical changes across the economy, particularly in relation to the way Ireland produces and uses energy'. It did not, however, deal in a comprehensive manner with the post-2012 scenario.

## The carbon budget

The Programme for Government (2007) contained a political commitment that Ireland will reduce its GHG emissions by 3 per cent per annum for the period of the Government. In addition, it was agreed that a carbon budget report would be presented in conjunction with the annual budget statement.[253] While the current Programme for Government does not contain any commitment to an emission-reduction target the reality is that Ireland has legally binding targets set by EU Directives.

Ireland's first carbon budget was presented on 6 December 2007 and its objectives were stated as follows:

• To integrate climate change considerations into the Government's budgetary policy and into the decision-making process across all sectors of government

• To provide a clear measure of the progress made towards meeting national targets for emission reductions

• To help efforts to increase public understanding of climate change and the Government's response.

The Government indicated that a significant proportion of Ireland's distance to Kyoto target will be met through the purchase of Kyoto flexible mechanisms. Furthermore, the NCCS projection of 66.2 Mt is about 2.2 Mt above what is required to meet the Programme for Government target of an annual average reduction of 3 per cent in GHG emissions.

The following additional measures were announced in the carbon budget statement: the motor tax regime will be based on the rated carbon emissions from vehicles and a mandatory labelling system will be introduced in tandem; new regulations will deliver energy and emissions savings of 40 per cent in new homes; the building standards will be further strengthened in 2010 to achieve a 60 per cent improvement in current levels; and a new national energy-efficiency standard for light bulbs was announced.

The (then) Minister for the Environment, Heritage and Local Government, John Gormley, presented the third carbon budget on 11 December 2009. The main points of the presentation were as follows:

- The report of the action group on the green economy has projected that 80,000 jobs could be created over the coming decade.

- A national action plan for green procurement will be introduced.

- The heads of the Climate Change Bill will be published before the end of March 2011.

- The carbon levy will yield of €330 million in a full year; with a reduction of emissions of 250,000 tonnes in the non-traded sector.

- €130 million to be spent on retrofitting homes in 2010 (6,000 jobs).

- Completion dates of 94 road projects to be reviewed in light of economic circumstances, falling road usage and climate change objectives.

- €20 million to be allocated over two years to improve energy efficiency in social housing.

- A risk-based national climate change adaptation framework will be published by the end of March 2011.

To date, decisions are still awaited on climate change legislation, and a national adaptation strategy. The Government abandoned the practice of making a separate statement on carbon as part of budget 2012.

## Adaptation

Adaptation is about ensuring that our society and economy are resilient to the realities of a changing climate; adaptation is about the consequences of climate change. Mitigation on the other hand involves reducing GHG emissions; it involves dealing with the causes of climate change. There is far more emphasis in Ireland on the latter to the detriment of the former.

The EU White Paper on adapting to climate change set out a framework to reduce the EU's vulnerability to the impacts of climate change.[254] The Commission recommended that Member States prepare adaptation programmes for the following five priority sectors: health and social systems; agriculture and forestry; biodiversity, ecosystems and water; coastal and marine areas; and production systems and physical infrastructure.

At the time of the publication of the NCCS (2007–2012), the Government committed to adopt a national adaptation strategy within two years i.e. by 2010. The strategy, which has yet to be published, will provide a framework for the integration of adaptation issues and options into decision-making at national and local levels. The EPA's Climate Change Research Programme has enabled the publication of research in support of adaptation planning, such as 'A summary of the state of knowledge on climate change impacts for Ireland'. Forfás is the only other public body to publish a report (from a business perspective) about the impacts of climate change and the implications and associated risks involved.[255]

As we await a national adaptation strategy it is instructive review what is happening in other countries. The first thing to note is that most other EU Member States already have national and even regional adaptation programmes as is evidenced from activity monitored by the European Environment Agency (December 2011). The UK's Climate Change Act 2008 requires that a national adaptation programme must be put in place and reviewed every five years to address the most pressing climate change risks to England. On foot of this legislation a number of actions have been put in place. For example, from October 2011, the Environment Agency took on a new role as the Government's delivery body for climate change adaptation in England. The UK's Climate Change Risk Assessment, which was presented to Parliament on 25 January 2012, presents the latest evidence on the risks and opportunities of climate change for the UK to 2100.[256] Its finding will now inform the development of adaptation plans by the UK and Northern Ireland Governments. Thus the CCAR report for Northern Ireland will inform the Northern Ireland adaptation programme. Adaptation planning is also centre stage in Scotland.

## Policy outlook

The Commission's climate change package, as adopted, will have a profound impact on Irish climate change policy in the post-2012 period. The removal of the EU ETS sector from the national inventory and establishing a cap set at EU level fundamentally changes the ground rules for Ireland and other Member States and restricts their room for manoeuvre in designing their post-2012 policies in relation to domestic measures.

Emissions covered by ETS operators represent approximately 34 per cent of Irish emissions, compared to 41 per cent across the EU. The aggregate reduction faced by the traded sector across the EU is 21 per cent, or 1.74 per cent per annum. Emissions will occur where they are cheapest across the EU, and thus the cost to Irish industry covered by the EU ETS would be capped at the EU marginal cost of abatement.[257] The price of CER permits should reflect the abatement cost to industry. Predictions of the price of permits in the post-2012 period vary (optimistically) from €20 to €50 per tonne. It is expected that these costs will be passed on to consumers in the form of higher energy and commodity prices.

The few Irish operators covered by the EU ETS who are exposed to external competitive pressures will to some extent be protected from the negative cost implications of the post-2012 EU ETS Directive. They will continue to receive free allocations of permits to an extent that will be determined in ongoing negotiations. In broad terms, according to the Commission, the intra-EU competitiveness effects of the EU ETS should be neutral.

The EU ETS Directive creates something of a contradiction for Irish policy-makers in that the emissions reductions arising from increased penetration of renewables and measures to improve energy efficiency in the powergen sector (for example the use of locally grown biomass in powergen installations) will not be counted in national emissions inventories in the non-traded side of the economy. Yet Government will not be indifferent to strategic choices made by the power sector bearing in mind it will be responsible for meeting the proposed renewables targets by 2020, not to mention its security of supply and competitiveness goals.

The full implications of this new policy environment need to be carefully assessed in the context of the post-2012 NCCS and Ireland's low-carbon strategy to 2050.

Government policy will of necessity be focused on the Irish domestic sector – agriculture, transport, commercial, residential and services and light industry – which account for 66 per cent of overall Irish emissions. The largest two of these are responsible for 70 per cent of domestic sector GHG emissions: agriculture (41 per cent) and transport (29 per cent). Emissions from these two sectors are projected to rise in the period to 2020.

Under the EU's effort-sharing Decision, the domestic sector would collectively be bound to reduce emissions by at least 20 per cent on 2005 levels by 2020. The use of flexible mechanisms will be restricted to 3 per cent of the overall target. Ireland will also have the option of buying allowances from those Member States who have a surplus because they over-achieved their targets, with each Member State limited to the sale of 5 per cent of its surplus. Although less onerous than either the (previous) Government's target of a 3 per cent annual emissions reduction if extrapolated to 2020, or even the calculations set out in the NCCS, this is an enormous challenge for Ireland.[258] Unlike the traded sector, the marginal cost of abatement in the domestic sector is not capped at the EU marginal cost and there are few cheap abatement options available. This is a major concern for Ireland's policy-makers given that the Commission's projected price of carbon may be no more than €16/tonne by 2020.

It is difficult to see how this target can be met in Ireland without a restructuring of the Irish economy and in the absence of very significant behavioural change.

In this context, the Government has announced a major review of Irish climate change policy.[259] This will involve an independent study to inform the policy development process to be carried out by the NESC (with an interim report to be published in July 2012); a stakeholder consultation; and the preparation of sectoral mitigation strategies. The review is seen as a first step towards a national 2050 low-carbon plan. In addition, the

Government will publish a review of Irish energy policy through to 2030 in 2012.

## Ireland's target in a minus 30 per cent scenario

Although revised EU emission-reduction targets in the event of a global agreement being reached have, as yet, to be agreed by Member States, it is difficult to envisage a significant renegotiation of Ireland's current tough targets as there are no objective criteria that would justify a softer target relative to other Member States. Even the use of GNP instead of GDP would not significantly affect Ireland's proposed -30 per cent target.

It might also be borne in mind that the negotiations will be zero-sum; one country's gain will come at the expense of another. It is hard to imagine any country agreeing to a unilateral increase in its target, making a renegotiation increasingly unlikely.

The Commission has conducted preparatory work in relation to the division of an EU target up to -30 per cent on 1990 levels. Ireland would face the prospect of shouldering a disproportionately large portion of this target, as the burden could be divided on a pro rata basis based on the division of the -20 per cent target. The question thus becomes how would Ireland deal with the target for the non-traded sector of between -20 per cent and -30 per cent on 2005 levels by 2020? Given the time lag that often exists between the adoption of policy, implementation of the required measures, and the emissions reduction it yields, this is a critical issue that has yet to be addressed.

Ireland's proposed share of the target for renewables of 16 per cent is broadly in line with the Government's own targets as set out in the Energy White Paper of 2007 and the Strategy for Renewable Energy 2012–2020. While it may be challenging and ambitious, it is within the bounds of what can be achieved.

That the targets proposed by the EU pose significant challenges for Ireland in the period to 2020 is clear. The first issue to be addressed is the precise quantification of Ireland's target. It is probable that current projections for 2020 are too low given the increases expected in car ownership, population and economic growth in the medium term.

The division of the economy into trading and non-trading sectors with differing marginal costs of abatement in each will have significant implications for Irish climate change policy. For example, there would be an incentive to migrate emissions from the domestic sector (residential and transport sectors) to the trading sector through electrification.[260]

The issue of cross-sectoral equity within the non-traded sector needs also to be addressed. It could be argued that it would be inequitable to place a disproportionate share of the burden on one or more sectors if other sectors did not engage in trying to secure a reasonable GHG emission-reduction strategy over the medium term. A general assessment of the allocation of burden between sectors will be required. This should be based on more complete MACCs than those to hand.

## Long-term target

The indicative EU targets of 60–80 per cent GHG emissions reductions by 2050 agreed at the spring European Council in March 2007 could be interpreted by Irish policy-makers as a guide to a long-term strategic direction. It is clear that decisions yet to be taken by Ireland on the Commission's climate change package will have major implications for the post-2020 period.

By 2050, on the basis of the (November 2007) Synthesis Report of the IPCC Fourth Assessment Report, Irish economic activity will need to be largely carbon-free. The Government's response to the EU's 2050 low-carbon roadmap (see below), which sets out possible trajectories at sectoral level, will be important.[261] Given this prognosis, the period to 2013 might be considered a window of opportunity, a chance to make the difficult decisions that will safeguard Ireland's future competitiveness in a new global environment.

The overall direction of Irish climate change policy will be determined at EU and international level. On the balance of probability, Ireland and other Member States will agree to a more onerous legally binding GHG emission-reduction target for the post-2012 period i.e. a target in excess of -20 per cent.

As per capita emissions in Ireland are high by EU standards and, given the degree of Ireland's economic convergence within the EU, a renegotiation of Ireland's target is unlikely. On the other hand, the EU's low-carbon strategy recognises that Ireland's farming and agri-business sector could be benchmarked for its carbon intensity against activity in other Member States. If such a proposition was reflected in an amended EU Directive then the emissions reduction challenge facing this strategically critical sector for Ireland would be much more manageable.

A new imaginative approach, cognisant of the division of the economy into two sectors and the removal of allocating allowances to the traded sector as a national competence, is now required. This reality will have to be reflected in future carbon budgets and the revised NCCS in the post-2012 period. Ireland faces a choice as it considers its long-term response to climate change. It is certain that the country will be faced with some kind of restraint on its emissions, as part of the EU effort to reduce overall emissions by at least 20 per cent by 2020, and possibly more. Figure 21 below presents a schematic of these two broad options.

**Figure 21: Policy Options for Ireland**

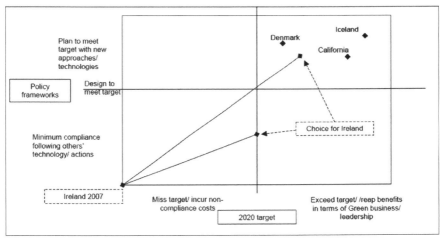

*Source:* EPA (2012), *Ireland's Greenhouse Gas Emissions Projections 2011–2020.*

There are two broad ways that Ireland could meet this constraint. On the one hand, Ireland could pursue technical compliance with its international commitments, through a minimalist application of policies and measures and wide use of flexible mechanisms such as international emissions trading.

On the other hand, Ireland could make a political commitment to meet or exceed its targets in a more ambitious way. Countries and regions like Denmark, Iceland and California have made unilateral commitments to position their economies as low-carbon societies. Denmark made a political decision in the 1970s to wean its electricity sector off fossil fuels and, as a result, is a leading exporter of wind-power technology to the rest of the world; the quid pro quo is that Denmark has the highest domestic electricity prices in Europe. Iceland has made a political commitment to be the world's first hydrogen economy. The US state of California has made a commitment to reduce its GHG by 80 per cent by 2050, even though there is no similar target in the US; other states are following California's lead by introducing legislation of their own. The UK's Energy Act 2011, which legislated for the Green Deal, is expected to revolutionise the energy efficiency of British properties. The experience of these countries suggests that early action can bring benefits to society as a whole, through the promotion of the industries of the future and through the development of knowledge and prestige that such initiatives often stimulate.

Ireland's position on this schematic in 2020 (and indeed beyond to 2050) is not yet determined. It is arguable that Ireland should aim to meet the challenge of climate change in an imaginative way, going beyond formal compliance and pursuing instruments and measures that set an international example and increase the chances that other countries will follow suit. Full and rapid implementation of all the measures in the NREAP and NEEAP would be a positive contribution. It would also help if the emission-reduction targets expected from the agriculture sector were balanced by an acknowledgement at EU level that Ireland's low-carbon intensive agri-food exports provide essential foods for Europe's consumers. Allowing forest carbon credits (see below) would also be a significant policy option for Ireland.

## The challenge and opportunity of climate policy in Ireland

Climate change is one of the most complex of policy challenges. GHG emissions are bound up in almost every aspect of the economy, often through complex and poorly understood causal relationships. Controlling emissions requires a degree of coordination across sectors, which is hard to achieve even in countries with the strongest systems of governance. The problem is compounded by the need to persuade other countries to act in tandem.

As explained earlier, climate change is also a form of market failure, the greatest and most wide-ranging example ever seen, by which many investment decisions are taken without complete information about the price of carbon in the future, or indeed without having to consider paying for them at all. As a result, and due to the novel nature of many interventions at both national and international levels the payoffs from reducing emissions are often uncertain, delayed or diffuse. The result is a policy challenge that requires action across many different sectors for uncertain gain. The presence or absence of strong climate policies will help determine whether Ireland invests in social and economic infrastructure that commits us to a carbon-intensive or a carbon-efficient future.

To date, Ireland's climate policy has been characterised by an insufficiently clear strategy or coordinated approach across different government departments and agencies. The 2000 NCCS contained a number of measures that could have helped constrain Ireland's GHG emissions but some critical policy proposals, particularly the carbon tax and the conversion of the Moneypoint coal-fired electricity-generating plant to natural-gas firing, were dropped for other policy considerations (a desire to increase fuel diversity in the face of concerns over security of supply in the latter case). Major infrastructure programmes were launched with an incomplete regard to climate change. For example, the national roads programme was an essential response to the poor quality of Ireland's primary roads and a prerequisite for future economic growth, but the focus on building roads without accompanying measures (e.g. equivalent investment in public transport; controls on urban sprawl) has driven up transport-related emissions.

Radical policy change in Ireland has been shown to be a hostage to important sectoral interests. The failure of the carbon tax in 2004 was partly due to active lobbying by business groups and the opposition from the (then) Minister for Finance, Charlie McCreevy, who said that the tax would bring minimal emissions reductions at a high bureaucratic cost, as well as by some trade unions, who said that a carbon tax would have a disproportionate effect on the poor. Both these claims were disputed at the time. The then chairman of SEAI, Frank Convery, said that the Government seriously underestimated the likely emissions reductions that a carbon tax would achieve.[262] The Economic and Social Research Institute showed that the potentially regressive effect of a carbon tax could be offset by directing some of the revenues to social welfare.[263] Arguably, opponents of the carbon tax in 2004 based their position on the possibility that the Kyoto Protocol might fail, and that no action was a plausible alternative to a carbon tax. Today that is no longer the case: 'no action' is no longer a possible response to the challenge of climate change.

It is clear that all sectors and all parts of society will be involved in what is essentially a decarbonisation project.

## Potential instruments and measures to reduce Ireland's emissions

Policy approaches to address climate change can be divided into the following broad categories:

- **Legislative,** e.g. legally binding time-bound targets
- **Economic and incentive-based,** e.g. environmental tax reform, emissions trading
- **Behavioural,** e.g. focusing on demand-side management
- **Technical,** e.g. performance- and technology-based standards.

Of course, there are other ways to categorise the galaxy of policy options but it is hoped that this taxonomy is reasonably comprehensive.

It is recalled that the UNEP (2010) estimates that emission levels of some 44 Gt in 2020 would be consistent with a 'likely' chance of limiting global warming to 2°C. BAU projections suggest emissions will rise to 56 Gt within eight years; a dramatic increase of 27 per cent. Depending on how the Cancún pledges are implemented, an overshoot of 5–9 Gt is a realistic prospect. To assist climate change negotiators (including the Irish delegation) the World Resource Institute has developed a series of policy options to advance governments' thinking. One such scenario suggests that countries (such as Ireland) with high per capita emissions have a responsibility to take on additional commitments.[264]

One of the universal ways to assess climate change policy options is to use a MACC.

### Ireland's MACC

A marginal abatement cost curve (MACC) adapted to meet Irish circumstances was carried out by McKinsey and Co. under the guidance of the SEAI (Figure 22). The MACC identifies the costs

### Figure 22: Ireland's MACC

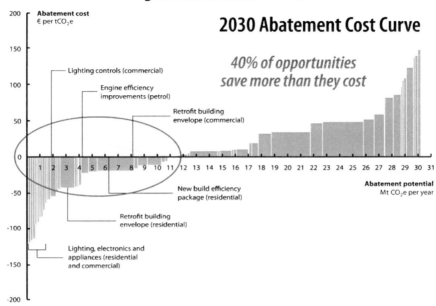

*Source:* Motherway, B. and Walker, N. (2009) *Ireland's Low-Carbon Opportunity*, report for SEAI.

of the principal measures that have the potential to reduce or significantly offset Ireland's GHG emissions. Two oil cost scenarios of $60 and $120 were investigated with different results for the resulting technology priorities. The two oil cost scenarios illustrate how the relative abatement cost of technology levers can depend on the expected costs of the counterfactual technology. The MACC says nothing about policy priorities nor behavioural change.

The results show that approximately one-third of projected GHG emission reductions relate to operators covered by the EU ETS (which requires no additional policy measures by Ireland). Of note is the assumption that new coal-fired capacity will replace the existing station at Moneypoint.

Of the remainder, some 8 Mt in the non-traded sector, half of the cuts could be achieved by behavioural changes such as a shift away from the use of private cars. Evidence is provided about the low/no-cost potential to abate carbon emissions from commercial buildings and domestic dwellings. The oil price scenarios show how the opportunities relating to electric vehicles are favoured by high oil prices. Investment in public transport and spatial planning are not included in the measures.

Given the complexities involved, the section on agriculture was the subject of intensive discussion prior to the publication of the MACC report and was clearly amended prior to publication. It notes, for example, that methane emissions associated with milk and beef production in Ireland are difficult to measure. The conclusions – three potential measures with an abatement potential of just 0.5 Mt – illustrate the difficulties facing the agricultural sector in reducing emissions.

The significant potential of LULUCF is illustrated by the effectiveness of maintaining the afforestation programme and increasing rates to around 20,000 hectares per annum with a carbon sink potential of some 3 Mt by 2030.

The MACC limits its consideration of effective measures at carbon price of €80/tonne. This is a multiple of the current price of nearer €7/tonne (January 2012). A higher and sustained international carbon price will be essential for the cost-effective implementation of some measures. As pointed out earlier, some measures will and should proceed without a carbon price market signal.

It is also notable that over 40 per cent of the opportunities save more money than they cost. This is because energy efficiency reduces energy bills over many years and the total savings add up to more than the initial investment required. The MACC is based on conservative assumptions about oil prices (Brent crude was $110/barrel in January 2012), and as the assumed future price rises so too do the economic benefits of taking action in all areas.

The potential costs of inaction to society as a whole must therefore be considered alongside the costs of action. At the same time, adaptation to climate change presents opportunities as well as challenges. Climate change policy is likely to be disruptive for some sectors, but this does not mean that its overall impact will be negative in the long term. Indeed, a European Commission study found that tackling climate change could have a limited, but positive, impact on overall employment across the EU provided that appropriate policies are in place, with some important shifts in employment patterns within sectors.[265] Moreover, businesses that have low energy requirements or deal with the technologies that are suited to a low-carbon economy will prosper in a carbon-constrained economy, and Ireland could benefit by being among the first movers in this significant area of future economic development. Ireland therefore has an opportunity to lead by example by showing that greener policies can be cost-efficient and beneficial to society.

Reducing emissions raises legitimate questions about costs, especially to Ireland's competitiveness. Although many companies and individuals can reduce emissions at little or no cost (many energy-saving measures can be affected at negative cost), a tough climate target raises legitimate concerns about real problems to Ireland's economic competitiveness and the effect on vulnerable sectors of society. As the targets become more ambitious, companies (and individuals) will exhaust the low-cost options and be forced to turn to more expensive means of reducing emissions. The effect of this on Ireland's competitiveness depends on the extent to which Ireland's competitors are similarly affected by emissions reductions. Most of Ireland's economic actors compete with firms in other EU countries, that are likely to be similarly constrained by domestic climate policies, rather than with developing countries who have lower environmental standards, so the impact on competitiveness for the economy as a whole might be relatively small compared to that for specific sectors. Affected sectors may require a targeted policy approach, but this should not be allowed to become a brake on national policy.

Consideration of costs must also include the costs to Ireland of relying on means other than reducing emissions at home. The current NCCS foresaw an outlay of €270 million to purchase credits on the international market. This forecast assumed a permit price of about €15 a tonne of $CO_2$ e. As emissions have dropped sharply, the Carbon Fund may not have to purchase any more credits this side of December 2012.

## The need for a Climate Change Act

The case to reduce GHG emissions in order to tackle climate change is overwhelming. The Stern Review, which was influential in bringing about the UK's climate change legislation, stated that the cost of inaction was far greater than the cost of taking action now. The benefits of strong action on climate change outweigh the costs and present real opportunities for Ireland to position itself as a low-carbon society.

It is envisaged that a climate change law will put in place a framework to facilitate Ireland meeting its EU and international commitments, in particular in relation to meeting the targets required to achieve these GHG emission reductions in the sectors not covered by the EU ETS.

Primary legislation is not required to implement the EU ETS Directive or the effort-sharing Decision.

A legislative approach was supported on a cross-party basis within the Oireachtas Joint Committee on Climate Change and Energy Security because this presents a degree of certainty in terms of future planning for government departments, businesses and other emitters. Due to the global, cross-generational importance of action to combat climate change the response must be cross-party. It must also inform policy-making across all government departments and it must extend beyond the five-yearly government election cycles. Hence there is cross-party support for the preparation of climate change legislation. Regardless of what combination of political parties are in power, meeting the climate change challenges will be a central task for any government.

Cooperation is required both across the political spectrum and within government structures. Climate change legislation needs to facilitate and encourage a streamlined approach. In effect, it can ensure 'joined-up' government. The Oireachtas Joint Committee's proposal that the Taoiseach become accountable for climate change targets is designed to ensure a cross-departmental approach and a dynamic for change. This approach, in the absence of a department responsible for climate change and energy (as exists in many countries) has twin advantages in that first the Taoiseach's authority extends across all departments and second that the Oireachtas is engaged in the project by providing accountability and scrutiny at parliamentary level.

The report by the Oireachtas Joint Committee reviewed the Acts in force and Bills under consideration in the following states with a view to informing the debate on Ireland's Climate Change Bill 2009.[266]

- The UK (Climate Change Act)

- The US (American Clean Energy and Security Act (Waxman–Hartley Bill))

- Canada
- California
- New Zealand
- Australia

Having assessed the climate change legislation in six jurisdictions, the Joint Committee proposed that an Irish Climate Change Act could provide framework conditions for the following:

- Setting of national GHG emission-reduction targets, including a long-term 2050 target with reference to 1990 baseline emissions and interim (five-year) targets
- Setting of energy and electricity efficiency targets by 2020 and a methodology for setting targets beyond that date in a NEEAP
- The setting up of an independent Climate Change Commission (CCC) with a clear advisory mandate and reporting requirements to the Oireachtas
- The role of the Oireachtas in relation to climate change
- The setting up of an Office on Climate Change and Renewable Energy (as an extension of the remits of the Environmental Protection Agency and Sustainable Energy Authority Ireland) under the auspices of the Department of the Taoiseach
- Nomination of the Taoiseach as the person with overall responsibility for climate change
- The determination and presentation of a multi-annual carbon budget
- The introduction of penalties (fines) for operators in the non-traded sectors who do not meet statutory targets
- Preparation of the NCCS (with reference to the SEAI MACC report) and adaptations to same based on economic, social and scientific evidence
- The setting up of a Climate Change Dividend Fund, under the guidance of the Office on Climate Change and Renewable Energy, with responsibility for managing the disbursement of carbon tax and auctioning revenues as decided by government

- Transferring responsibility for setting policy in relation to Ireland's Carbon Fund to the Office of Climate Change and Renewable Energy

- Having regard to the independent opinion of the CCC, the possible exploitation of carbon offsets (such as forest carbon sequestration) should the post-Kyoto global agreement allow this and the issuing of Irish carbon units by the Office on Climate Change and Renewable Energy

- Possible restrictions on the use of CDM and JI credits and the conditions attaching to same

- Coordination of all R&D activity in the field of climate change and renewable energy falling under the remit of the Office on Climate Change and Renewable Energy

- Framework conditions for the deployment of electric vehicle, domestic and public sector energy-efficiency retrofitting schemes and a smart grid investment programme

- The implementation of the EU Directives of carbon capture and storage (2009/31/EC) and on the promotion of the use of energy from renewable sources (2009/28/EC)

- Monitoring and reporting of all GHG emissions from both the traded and non-traded sectors

- The introduction of provisions about the duties of public bodies in relation to climate change.

Climate change legislation will also provide certainty for industry and other emitters. It is worth noting that business leaders pressed for the introduction of legislation on climate change in the UK. Their argument was that they required certainty in order to invest in low-carbon technologies. The legislation that followed provided certainty that it would not be undone at the next general election. In Ireland, certainly in these difficult times, certainty is an important factor for business, in particular for those looking to invest in low-carbon technologies or embarking on energy-efficiency programmes. The Irish Corporate Leaders Group on Climate Change called on the Taoiseach to introduce a robust climate change law.[267] IBEC on the other hand estimated that the regulatory burden of the proposed legislation for businesses and households was some €400 million per annum and called for a proper debate on the implications of the proposed legislation.

In order to tackle climate change we need both a 'top-down' approach from government but also a 'bottom-up' approach from public bodies, local authorities, universities and individuals.

Unless and until government, state bodies, businesses, farmers, employees and householders operate and live within a legal framework, including binding climate change targets, changes in personal and corporate behaviour that are critical if GHG emissions reductions are to become a reality will not happen at the pace required.

In addition, Ireland needs to have political leadership with supporting institutions in the climate change space and greater and more proactive engagement by all stakeholders.

The last Government's Climate Change Response Bill has lapsed apparently because the Department of Finance resisted the setting of binding emission-reduction targets. The more ambitious Climate Change Bill proposed on a cross-party basis by the Oireachtas Joint Committee on Climate Change and Energy Security has also been shelved. Government intends to publish a bill in 2012 following stakeholder consultation on Ireland's low-carbon strategy with a view to having legislation enacted by the end of 2013.[268] Among the strategic issues to be decided are whether it is in Ireland's interest to legislate for emission-reduction targets for the non-ETS sectors that are more onerous than those already agreed in the effort-sharing Decision; whether Ireland should reveal more ambitious targets prior to the presentation by the Commission of proposals to amend both the ETS Directive and effort-sharing Decision; and whether binding targets post-2020 should be enshrined in primary legislation in the absence of an agreed policy at EU level on the 2050 low-carbon framework. It is expected that a detailed regulatory impact assessment will be prepared to inform debate about the Bill.

In an important contribution to the debate on climate change legislation, the IIEA set out a series of options about the enactment of an effective and tailored climate policy for Ireland.[269]

In an ideal world Ireland, in common with many other countries, would have a department responsible for climate change and energy.

Finally, while legislation is necessary, putting in place the processes and institutional structures to facilitate implementation is more important.

## Carbon taxation in Ireland

Carbon taxation can correct the market failure presented by many types of energy use by internalising some of the external costs of $CO_2$ emitted from carbon-intensive energy sources. Carbon taxation is a more effective instrument for reducing energy-sector $CO_2$ emissions than other kinds of energy taxation because it discriminates between energy sources according to their contribution to GHG emissions.[270] A 2002 study by ESRI found that a carbon tax of €20/tonne $CO_2$ in Ireland would reduce projected emissions in 2010 from around 27 per cent above 1990 levels (the BAU projection) to being only 18 per cent above the 1990 level. It would also cause a 'modest' reduction in GHG emissions over ten years. This has not happened. Research by the ESRI also showed that the regressive nature of a carbon tax could be countered by a rebate or compensation for low-income households, for instance by increasing the amount of fuel allowances.[271] Revenues could be used not just to compensate low-income households but also, as proposed by the ESRI, to remove other distorting taxes in general and improve the functioning of the economy. The ESRI suggests that the long-term cost to the Irish economy of a carbon tax, if the revenues were used to reduce income tax or value added tax and increase welfare payments, would be small, or might even have a positive effect. This also has not happened as the revenue received has not been ringfenced for any purpose. The ESRI said the longer-term effect of a carbon tax would be to provide incentives for consumers to switch to more energy-efficient heating systems or implement energy-saving measures, such as improving insulation. Measures to support energy-efficiency measures at home (such as window replacement, loft insulation) would not only bring about savings of, on average, 2.6 tonnes of $CO_2$ per household per year, but also increased warmth and comfort for the houses' inhabitants. As will be explained later, the SEAI's Better Energy programme has not reached its full potential and will not in the absence of a pay and you save scheme, which has nothing to do with carbon taxation. Moreover, according to the ESRI, a carbon tax would generate large revenues, estimated by the ESRI at about €2.8 billion.[272]

The potential abatement achieved by a carbon tax and the effect of the tax on the economy will depend on several factors, including the point of application of the tax, the rate and what critically is done with the revenue.

The Programme for Government (June 2007) stated: '... in the context of maintaining a strong economy, [the Government will] investigate fiscal measures to protect and enhance the environment including the introduction of a carbon tax'.

The Commission on Taxation saw rebalancing (environmental) tax revenue as an opportunity to alleviate actual or future tax burdens in other parts of the economy, for example by funding cuts in social insurance payments.[273] The context for the proposed introduction of a carbon tax in Ireland was 'to change the relative price of fossil fuels based on $CO_2$ emissions, in order to change consumption patterns, encourage fuel efficiency and lead to an improvement in environmental quality'. That said the Commission pointed out the purpose of the carbon tax was not to achieve a given level of emissions reduction.

A carbon tax of €15 per tonne of $CO_2$ emissions was introduced in the 2010 carbon budget, which applies to petrol, diesel and home heating oil and gas from May 2010. A further increase of €5/tonne was announced in budget 2012.

An excise duty, the natural gas carbon tax (NGCT), and at a rate of €3.07 per megawatt hour, applies to supplies of natural gas to consumers from 1 May 2010.[274] Full relief is granted for natural gas supplied for use in the generation of electricity; chemical reduction; and electrolytic or metallurgical processes. Partial relief is granted for natural gas delivered for use in an installation that is covered by a GHG emissions permit. In this case, the natural gas concerned is charged at the minimum rate specified in the EU Energy Tax Directive, which is €0.54 per megawatt hour at gross calorific value.

In addition, the Finance Act 2010 introduced a minerals oil tax carbon charge and a solid fuel carbon tax with similar reliefs. There is full relief for supplies of peat and any solid fuel manufactured from peat that is supplied to ETS installations.

The National Recovery Plan envisages a doubling of the rate within four years.

Using ESRI estimates, a carbon tax at €20/tonne could raise some €500 million in 2012. A €20/tonne tax is the equivalent of increasing premium unleaded gasoline by some €0.047/litre (5 cents), or by some 4.8 per cent. Even at 10 cents a litre carbon tax will have no impact in terms of reducing GHG emissions. The rate would have to be as high as €180/tonne if a carbon tax was to have any noticeable impact of emissions reductions (in the region of 20 per cent).

The Government has not yet addressed how to use the potential revenues from auctioning of EU ETS allowances and the impact this will have on carbon taxation.

The particular concern for the Minister for Finance (in the context of the negotiations on the draft proposal for an EU Energy Taxation Directive) is to ensure that any measures advanced to promote energy saving do not adversely affect Ireland's international competitiveness, particularly in relation to countries that compete with us and that may have very low taxes or non-existent taxes on energy.[275]

Energy costs as a percentage of gross output vary considerably across industry. According to a (2002) report by Indecon Consultants, some 14 per cent of industry sectors by employment (and excluding electricity, gas and water supply) may be classified as 'above-average' energy users i.e. their energy costs as a percentage of their gross output are between 3 and 10 per cent. Some of the sectors at the top end of this range, however, contain sub-sectors where energy costs exceed 10 per cent of gross output, and substantially more in the case of individual firms. Such firms are hit hard by the imposition of a carbon energy tax. However, in the interest of equity all operators included in the ETS should be exempt to avoid the imposition of double taxation.

Ireland currently collects a considerable proportion of its revenue from environmentally related taxes, especially in the transport sector. If additional environmental taxation is introduced then, in order to minimise the adverse competitiveness impacts, a number of principles should be adopted:

- Lower cost alternatives should be put in place simultaneously.

- Incentives in the area of renewable energy generation should be introduced.

- EU ETS sites should be excluded or partially exempted from the tax as such sites have signed up to emissions ceilings and must pay for additional carbon permits, thereby internalising carbon costs.[276]

- Firms engaged in legally binding negotiated agreements on energy efficiency should be exempted from the tax, as is the case in other Member States.

- Carbon taxes must be revenue neutral and revenues from industry should be recycled to industry.

Carbon taxation is now a political reality in Ireland – it is a 'fundamental element of national climate policy'[277] – despite the fact that its imposition will not have any material impact on reducing Ireland's GHG emissions. As none of the revenue will be used to address climate change mitigation or adaptation measures it should be seen for what it is: a crude revenue-raising instrument.

## Taxation of carbon trading

The Government has already in place a suite of legislation to facilitate the trading of carbon in Ireland provided the company in question is resident for the purposes of tax in Ireland i.e. it is centrally and effectively managed and controlled in Ireland. As a general rule, the calculation of profits from carbon trading for tax purposes is no different than the calculation of profits under current accounting rules. Operators have the option of setting up a qualifying company that can avail of a special tax regime in respect of 'qualifying assets', which include carbon offsets and carbon credits and allowances.[278] There is also a specific exemption from Irish stamp duty for instruments for the sale, transfer of ETS allowances and permits.[279] The exemption also covers financial services instruments relevant to carbon trading from an Irish location. Finally, a company engaged in carbon trading is likely to get a VAT exemption as financial services consisting of issuing, transferring or otherwise dealing in stocks, shares and other securities are exempt from Irish VAT.[280]

The Finance Act 2012 extends the range of carbon offsets that a section 110 company can acquire to include forest carbon credits. A consequential amendment to the Stamp Duty Consolidation Act will be made to facilitate this provision. The Act also deals with the deductibility of expenses incurred in the purchase of carbon emission allowances and the capital gains tax treatment of sales of surplus allowances granted free of charge under the EU ETS.

## REFIT

On 1 May 2006, the Minister for Communications, Marine and Natural Resources announced the official launch of the renewable energy feed-in tariff (REFIT) scheme. REFITs are intended to provide price certainty to renewable electricity generators.

It operates on a sliding scale, acting to ensure a guaranteed floor price for each unit of electricity exported to the grid by paying the difference between the wholesale price of electricity and the REFIT price. The programme provides support to renewable energy projects over a fifteen-year period. This support mechanism was a change from the previous programme in that it is a fixed feed-in tariff mechanism rather than a competitive tendering process; the Alternative Energy Requirement (AER) programme ran until the mid 2000s. Applicants in REFIT must have planning permission and a grid connection offer for their projects and they will then be able to contract with any licensed electricity supplier up to the notified fixed prices. REFIT 1 (which assists 1,242 MW of renewable generation capacity) closed to new entrants on 31 December 2009.[281] In addition, it took almost two years after REFIT 1 had been sent to the Commission for approval (August 2006) before the Department published the statutory instrument bringing the scheme into force.

The tariffs (2011) under REFIT 1 are:

- Large wind energy (over 5 Megawatts) – 6.9 cent per Kwh
- Small wind energy (under 5 Megawatts) – 6.6 cent per Kwh
- Biomass (landfill gas) – 8.1 cent per Kwh
- Hydro and other biomass technologies – 8.4 cent per Kwh.

REFIT policy is an important dimension of Europe's single energy market. In that context the ESRI has assessed the implications of current REFIT policy.[282]

The Department has EU state aid clearance for REFIT 2; a 15-year scheme that covers small and large scale onshore wind, biomass landfill gas and hydro (below 5 MW) technologies. An application form and guidance has been published.

In May 2010, a new support price structure for bio-energy (i.e. the use of natural materials for the production of electricity) was announced. REFIT 3 – a scheme to cover certain biomass categories – was approved in October 2011 under the EU state aid rules. The categories include 50 MW of anaerobic digestion broken down into separate sub-categories, 100 MW of biomass combined heat and power broken down into separate sub-categories and 160 MW of bio-combustion and cofiring of biomass with peat (at the peat plant at Edenderry). The scheme, now approved by Government, will cover 310 MW of capacity. Of this, 150 MW will be high efficiency CUP, using anaerobic digestion and the thermo-chemical conversion of solid biomass, while 160 MW will be reserved for biomass combustion and biomass co-firing. REFIT 3 will also support an expansion of the market for forest-based biomass. The guaranteed support price ranges from 15 cent per kilowatt hour to 8.5 cent depending on the technology deployed. REFIT 3 will also support an expansion of the market for forest-based biomass. An application form and guidance has been published. There are some 29 anaerobic digestion plants with planning permission (and an investment of around €250 million) awaiting decisions on their REFIT.[283]

In order to be eligible for REFIT 2 and 3, proof of planning permission and grid connection must be in place. This should prevent speculative applications from being allocated capacity before the necessary project pre-requisites have been secured. It is likely that the upcoming schemes will also mandate that projects must neither have been built, nor have been under construction by 1 January 2010, thereby ensuring that it is new developments which benefit from the new support scheme. Many sites with a grid offer under Gate 3 do not have and may never get planning permission.

The Minister for Communications, Energy and Natural Resources does not intend to make a state aid application in respect of offshore wind as it is twice as expensive as onshore wind (at €3 million per MW) and because Ireland can meet its renewable energy targets from onshore capacity, biomass and related technologies.[284] However, if in the future the British Government contracted to purchase Irish renewable energy (using guarantees of origin) from on and offshore sources and via interconnectors at the market rate the Government might reconsider its decision.

There is a strongly held view within the offshore renewables industry that the Government is not sending out the proper investment signals to encourage investors to enter the Irish market. For example, NOW Ireland has criticised the REFIT policy on the grounds that it needs to be more competitive to attract major capital projects, a view shared by many project promoters. For these technologies, despite the resources at our disposal, it is apparent that Ireland has still not got its act together.

## Green public procurement

The long-awaited Government action plan on green public procurement (GPP) has been published.[285] The action plan will cover tenders in the following sectors: construction, energy, transport, food and catering, cleaning products and services, paper, uniforms and other textiles and ICT equipment. The plan seeks to make sure that existing legislative requirements, for example in relation to waste and energy efficiency, are factored into future tender competitions.

Suppliers in these priority sectors would be well advised to read the GPP action plan carefully as selection and evaluation marks will depend on how you 'green' your tender bid responses. For example, buyers may require that for the tenders covered by GPP suppliers should have certification in environment management systems (EMAS).

This is voluntary approach as a statutory instrument has not been enacted to give effect to GPP in Ireland.

On the other hand, while details are as yet sketchy, Government has made it clear that a life-cycle costs approach should be considered by buyers when evaluating costs.

Detailed guidelines will have to be issued to public buyers before the GPP goes 'live'. For example, there are as yet no assessment criteria for the use of construction products. On the other hand, the GPP action plan requires, for instance, that food and catering companies must have ISO 14001 certification (or equivalent) and that all ICT equipment meets energy star or equivalent criteria. There is no reference (quite a surprise let it be said) to carbon footprinting i.e. the identification of the carbon component of the goods to be supplied.

It is envisaged that before full roll-out a detailed implementation plan for each of the eight sectors will need to be prepared in consultation with industry stakeholders. The marketing development programme (or rx3 as it is now called) will work to define the most appropriate methodology for each sector. First and foremost, the public servants who have been asked to implement GPP will have to be trained. Funds for such training are limited so the introduction of GPP will be gradual, but soon enough it will be embedded in national procurement policy.

GPP will work provided the National Procurement Service engages with suppliers in a proactive manner. The fact that the NPS is moving cautiously is also to be welcomed given the limited experience that Irish suppliers have in this area.

## Conclusions

A review of national climate change and energy policies will take place during 2012 and the former exercise will be informed by evidenced-based research to be completed by the National Economic and Social Council.

The post-2012 NCCS will have to address the EPA's assessment about the inadequacy of existing and/or planned policies and measures for the purposes of delivering on the post-2012 climate mitigation agenda, even in the short term. In addition the revised NCCS should be based inter alia on Ireland's MACC. The NCCS needs to be fully costed, assessed by means of a regulatory impact statement, and then implemented in the most efficient basis. It could be argued that Ireland currently does not have the institutional arrangements to deliver the strategy and that a separate Climate Change Office should be established.

The NCCS should also address Ireland's desired pathway to a low-carbon economy by 2050 and set out complementary measures to the Irish Energy Plan 2030.

Intensive stakeholder consultation in line with the Government's Better Regulation principles is essential.

The importance of energy efficiency in meeting Ireland's Kyoto commitments at least cost while improving our competitiveness should be given a higher priority. For example, Government should introduce the supports and incentives that other Member States have in place – for example, the Enhanced Capital Allowances Scheme, the Low Carbon Technology Incubator Scheme and the Energy Efficiency Loan Scheme managed by Carbon Trust covering fifteen categories of technology and 13,000 products.

Ireland's energy supply structure, large agricultural sector, increasing transport sector, and relatively modern and efficient industrial base make the economy more susceptible to loss of competitiveness and more dependent on achieving emissions reductions elsewhere in the EU and globally to protect national competitiveness. In addition, our distance to target estimates make it evident that Ireland may become more reliant on purchases by the Carbon Fund of carbon allowances on the open market. Restrictions on the use of flexible mechanisms will significantly impact the cost of compliance and competitiveness.

The expansion and development of north–south and east–west interconnectors are critical to increase diversity, capacity, security, and reduce energy peripherality. They will be key enablers in realising the benefits of renewable energy resources by sharing of resources and trading, as well as enhanced system security and reduced system costs.

Efforts must be made to engage with the investment and financial services sector to raise awareness of climate change and to encourage the emergence of a low-carbon technology sector through direct venture capital investment. In this respect, and in others, the UK's Carbon Trust should be examined and its usefulness as a business model for promoting a low-carbon economy should be considered in Ireland. The enterprise sector must seize the benefits that will arise through opportunities in the environmental goods and services sector, which is forecast to be a key growth area across the EU and Ireland.

Thankfully, as the next chapter will explain, considerable international research is available about Ireland's options as the economy transitions towards a low-carbon future.

## Chapter 9

# Towards a low-carbon future in 2050

The global warming scenario is pretty grim. I'm not sure I like the idea of polar bears under a palm tree.

Lenny Henry

## Europe's key challenges

The European Commission provides its Member States with a long-term policy framework for dealing with the issue of sustainability and the cross-border effects of phenomena such as climate change that cannot be dealt with at the national level alone.

For example, the Commission proposed the *Europe 2020* flagship initiative for a resource-efficient Europe and within that framework has put forward a series of long-term policy plans in areas such as transport, energy and climate change.[286] Most importantly, the Commission's Communication for moving to a low-carbon economy in 2050 sets the scene for a potentially seismic shift in policy that would see Ireland and other Member States moving inexorably towards a low-carbon economy. This Communication sets out key elements of climate action so that the EU and its Member States become a competitive low-carbon economy by 2050. The approach is based on the view that innovative solutions are required to mobilise investments in energy, transport, industry and information and communication technologies, and that more focus is needed on energy-efficiency policies.[287]

The *Europe 2020* strategy for smart, sustainable and inclusive growth includes five headline targets that set out where the EU should be in 2020. One of them relates to climate and energy. Member States have committed themselves to reducing GHG emissions by 20 per cent, increasing the share of renewables in the EU's energy mix to 20 per cent, and achieving the 20 per cent energy-efficiency target by 2020. The EU is currently on track to meet two of those targets, but will not meet its energy-efficiency target unless further efforts are made.[288] Hence, the priority remains to achieve all the targets already set for 2020.

In order to keep climate change below 2°C, the European Council reconfirmed in February 2011 the EU's objective of reducing GHG emissions by 80–95 per cent by 2050 compared to 1990, in the context of the required reductions according to the IPCC by developed countries as a group.[289] This is in line with the position endorsed by world leaders in the Copenhagen and subsequent COPs. These agreements include the commitment to deliver long-term low-carbon development strategies. Some Member States have already made steps in this direction, or are in the process of doing so, including setting emission-reduction objectives for 2050.

Together with the EU's White Paper on Transport[290] and the Energy Efficiency Plan, the Communication presents a roadmap for possible action up to 2050 that could enable the EU to deliver GHG emission reductions in line with the 80–95 per cent target agreed. It outlines milestones that would show whether the EU is on course for reaching its target, policy challenges, investment needs and opportunities in different sectors, bearing in mind that the 80–95 per cent reduction objective in the EU will largely need to be met internally.

The EU's transition towards a competitive low-carbon economy – an ambition shared by all Member States (apart from Poland) – means that Ireland will have to consider how best to reduce its emissions by perhaps 80 per cent by 2050.[291] A critical and over-arching consideration will be the relative contributions that will be made by the traded (ETS) and non-traded (non-ETS) sectors of the economy.

## Milestones to 2050

The Commission has carried out an extensive modelling analysis with several possible scenarios showing how this could be done at EU level, as explained below.

### Modelling approach for the 2050 low-carbon roadmap

The results and findings presented in the Communication are based on a comprehensive global and EU modelling and scenario analysis on how the EU could shift towards a low-carbon economy by 2050 against the backdrop of continued global population growth, rising global GDP and varying global trends in terms of climate action, energy and technological developments.

A set of global projections were used to look at global impacts of climate action, how it relates to the energy sector, agriculture and deforestation. Furthermore, impacts on the EU's competitive sectors were projected to assess the possible risks of ambitious actions in the context of fragmented global action on climate.

Detailed EU projections were made within a wide set of potential future scenarios, focussing on the sensitivity regarding assumptions on global fossil fuel price developments and rate of technological innovation to analyse the sectoral contribution, including from agriculture and other land uses. While there are always uncertainties relating to long-term projections, results have been made more robust by developing a wide set of scenarios with different assumptions.

This analysis of different scenarios shows that domestic emission reductions of the order of 40 per cent and 60 per cent below 1990 levels would be the cost-effective pathway by 2030 and 2040, respectively. In this context, it also shows reductions of 25 per cent in 2020.

Such a pathway would result in annual reductions at EU level compared to 1990 of roughly 1 per cent in the first decade until 2020; 1.5 per cent in the second decade from 2020 until 2030; and 2 per cent in the last two decades until 2050. The effort would become greater over time as a wider set of cost-effective technologies becomes available.

Figure 23 illustrates the pathway towards an 80 per cent reduction by 2050, shown in five-year steps. The upper 'reference'

**Figure 23: EU GHG emissions towards an 80% domestic reduction (100% = 1990)**

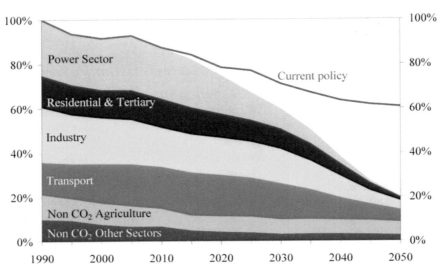

*Source:* European Commission (2011), *A Roadmap for Moving to a Competitive Low Carbon Economy by 2050*, COM (2011) 112 final.

projection shows how domestic GHG emissions would develop under current policies. A scenario consistent with an 80 per cent domestic reduction then shows how overall and sectoral emissions could evolve, if additional policies are put in place, taking into account technological options available over time.

Emissions, including international aviation, were estimated to be 16 per cent below 1990 levels in 2009. With full implementation of current policies, the EU is on track to achieve a 20 per cent domestic reduction in 2020 below 1990 levels, and 30 per cent in 2030. However, with current policies, only half of the 20 per cent energy-efficiency target would be met by 2020.

If the EU delivers on its current policies, including its commitment to reach 20 per cent renewables, and achieve 20 per cent energy efficiency by 2020, this would enable the EU to outperform the current 20 per cent emission-reduction target and achieve a 25 per cent reduction by 2020. This would require the full implementation of the EU's Energy Efficiency Plan, which identifies measures that would be necessary to deliver the energy-efficiency target. The amount of currently allowed offsets would not be affected.[292]

The Commission's analysis also shows that a less ambitious pathway could lock in carbon-intensive investments, resulting in higher carbon prices later on and significantly higher overall costs over the entire period. In addition, R&D, demonstration and early deployment of technologies, such as various forms of low-carbon energy sources, carbon capture and storage, smart grids and hybrid and electric vehicle technology, are of paramount importance to ensure their cost-effective and large-scale penetration later on. Full implementation of the Strategic Energy Technology Plan, requiring an additional investment in R&D and demonstration of €50 billion over the next ten years, is indispensable.[293]

The European Climate Foundation (ECF) has also assessed in considerable detail (from a technical and economic perspective) the implications for European industry, in particular the electricity sector, of reducing GHG emissions by 80 per cent by 2050; Figure 24 sets out their win–win scenario.[294]

**Figure 24: Roadmap 2050: a prosperous, low-carbon Europe**

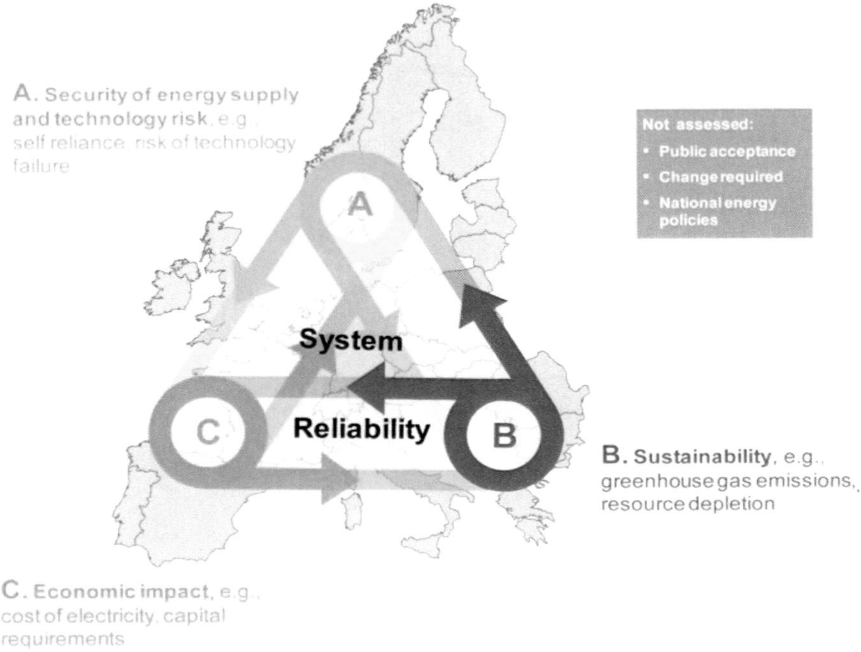

A. Security of energy supply and technology risk, e.g., self reliance, risk of technology failure

Not assessed:
• Public acceptance
• Change required
• National energy policies

System

Reliability

B. Sustainability, e.g., greenhouse gas emissions, resource depletion

C. Economic impact, e.g., cost of electricity, capital requirements

*Source:* European Climate Foundation (2011), *Roadmap 2050 – A Practical Guide to a Prosperus Low-Carbon Europe.*

The Commission has urged Ireland and other Member States to consider using auctioning revenue and cohesion policy (i.e. structural funds) as financing options. In addition, increasing resource efficiency through, for instance, waste recycling, better waste management and behavioural change, as well as enhancing the resilience of ecosystems, can play an important role. Also, continued effort to strengthen research on climate mitigation and adaptation technologies will be required.

## A sectoral perspective

The Commission's analysis has also explored pathways for key sectors. This analysis looked at a range of scenarios assuming different rates of technological innovation and different fossil fuel prices. They produced largely convergent results with respect to the magnitude of reductions needed in each sector in 2030 and 2050 as indicated by the ranges presented in Table 10. The development of sectoral policy options at national level will have to go into greater depth on costs, trade-offs, and uncertainties.

### Table 10: Sectoral reductions

| GHG reductions compared to 1990 | 2005 | 2030 | 2050 |
|---|---|---|---|
| Total | -7% | -40 to -44% | -79 to -82% |
| **Sectors** | | | |
| Power ($CO_2$) | -7% | -54 to -68% | -93 to -99% |
| Industry ($CO_2$) | -20% | -34 to -40% | -83 to -87% |
| Transport (incl. CO2 aviation, excl. maritime) | +30% | +20 to -9% | -54 to -67% |
| Residential and services ($CO_2$) | -12% | -37 to -53% | -88 to -91% |
| Agriculture (non-$CO_2$) | -20% | -36 to -37% | -42 to -49% |
| Other non-$CO_2$ emissions | -30% | -72 to -73% | -70 to -78% |

*Source:* European Commission (2011), *A Roadmap for Moving to a Competitive Low Carbon Economy by 2050*, COM (2011) 112 final.

## World energy outlook

The latest forecasts from the IEA come to the same strategic conclusions as the EU's 2050 low-carbon roadmap.[295] Despite the economic recession global primary energy demand rebounded by a remarkable 5 per cent in 2010, pushing global GHG emissions to a new high. While below its 2007 +60 per cent forecast, the IEA predicts demand for energy will grow by a third from

2010 to 2035, with non-OCED countries accounting for 90 per cent of the energy demand growth. China will consolidate its position as the world's largest energy consumer; by 2035 China will consume nearly 70 per cent more energy than the US. In practical terms, oil demand (excluding bio-fuels) rises from 87 million/day to 99 million/day by 2035. As the following figure shows, cumulative investment of some $38 trillion is required over this period to meet projected demand.

**Figure 25: Cumulative investment in energy-supply infrastructure (2010–2035)**

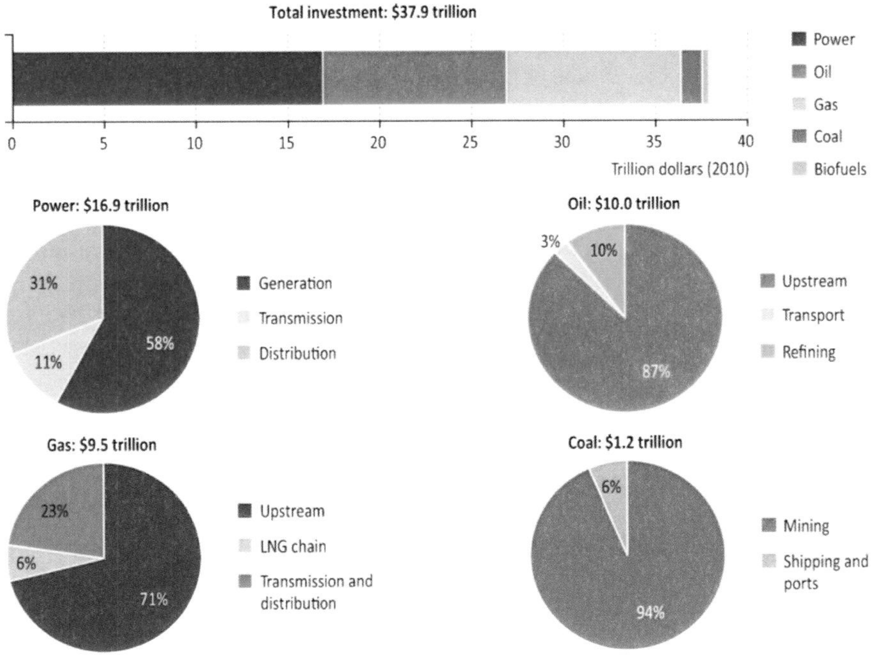

*Source:* IEA (2011), *World Energy Outlook 2011.*

The IEA's New Policies Scenario will result in a level of emissions consistent with a long-term average temperature increase of more than 3.5°C and some 6°C or more if BAU policies are adopted. A reason for this gloomy prediction is that some 80 per cent of total energy-related carbon emissions permissible by 2035 in the -2°C scenario are already 'locked in' to the existing capital stock. Unless new stringent action is taken by 2017, the IEA says that the energy-related infrastructure then in place will generate all the carbon emissions allowed under this scenario up

221

to 2035. This leaves no room for additional power plants unless they are zero-carbon, an unlikely prospect for at least a decade.

**Figure 26: Locked-in carbon infrastructure**

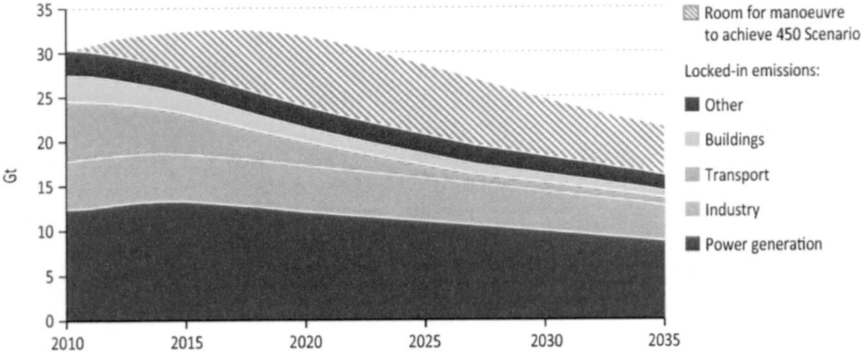

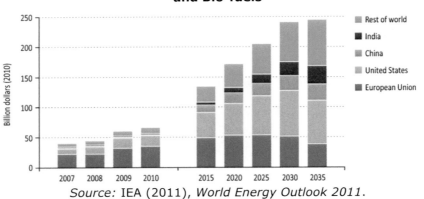

*Source:* IEA (2011), *World Energy Outlook 2011.*

With the EU and China as the main drivers, the share of non-hydro renewables in power generation is forecast to increase from 3 per cent in 2009 to 15 per cent by 2035. The IEA argues that even though the subsidy cost per unit of output is expected to decline, most renewable-energy sources need continued support in order to compete in electricity markets; such subsidies amounted to $66 billion and may rise to $250 billion by 2035.

**Figure 27: Global Subsidies to Renewables-Based Electricity and Bio-fuels**

*Source:* IEA (2011), *World Energy Outlook 2011.*

## A fully decarbonised power sector

The IEA's main findings and projections are broadly shared by the EU's Energy Roadmap 2050. This seminal document will have a considerable impact on the policy choices facing Ireland.[296]

In each of the seven scenarios presented, gas along with renewable sources are named as 'critical energy sources'. Dieter Helm, Professor at Oxford University and chairman of the ad hoc advisory group that assisted the Commission prepare the 2050 Energy Roadmap, is strongly supporting shale gas. He has also called into question conventional peak oil theory.

Electricity will clearly play a central role in the low-carbon economy. The analysis shows that it can almost totally eliminate $CO_2$ emissions by 2050, and offers the prospect of partially replacing fossil fuels in transport and heating. Although electricity will increasingly be used in these two sectors, electricity consumption overall would only have to continue to increase at historic growth rates, thanks to continuous improvements in efficiency.

The share of low-carbon technologies under various scenarios in the electricity mix is estimated to increase from around 45 per cent today to around 60 per cent in 2020, to between 75 per cent and 80 per cent in 2030, and nearly 100 per cent in 2050. As a result, and without prejudging Member States' preferences for an energy mix that reflects their specific national circumstances, the Commission believes that the EU's electricity system could become more diverse and secure.

A range of existing technologies will need to be widely deployed, including more advanced technologies, such as photovoltaics, that will continue to become cheaper and thus more competitive over time.

Energy-specific scenarios and the means of achieving such decarbonisation, while ensuring energy security and competitiveness, are examined in the EU's Energy 2050 Roadmap. This will build on the established EU energy policy and the *Europe 2020* strategy.

The EU ETS will be critical in driving a wide range of low-carbon technologies into the market, so that the power sector itself can adapt its investment and operational strategies to changing energy prices and technology. For the ETS to play this role on the identified pathway to 2050, both a sufficient carbon price signal and long-term predictability are necessary. In this respect, appropriate measures need to be considered, including revisiting the agreed linear reduction of the ETS cap.[297] Other tools, such as energy taxation and technological support may also be appropriate to ensure that the power sector plays its full part.

Given that the central role of electricity in the low-carbon economy requires significant use of renewables, many of which have variable output, considerable investments in networks are required to ensure continuity of supply at all times.[298] Investment in smart grids is a key enabler for a low-carbon electricity system, notably facilitating demand-side efficiency, larger shares of renewables and distributed generation and enabling electrification of transport. For grid investments, benefits do not always accrue to the grid operator, but to society at large (with co-benefits for consumers, producers, and society at large: a more reliable network, energy security and reduced emissions). In this context, future work should consider how the policy framework can foster these investments at EU, national and local level and incentivise demand-side management.

## Reducing Europe's energy bill

Taken over the whole 40-year period, it is estimated that energy efficiency and the switch to domestically produced low-carbon energy sources will reduce the EU's average fuel costs by between €175 billion and €320 billion per year. The actual cost saving depends on the extent to which global action on climate change is undertaken. In a scenario of global climate action, less fossil fuel would need to be imported into the EU and the cost of what would still be imported would decline.

The ECF has produced evidence that suggests lower energy costs under the decabonised pathways will reduce costs (Figure 28).

If the rest of the world does not take coordinated action, however, a major benefit of EU action would be to protect the economy against high fossil fuel prices. The Commission's analysis, as well as the IEA World Energy Outlook 2011, clearly demonstrates that fossil fuel prices are indeed projected to be significantly higher in case of limited global action. This is not only a long-term issue. Even following the current recession, oil prices are about twice as high as in 2005. The IEA estimated that the EU has seen its import bill rise by $70 billion from

## Figure 28: Decarbonising the Economy Saves Money

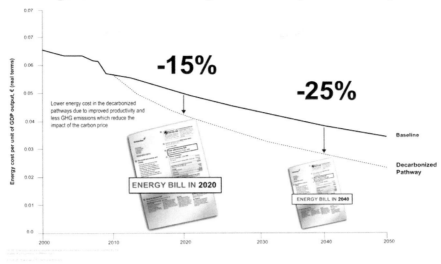

*Source:* European Climate Foundation (2011), *Roadmap 2050 – A Practical Guide to a Prosperus Low-Carbon Europe.*

2009 to 2010, and that further rises in the foreseeable future are probable. As we experienced in the 1970s and early 1980s, oil price shocks can lead to inflation, increasing trade deficits, reduced competitiveness and rising unemployment.

In 2050, the EU's total primary energy consumption could be about 30 per cent below 2005 levels. More domestic energy resources would be used, in particular renewables. Imports of oil and gas would decline by half compared to today, reducing the negative impacts of potential oil and gas price shocks significantly. Without action, the oil and gas import bill could instead double compared to today, a difference of €400 billion or more per annum by 2050; the equivalent of 3 per cent of today's GDP.[299]

## Transport

Technological innovation can help the transition to a more efficient and sustainable European transport system by vehicle efficiency through new engines, materials and design; cleaner energy use through new fuels and propulsion systems; better use of networks and safer and more secure operation through information and communication systems. The EU's White Paper on Transport identifies a comprehensive set of measures to increase the sustainability of the transport system.

Up until 2025, the main driver for reversing the trend of increasing GHG emissions in this sector is likely to remain improved fuel efficiency. Emissions from road and rail could in fact be brought back to below 1990 levels in 2030, in combination with measures such as pricing schemes to tackle congestion and air pollution, infrastructure charging, intelligent city planning and improving public transport, whilst securing affordable mobility. Improved efficiency and better demand-side management, fostered through $CO_2$ standards and smart taxation systems, should also advance the development of hybrid engine technologies and facilitate the gradual transition towards large-scale penetration of cleaner vehicles in all transport modes, including plug-in hybrids and electric vehicles (powered by batteries or fuel cells) at a later stage.

The synergies with other sustainability objectives such as the reduction of oil dependence, the competitiveness of Europe's automotive industry as well as health benefits, especially improved air quality in cities, make a compelling case for the EU (and Ireland) to step up efforts to accelerate the development and early deployment of electrification and, in general, of alternative fuels and propulsion methods, for the whole transport system. In this respect, it is not surprising also to see automotive industries in the US, Japan, Korea and China increasing their investments in battery technology, electric vehicles and fuel cells.

Sustainable bio-fuels could be used as an alternative fuel especially in aviation and heavy duty trucks, with the Commission envisaging strong growth in these sectors after 2030. If electrification were not deployed on a large scale, bio-fuels and other alternative fuels would need to play a greater role to achieve the same level of emissions reduction in the transport sector. For bio-fuels this could lead, directly or indirectly, to a decrease of the net GHG benefits and increased pressure on bio-diversity, water management and the environment in general. This reinforces the need to advance second and third generation bio-fuels and to proceed with the ongoing work on indirect land use change and sustainability.

## The built environment

The built environment provides low-cost and short-term opportunities to reduce emissions, first and foremost through improvement of the energy performance of buildings. The Commission's analysis shows that emissions in this area could be reduced by around 90 per cent by 2050; a larger than average contribution over the long term. This underlines the importance of achieving the objective of the recast Directive on energy performance of buildings, which requires that new buildings built from 2021 onwards will have to be nearly zero-energy buildings.[300] This process has already started, with many Member States implementing stricter energy-performance standards for buildings. On 4 February 2011 the European Council, taking account of the EU headline target, decided that from 2012 onwards all Member States should include energy-efficiency standards in public procurement for relevant public buildings and services. The Commission's forthcoming Communication on sustainable construction will set out a strategy on how to boost the competitiveness of this sector while improving its environmental and climate performance.

Efforts will need to be strengthened significantly over time. Today, new buildings should be designed as intelligent low- or zero-energy buildings. The extra cost of this can be recovered through fuel savings. A greater challenge, however, is the refurbishment of the existing building stock, and in particular how to finance the necessary investments. The analysis projects that over the next decade investments in energy-saving building components and equipment will need to be increased by up to €200 billion. Several Member States have already implemented smart financing schemes, such as preferential interest rates, for leveraging private sector investments in the most efficient building solutions. Other private financing models will need to be explored.

As in the transport sector, shifting energy consumption towards low-carbon electricity (including heat pumps and storage heaters) and renewable energy (e.g. solar heating, biogas, biomass), also provided through district heating systems, would help to protect consumers against rising fossil fuel prices and bring significant health benefits.

## Industrial sectors

The Commission's analysis shows that GHG emissions in the industrial sector could be reduced by between 83 per cent and 87 per cent in 2050. The application of more advanced resource and energy-efficient industrial processes and equipment, increased recycling, as well as abatement technologies for non-$CO_2$ emissions (e.g. nitrous oxide and methane), could make a major contribution by allowing the energy-intensive sectors to reduce emissions by half or more. As solutions are sector-specific, the Commission sees a need to develop specific roadmaps in cooperation with the sectors concerned.

In addition to the application of more advanced industrial processes and equipment, carbon capture and storage would also need to be deployed on a broad scale after 2035, notably to capture industrial process emissions especially in the cement and steel sectors. This would entail an annual investment of more than €10 billion. In a world of global climate action, this would not raise competitiveness concerns. But if the EU's main competitors do not engage in a similar manner, the EU would need to consider how to further address the risks of carbon leakage due to these additional costs.

As the EU develops its climate policy framework, there will be a need to continue to monitor and analyse the impacts of these measures on the competitiveness of energy-intensive industries in relation to efforts by third countries, and to consider appropriate measures where necessary. The Commission's analysis confirms earlier findings that the current measures provide adequate safeguards in the current context and notes the findings on options for addressing carbon leakage as set out in the Communication of May 2010.[301] The Commission will continue to update the list of sectors at risk of carbon leakage as foreseen in the EU ETS Directive.[302] Clearly, the best protection against the risk of carbon leakage would be effective global action.

## Agriculture, land use and forestry

The Commission's analysis shows that by 2050 the agriculture sector can reduce non-$CO_2$ emissions by between 42 per cent and 49 per cent compared to 1990. For Ireland, it is almost unimaginable that agriculture emissions would have to be cut almost in half. The sector will have to be modelled in much more detail reflecting the different abatement technologies applicable to arable versus pasture.

The sector has already achieved a significant reduction in emissions and more are feasible in the next two decades. It is proposed that agricultural policies should focus on options such as further sustainable efficiency gains, efficient fertiliser use, bio-gasification of organic manure, improved manure management, better fodder, local diversification and commercialisation of production and improved livestock productivity, as well as maximising the benefits of extensive farming.

Improved agricultural and forestry practices can increase the capacity of the sector to preserve and sequester carbon in soils and forests. This can be achieved, for instance, through targeted measures to maintain grasslands, restore wetlands and peat lands, low- or zero-tillage, to reduce erosion and allow for the development of forests. Agricultural and forestry are also providing the resources for bio-energy and industrial feedstocks, and this contribution is bound to increase further.

The above elements will be further addressed in the CAP legislative proposals for 2013,[303] of which the positive impacts have not yet been taken into account in the analysis, as well as the forthcoming Communication on the bio-economy.

After 2030, the rate of emission reductions in the agricultural sector could slow down, in part because of increased agricultural production due to the growing global population. However, it is important to note that, by 2050, agriculture is projected to represent a third of total EU emissions, tripling its share compared to today. Its importance in terms of climate policy is, therefore, set to increase: if it does not achieve the projected emissions reductions, other sectors would need to reduce even more, which would come at a high cost. The farming sector is also potentially at some risk of carbon leakage, so changes in production and trade patterns should not in the longer term undermine global reduction of emissions.

The Commisison's analysis also considers implications for the agricultural and forestry sector in a global perspective. In 2050, the world will have to feed around nine billion people. At the same time, tropical forests will have to be preserved as an essential component of tackling climate change and preserving world biodiversity. In addition, mitigation efforts are expected to increase demand for bio-energy alongside existing and increasing demand for feed for animals, timber, paper production and bio-industries. The dual challenges of global food security and action on climate change need to be pursued together. In order to cope with these increased land use requirements in the EU and on a global scale sustainable increases in the productivity delivered by diverse agricultural and forestry systems (both intensive and extensive) will need to continue at a rapid pace, not least in developing countries. Any negative impacts on other resources (e.g. water, soil and biodiversity) will need careful management. Accelerating climate change could endanger these productivity improvements in a world of insufficient action on climate change.

This also underscores the need to consider all land uses in a holistic manner and address LULUCF in the EU's climate policy. The Commission is preparing an initiative on this issue, which may facilitate the introduction of a forest carbon offset programme in Ireland.

## Investing in a low-carbon future

Various forms of low-carbon energy sources, their supporting systems and infrastructure, including smart grids, passive housing, carbon capture and storage, advanced industrial processes and electrification of transport (including energy-storage technologies) are key components that are starting to form the backbone of efficient, low-carbon energy and transport systems after 2020. This will require major and sustained investment: the increase in public and private investment at EU level is calculated to amount to around €270 billion annually. This represents an additional investment of around 1.5 per cent of EU GDP per annum on top of the overall current investment representing 19 per cent of GDP in 2009.[304] It would take us back to the investment levels before the economic crisis.

Investments today will determine the future competitiveness of economies. In this context, it is interesting to note the much larger shares of GDP allocated to investments in China (48 per cent), India (35 per cent), and Korea (26 per cent) in 2009, showing emerging economies' need to build up infrastructure but also the potential in leapfrogging towards a competitive, low-carbon economy.[305]

Unlocking the investment potential of the private sector and individual consumers presents a major challenge. While most of this extra investment would be paid back over time through lower energy bills and increased productivity, markets tend to discount future benefits, and disregard long-term risks. A key question is, therefore, how policy can create the framework conditions for such investments to happen, including new financing models.

In the implementation of the 20 per cent energy-efficiency target, Ireland will have to monitor the impact of new measures on the ETS in order to maintain the incentives in the ETS rewarding low-carbon investments and preparing the ETS sectors for the innovations needed in the future. In this respect, appropriate measures need to be considered, including recalibrating the ETS by setting aside a corresponding number of allowances from the part to be auctioned during the period 2013–2020 should a corresponding political decision be taken. This would also ensure that the contribution to the energy-efficiency target would be made in a cost-efficient manner in both the ETS and non-ETS sectors.

The ECF has assessed the required level of capital investment under various scenarios (Figure 29).

## Figure 29: Annual capex development (2010–2050)

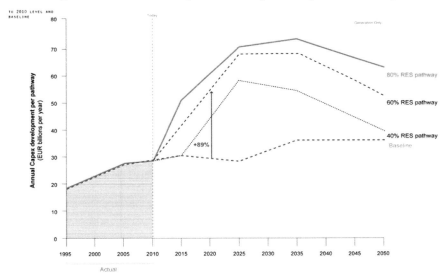

*Source:* European Climate Foundation (2011), *Roadmap 2050 – A Practical Guide to a Prosperus Low-Carbon Europe.*

Additional public–private financing mechanisms are key in order to overcome initial financing risks and cashflow barriers. Public finance through innovative financing instruments, such as revolving funds, preferential interest rates, guarantee schemes, risk-sharing facilities and blending mechanisms can mobilise and steer the required private finance, including for SMEs and consumers. In this way, limited public finance can leverage a multitude of private sector investments.[306] The European Investment Bank, the European Bank for Reconstruction and Development, as well as dedicated funding in the next Multi-Annual Financial Framework (the EU multi-annual budget 2013–2020) will play a role in providing additional financing for energy-efficient and low-carbon technologies.

Increasing domestic investments also provide a major opportunity for increased productivity, added value and output from a wide range of EU manufacturing industries (e.g. automotive, power generation, industrial and grid equipment, energy-efficient building materials and the construction sector), which are key industries for the creation of future growth and jobs.

## New jobs

Investing early in the low-carbon economy would stimulate a gradual structural change in the economy and can create in net terms new jobs both in the short and the medium term. Renewable energy has a strong track record in job creation. In just five years, the EU's renewable industry increased its workforce from 230,000 to 550,000. Also for the construction sector low-carbon investment offers large short-term job opportunities. With some 15 million employees in the EU, it was particularly hard hit by the economic crisis. Its recovery could get a significant boost through a major effort to accelerate the renovation and building of energy-efficient houses. The EU's Energy Efficiency Plan confirms the large job-creation potential from promoting investments in more efficient equipment.

The ECF draws attention to where jobs will be lost (in the petroleum, gas and oil industries), which will be more than compensated by increased employment in the low-carbon sector and jobs resulting from energy efficiency and fuel switching (Figure 30).

**Figure 30: EU job creation**

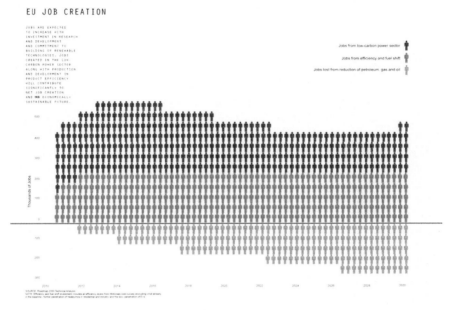

*Source:* European Climate Foundation (2011), *Roadmap 2050 – A Practical Guide to a Prosperus Low-Carbon Europe.*

In the longer term, the creation and preservation of jobs will depend on the EU's ability to lead in terms of the development of new low-carbon technologies through increased education, training, programmes to foster acceptability of new technologies, R&D and entrepreneurship, as well as favourable economic framework conditions for investments. In this context, the Commission has repeatedly emphasised the positive employment benefits if revenues from the auctioning of ETS allowances and carbon taxation are used to reduce labour costs, with the potential to increase total employment by up to 1.5 million jobs by 2020.

As industry takes advantage of the economic opportunities provided by the low-carbon economy, the need to ensure a skilled workforce, especially in the construction sectors, technical professions, engineering and research, becomes more pressing. This will require targeted vocational training of the existing workforce towards 'green-collar' job opportunities, addressing emerging skills bottlenecks and fostering these skills in education systems. The Commission is currently working on assessing the employment effects of greening the economy, for instance through the implementation of the Agenda for New Skills and Jobs.[307]

## Ireland's response

In the light of the Commission's assessment, there is a compelling case that Ireland should develop a resource-efficient national low-carbon roadmap through to 2050 reflecting our particular circumstances. We need to start thinking outside the box if we really want to take advantage of the investment opportunities in a European low-carbon economy.

We need to position the economy way beyond the timescale through to 2020 that will be the focus of the forthcoming National Climate Change Strategy. The NCCS will, in large, be a compliance response setting out a range of domestic measures to give effect to the legal obligations we have to cut GHG by at least 20 per cent by 2020.

Strategic thinking is needed with a much longer time horizon than is currently contemplated.

### The big issues

- The complete electrification of the public transport system
- An accelerated investment programme to roll out the supporting infrastructure for electric vehicles
- Reducing energy efficiency in buildings by 50 per cent as part of an accelearted implementation of the NEEAP
- Unless needed on grounds of fuel diversity, the phasing out of generation at the coal-fired station at Moneypoint (the largest emitter of GHG on the island: some 4 million tonnes per annum)
- Investment in high volume pump storage generation capacity on the western seaboard
- Planning for a considerable expansion of offshore renewables coupled with investment in higher capacity interconnectors [308]
- A tripling of the current levels of afforestation (linked to the introduction of a forest carbon offset programme).

For companies who want a free resource efficiency assessment contact www.greenbusiness.ie.[309]

## Conclusions

The Commission's detailed analysis of cost-effective ways of reducing GHG emissions by 2050 has produced a number of important findings for Irish policy-makers, project promoters and investors.

First, in order to be in line with the 80–95 per cent overall GHG reduction objective by 2050, the Commission's assessment indicates that a cost-effective and gradual transition would require a 40 per cent domestic reduction of GHG emissions compared to 1990 as a milestone for 2030, and 80 per cent for 2050. Building on what has already been achieved, the EU needs to start working now on appropriate strategies to move in this direction.

Second, the analysis also shows that with existing policies, the EU will easily achieve the goal of a 20 per cent GHG reduction domestically by 2020. If the revised EU Energy Efficiency Plan was fully and effectively implemented (meeting the 20 per cent energy-efficiency target) this would enable the EU to out-perform the current 20 per cent emission-reduction target and achieve a -25 per cent emission-reduction target. The Commission is not suggesting to set new 2020 targets, nor does it affect the EU's offer in the international negotiations to take on a 30 per cent reduction target for 2020, if the conditions are right.

Third, as well as reducing the threat of dangerous climate change as part of ambitious global action, deep reductions in the EU's emissions have the potential to deliver benefits in the form of savings on fossil fuel imports and improvements in air quality and public health.

Fourth, the low-carbon roadmap gives ranges for emissions reductions for 2030 and 2050 for key sectors. To realise these milestones as cost-effectively as possible, and to maximise benefits for EU manufacturing industries, the implementation of the Strategic Energy Technology Plan is of crucial importance. It would be useful if Ireland could develop sectoral strategies using the IEA's technology roadmap model.

Finally, considering the important labour market implications, the EU's New Skills and Jobs Agenda will need to support the transition process.

In the coming years, implementing these pledges will be a key step in globalising climate change policies. Ireland should use this opportunity to strengthen its cooperation with other Member States and emerging economies to work towards a gradual development of global carbon markets to support efforts of developed and developing countries to implement low-emission development strategies, and ensure that all climate financing contributes to 'climate proof' development opportunities. The Commission intends to use the roadmap as a basis for developing sector-specific policy initiatives and roadmaps, such as the 2050 Energy Roadmap and the EU White Paper on Transport. The Commission will continue to ensure that the EU ETS remains a key instrument to drive low-carbon investments in a cost-efficient manner.

The critical question for Ireland is whether we become a policy-taker or a policy-maker. The latter requires strong leadership from the public sector, which to date is lacking.

Our level of ambition needs to be recalibrated. We must start planning for a post-Troika economy.

**Part 2**

# Green economy: the business opportunities

**Chapter 10**

# The green economy – global trends

Nations that lead the world in clean energy technology will lead the global economy of the 21st century.

President Barack Obama, 'Winning the Future'
speech, January 2011

## Introduction

The traditional market for environmental goods and services comprises suppliers of pollution control, including waste management, water treatment and land remediation technologies, as well as energy management and renewable energy companies. In recent years, the global market has been mainly driven by compliance and regulatory concerns and the deregulation of utilities. However, it is becoming increasingly evident that the threat of climate change and the pressure to reduce carbon emissions is beginning to have a major impact on investment decisions in the sector.

Because the sector is so diverse it is extremely difficult to define and quantify. One study estimated that the value of the sector was likely to exceed $800 billion by 2015.[310] To put this in context, and to underline the growing importance of the sector, this is triple the size of the global aerospace industry.[311] The US market is valued at $327 billion (2010).[312] The UK Government's Green Economy Strategy estimates that the sector will be worth £4 trillion by 2015; using a broad definition of what comprises 'the green economy'.

Ireland has some 240 cleantech companies employing 6,000 people. The top 50 indigenous SMEs employ 2,000 and have a turnover (2011) of €394 million with exports valued at €135 million.

In terms of regional breakdown, firms in OECD member countries are estimated to account for about 90 per cent of the global green economy market. However, this situation is beginning to change and many economies in transition, in particular China, are now seeing the most rapid growth, in response to concerted environmental problems arising from their rapid industrialisation and urbanisation.

In May 2011, the OECD embarked upon a green growth strategy. Country-specific reports have been published as have green growth indicators. The OECD also addresses foreign direct investment trends and innovation and technology transfers. However, the OECD did not attempt to quantify the size of the global green economy. One study set out to measure what is called 'eco-innovation' in the 30 OECD members. This included the identification of mechanisms that influence 'eco-innovation' and the promotion of policies that enable better diffusion of environment-related technologies.

The following policy instruments were examined as part of this study:[313]

- Framework conditions (innovation, investment)
- Public finance for R&D
- Environmental technology verification
- Performance targets
- Mobilisation of finance (move from grants to loans)
- Market-based instruments (tax incentives, non-tax instruments)
- Green procurement
- Awareness raising (showcasing technologies, eco-labeling)
- Acting globally (institutional problems, developing countries, IP rights).

The OECD study reflects the rapidly changing nature of the sector, driven by the multiple responses to climate change, declining commodity availability and energy security.

## Defining the sector

The environmental goods and services sector – the green economy – encompasses a wide range of activities, and definitions of the sector can, and do, differ. For example, the US Department of Commerce defines the green economy market, or more generally the 'environmental technology' market, as those environmental technologies that 'advance sustainable development by reducing risk, enhancing cost-effectiveness, improving process efficiency, and creating products and processes that are environmentally beneficial or benign'.[314]

The European Commission has adopted the OECD/Eurostat definition, which states that:

> The environmental goods and services industry consists of activities which produce goods and services to measure, prevent, limit, minimise or correct environmental damage to water, air and soil, as well as problems related to waste, noise and eco-systems. This includes cleaner technologies, products and services that reduce environmental risk and minimise pollution and resource use.[315]

A similar definition is used by the UK Department of Environment, Fisheries and Rural Affairs which concluded this is a cross-cutting and emerging sector, which includes both companies that have been created specifically to serve this market and companies sitting in more traditionally defined sectors (such as engineering) that are diversifying in response to this opportunity. There is no exact boundary around the sector. The key point is that there is a sector with common issues arising from the nature of the market it is serving.[316]

With the drive towards cleaner, greener processes and products and an increased focus on energy management and the development of alternative energy sources, the scope of the sector has widened considerably.

## Investment in the green economy

While reliable figures on the economic value of the green economy sector are difficult to arrive at, the sharp increase in investment in the sector helps to underline the growing importance of the sector at global level and the recognition of its future potential.

This has been particularly noticeable in the figures for global venture capital companies who have assigned the moniker 'greentech' or 'cleantech' to this sector, which is indicative of what areas the investment money is following.

---

**Surge in investment**

- Bio-fuels sales were over $56 billion in 2010 (27 billion gallons) and are projected to grow to $113 billion by 2020.

- Wind power (new installation capital costs) is projected to expand from $60 billion in 2010 to $123 billion in 2020. Installed installations now account for 35.2 GW of capacity with China, the global leader of new installations for the third year in a row, accounting for 16 GW.

- Solar photovoltaics are projected to grow from $71 billion (2010) to $114 billion by 2020, with 15.6 GW of installed capacity worldwide.[317]

---

While the overall European figures may be somewhat disappointing, the upward trend is clear. In the UK, for example (which the CEMEP report claims leads in Europe in share and spread of venture capital for clean technology, and accounts for almost a third of the total €1.9 billion invested across Europe in recent years), investment in the sector is beginning to become more diverse. While energy continues to attract most investment, investments are increasingly being targeted at a wide range of environmental sectors including materials, transport, logistics, water and air quality. As a result, UK investments are now claimed to be far more diverse than in Germany, for example, where energy accounts for 92 per cent of green economy activity. It was also noted, however, that while the UK is the leading venture capital market in Europe, it lags significantly behind the US in scale and pace of growth. The relative lack of investment in the UK means that the so-called 'valley of death', whereby innovative firms fail because of a gap in funding on the path to commercialisation is still a problem, particularly when large-scale demonstration projects are required.[318]

New Energy Finance has suggested a number of reasons why Europe has been falling behind, including the traditional weakness of Europe's venture capital industry, compared with that of the US, 'Balkanised' national markets and bureaucratic processes for technology support.[319] New Energy Finance made recommendations for policy-makers wishing to promote the business environment for venture capital spending in the renewable energy sector.

## How to promote venture capital activity

- Improve general macro-economics for innovation and entrepreneurship
- Identify and breakdown regulatory barriers to markets for clean energy providers
- Reduce investment risk by improving stability and longevity of clean energy support mechanisms
- Use the public sector to create markets through preferential procurement of clean solutions
- Introduce pan-European standards for clean energy, fuels and technologies
- Promote the development of supporting services such as testing and certification, training, information provision and insurance
- Avoid the temptation to pick winners, whether through green funds or any other mechanism
- Decouple technology support programmes from social and political goals.

The political and regulatory changes spurring such investments are unlikely to subside soon. These, allied to a strong innovation pipeline and confidence in the global drivers supporting growth in the clean technology market (such as government policies, consumer awareness, energy prices and concern about carbon emissions), will continue to drive venture capital investment.

The climate change roadmap and energy pricing are uniquely intertwined; the collective global response to climate change will involve a 'decarbonisation' of economies where the prospective pricing of a tonne of $CO_2$ at perhaps $40, will place both energy efficiency and renewable energy generation at a competitive advantage over traditional energy sources. Some commentators suggest that the impact of carbon pricing may be overtaken by hugely escalated prices for oil and gas – the so-called 'peak oil' concept. These factors will drive further investments in renewable sources of energy in particular.

## Global investments and foreign direct investment opportunities

Environmental goods and services in the US have over the past number of years become defined into a more distinct and documented sector of the economy. This has attracted the attention of the major fund managers who have packaged together 'green funds'; one of the biggest of these, the S&P Global Eco Index, comprises 40 of the largest publicly traded companies in ecology-related industries that meet specific investability requirements. The index is designed to provide liquid exposure to the leading publicly listed companies in these industries. The index includes stocks in six different clusters, which represent ecology-related industries. A review of this index provides an insight into the operations of the top 40 companies and what opportunities exist for prospective inward investment activity into Ireland.

In the very recent past here is considerable investment activity worldwide in the green economy sector as the following tables illustrate.[320]

**Table 11: Global asset finance and VC investment in clean energy (Q3/2011) ($billion)**

| Region | Asset Finance | | VC Investment | |
|---|---|---|---|---|
| | Amount | No. of Deals | Amount | No. of Deals |
| United States | 15.1 | 32 | 1.8 | 87 |
| China | 12.2 | 127 | 0.1 | 1 |
| EU | 8.8 | 23 | 0.2 | 14 |
| India | 2.6 | 38 | 0.1 | 4 |
| Brazil | 1.2 | 15 | | |
| Other | 2 | 14 | 0.3 | 12 |
| | $41.8 billion | 249 | $2.2 billion | 117 |

**Table 12: Global asset finance and VC investment – sector split (Q3/2011) ($billion)**

| Region | Asset Finance | | VC Investment | |
|---|---|---|---|---|
| | Amount | No. of Deals | Amount | No. of Deals |
| Solar | 19.5 | 100 | 0.5 | 30 |
| Wind | 18 | 112 | 0.2 | 9 |
| Geothermal | 1.2 | 4 | 0.1 | 2 |
| Biofuels | 1.2 | 5 | 0.3 | 13 |
| Biomass/waste | 0.9 | 12 | 0.03 | 5 |
| Hydro/Smart technologies | 0.8 | 14 | 1 | 52 |
| Marine | 0.03 | 2 | 0.03 | 2 |
| Other | | | 0.07 | 6 |
| | $41.8 billion | 249 | $2.2 billion | 117 |

*Source:* Bloomberg New Energy Finance (2011).

Although venture capital investment activity has slowed somewhat since 2008, US analysts Cleantech figures show that the $2.23 billion invested globally in Q3/2011 represents a fivefold increase since 2005. Despite a slowdown in venture capital funding, Government supports at $194 billion globally since 2008 and corporate and academic interest are at unprecedented levels.

Interestingly, the top five public market transactions in Q3/2011 were all in solar energy. It should also be borne in mind that while there is a limited history of solar manufacturing or development in Ireland, if one considers the constituent parts, extensive silicon fabrication and optics experience with the like of Analog Devices, Intel, Vistakon and Bausch and Lomb is already in place. A review of other possible foreign direct investment (FDI) targets such as wind turbines and associated components could be matched with the engineering capability of the marine engineering and aerospace industries of the Belfast region.

There are other factors that would be vital in demonstrating the readiness and commitment to attract new FDI projects into Ireland. Most significantly, the announcement of clean technology as the third pillar of the Government's investment in science and technology sends a clear signal to prospective investors of the commitment in the future. The industrial development agencies can point to developments such as the refurbishment of the wave tanks in UCC and Queens University

Belfast, the development of Galway as a Smartbay to facilitate development of wave energy and the iconic wind turbine based in the Dundalk Institute of Technology.

Unless and until Ireland commits to invest public funding for environmental R&D on a scale comparable to competitor countries such as the UK, Austria and Denmark, and unless the scientific and engineering skills base is in place, there is little prospect of securing a world class R&D presence in this area. On the other hand, as has happened in the past in relation to life sciences and ICT, declaring the green economy sector as a new pillar for science and technology endeavour will send the right signals to both global sustainable companies, investors and academia internationally.

The approach in attracting FDI should differ between the maturing energy technologies (e.g. wind energy and solar thermal) and emerging energy technologies (e.g. solar PV and battery technology). Wind energy is considered a maturing sector from a technology perspective but the global demand continues to outstrip supply. In the UK, the cost per MW of energy produced from offshore wind farms is approximately €3.5 million, with turbines representing around 70 per cent of the investment cost.

The main players in the wind turbine manufacturing market are as follows:

**Table 13: Wind turbine manufacturers' market share**

| | | |
|---|---|---|
| 1. | Vestas | 14.3% |
| 2. | Sinovel China | 10.7% |
| 3. | GE Wind, US | 9.3% |
| 4. | Goldwind, China | 9.2% |
| 5. | Enercon, Germany | 7% |
| 6. | United Power, China | 4.1% |
| 7. | Siemens, Denmark | 5.7% |
| 8. | Gamesa, Spain | 6.4% |
| 9. | Dongfang, China | 6.5% |
| 10. | Suzlon Group, India | 6.7% |
| 11. | Others | 20% |

*Source:* Renewable Energy Policy Network (2011), *REN21 Renewables 2011 Global Status Report.*

Turbines can be manufactured at a dedicated site by the top tier company or sub-contracted to original equipment manufacturers (OEMs). Turbines are generally not assembled and tested prior to shipping so the proximity of the tiered supply base to the primary manufacturing is not that critical. A possible strategy would be to engage with companies throughout the supply chain with a view to them establishing operations in Ireland to cater for the increased global demand and at the same time seeking R&D and back office elements as part of this investment.

C&F Green Energy of Athenry (now employing 165 people) has transformed from being a tooling company into a significant manufacturer of small-scale wind turbines. This shows how Ireland can become a niche player by using our skills base to good effect.

Branded Indian and Chinese wind turbine manufacturers have emerged in the past couple of years. There is every prospect that they will expand their domestic operations and seek to establish a presence in Europe to service the European market. By 2007, there were four Chinese manufacturers, six major foreign subsidiary/JV manufacturers, and 40 other Chinese firms aspiring to produce turbines and developing prototypes.[321]

For the emerging technologies the FDI strategy would differ; the industry is at a much different stage in its lifecycle with a plethora of start-ups, highly funded and eager for expansion. The solar PV industry appears (gauging on the level of expansion and investment) to be the most likely prospect for FDI. Again the focus should be directed at attracting these companies to establish Europe, Middle East and Africa operation in Ireland with manufacturing and back office services (design, treasury, supply chain). As well as the leading edge solar PV companies, each of these components in the tiered supply chain offers the potential to attract FDI. At present, current solar PV investment appears to be concentrated on the flow of investment between Germany and the US. In the same way as the location of Gammaster and Isotron were critical to the expansion of the medical device industry, there may be a similar infrastructural capability required to enable the development of the solar PV industry.

Other emerging technologies that could be possibilities for European expansion include load management/demand response solutions, new battery technologies and next generation bio-fuels technology.

Presentation of capability as much as an educated work-force and a generous tax regime will define Ireland's success at attracting inward investment from this growing sector. Another possibility would be to 'zone' the island on the basis of capability and infrastructure for inward investment and sub-market on this basis; as a broad-brush example:

## Ireland's clusters

Dublin = The Green Way (an tSlí Ghlas)
Belfast – Newry – Dundalk – Wexford = Wind Energy Zone
Limerick – Shannon = Solar Energy Zone and 'Green' Manu-facturing Zone
Galway – Mayo = Wave/Ocean Energy Zone
Cork = Bio-fuel Zone

According to the Global Cleantech Innovation Index 2012 it is encouraging that Ireland is ranked ninth out of 38 countries. One strong feature is our relative potential to produce entre-preneurial cleantech start-up companies and commercialise clean technology innovations. While placed ahead of the UK, the research concludes that Ireland lacks public cleantech R&D spending and has only average scores for supporting govern-ment policies and access to private finance.

Ireland has proven itself in the past in the FDI market by trend spotting and identifying the next inward FDI wave; tar-geting the right sub-sectors; examining the different elements of the supply chain; proving capability and infrastructure; and possibly sub-branding through zoning or clustering will ensure a slice of the rapidly expanding 'green collar' job market. A very good example of what Ireland can achieve is the announce-ment by Intel that it is setting up an energy and sustainability lab headquartered in Leixlip. The lab is an active member of research consortiums and research clusters lead by Irish uni-versities and is actively partnering with IDA Ireland's I2E2 energy-efficiency technology centre.

## ICT opportunities – convergence

*High Tech: Low Carbon*, a report of EICTA, the industry body representing the information and communications technology and consumer electronics industries in the EU has highlighted how the digital technology industry will enhance, enable and transform Europe to help achieve its climate change targets, if used to its full potential.[322] The European Commission has also highlighted the contribution that ICT can make to energy efficiency.[323] EICTA believes that there are two interdependent solutions to the problem of carbon emissions – product innovation by manufacturers and the intelligent use of digital technology by consumers, businesses and authorities.

The report identifies how more than 25 different technologies can be applied by other sectors of the economy to enhance existing processes, enable new ways of working and transform our everyday activities, and to reduce their overall carbon emissions and energy consumption. EICTA member companies manufacturing digital technologies are identifying the best low-carbon technologies and accelerating their development so that Europe can achieve its emission-reduction targets. EICTA argues that improving the efficiency of ICT products is not enough. Ways have to be found to decouple completely economic growth from energy consumption. This can only happen if the best in class carbon-reducing technology devices are more rapidly applied at a large scale by all other sectors of the economy. The report commits Europe's digital technology industry to monitor the emissions associated with their products, share best practices through their supply chain, assist to encourage behavioural change and further develop low-carbon technologies.

EICTA appears to suggest that market conditions and not industry guidelines will drive investment in carbon-abatement technologies and energy-efficiency measures.

More recently, the IEA has also stressed the critical importance of technology as a driver of the low-carbon economy.[324]

The ICT sector in Ireland will almost certainly benefit as a supplier and enabler to some green economy products and services as we have particular strengths in areas such as sensors, software and data analytics. The potential of ICT convergence opportunities for Irish companies is an important area and should be the subject of a dedicated piece of research that takes account of work done at global level.[325]

## EU state aid guidelines on environmental protection

A report prepared for the industrial development agencies identified a number of new state aid schemes that could be introduced to assist the Irish green economy sector.[326] The pro-posed measures were based on schemes in operation in other Member States, which were approved under the (then) EU state aid guidelines on environmental protection.

### Possible support schemes

- The WRAP Capital Grants Scheme (UK)
- The Carbon Trust Low Carbon Innovation Programme and Enhanced Capital Allowance Measure (UK)
- The kfW Bank's ERP Environmental Protection and Energy Saving Programme (Germany)
- The kfW Bank's Programme to Promote Renewable Energies (Germany)
- The Fideme Investment Fund (France)
- SenterNovem's Carbon Reduction Plan (the Netherlands)
- SenterNovem's Energy Investment Tax Relief Scheme (the Netherlands).

In the meantime, the Commission has published revised guidelines for environmental protection that will have to be taken into account in the preparation of any new Irish schemes to support the green economy sector.[327] The basic principles underpinning the revised guidelines remain the same. There are some subtle but important changes as follows:

- The guidelines apply to aid for environmental studies, district heating, aid for waste management and aid involved in tradable permit schemes.

- The permissible levels of aid intensities have increased considerably. If aid is awarded on foot of a competitive tender (e.g. to build an all-island waste or recycling plant) up to 100 per cent public funding may be provided.

- In certain situations tax reductions may be considered as compatible aid.

- Where large amounts of aid are proposed a detailed assessment will be carried out. However, once a scheme is approved individual company assessments will not be undertaken.

Under a Block Exemption Regulation, environmental aid under a certain amount does not have to be notified.

## Renewables – global forecasts

While global energy consumption rebounded in 2010 after the previous year's downturn, renewable energy growth in all end-use sectors – power, heat and transport – was strong, so much so that renewable sources (RES) now represents 16 per cent of global final energy consumption. RES accounted for almost half of the estimated 194 GW of new electricity capacity generated during 2010 and now accounts for a quarter of global power capacity from all sources.[328]

A record 71 per cent of all new power-generating capacity in Europe in 2011 (some 32 GW) came from solar panels, wind turbines and other renewable energy sources; the corresponding figure for 2010 was 23 GW. The rise was especially pronounced in solar.[329] In the US, RES accounted for nearly 11 per cent of domestic primary production (nuclear's share is 11.3 per cent); an increase of 5.5 per cent relative to 2009. China added an estimated 29 GW of RES grid-connected capacity; an annual increase of 12 per cent. Germany met 11 per cent of its total final energy consumption from RES. Several countries met higher shares of their electricity demand from wind power in 2010, including Denmark (22 per cent), Portugal (21 per cent), Spain (15.4 per cent) and Ireland (10.1 per cent).

Trends reflect strong demand and investment across all market sectors with growth in equipment manufacturing, sales and installation. Technology cost reductions in solar PV meant high growth rates in manufacturing.

By early 2011, at least 118 countries had some type of policy target or RES support policy. As a consequence wind energy now exists in some 83 countries and solar can be found in 100 countries.

China leads in several indicators of market growth. In 2010, it was the top installer of wind turbine and solar thermal systems and was the top hydropower producer. India is fifth worldwide in total existing wind power capacity and is rapidly expanding many forms of rural renewables such as biogas. Brazil produces virtually all of the world's sugar-derived ethanol. At least twenty countries in the Middle East, North Africa and sub-Saharan Africa have active renewable energy markets.

Globally, there are more than 3.5 million direct jobs in RES industries, about half of them in the bio-fuels sector. Total investment in RES reached $211 billion in 2010; up from $160 billion in 2009. Asset finance of new utility-scale projects accounted for almost 60 per cent of the total, with China attracting almost a third of the total investment.

An operating subsidy by way of a feed-in tariff (REFIT) remains the most widely implemented policy in place.

Sectoral trends could be summarised as follows (Table 14).

### Table 14: Market and industry highlights

| | |
|---|---|
| **Wind** | The global wind industry installed more than 41 GW of wind power capacity in 2011, up 21% on 2010, bringing total installed capacity to 238 GW.[1] For the first time, the majority of new wind power capacity was added in developing countries and emerging markets. China alone, with a cumulative capacity of 62 GW, is expected to install more than 30 GW of wind power capacity during 2011 and 2012. Average turbine sizes continued to increase, with some manufacturers launching 5 MW and larger machines. Some 75 countries now have commercial wind power installations. |
| **Solar Photovoltaics** | The PV industry had an extraordinary year with global production and markets doubling; an estimated 17 GW of capacity being added. Italy and Germany installed more PV in 2010 than the entire world did in the previous year. The trend towards utility-scale PV plants continued; some 5,000 plants now account for 25% of global PV capacity. Cell manufacturing continued its shift to Asia, with 10 of the top 15 manufacturers located in the region. At least 5.4 GW of solar PV capacity was under contract in the US at the end of 2010, with a further 2.6 GW of additional CSP capacity under construction. |
| **Concentrating Solar Thermal Power** | After years of inactivity, the CSP market has come back to life with nearly 740 MW added between end 2007 and 2011. Parabolic trough plants dominate the market. Dramatic reductions in PV costs are challenging the growing market for CSP, at least in the US. |
| **Biomass** | An estimated 62 GW of biomass power capacity was in operation by the end of 2010, with markets expanding steadily in most countries. Trends include increasing consumption of solid biomass pellets (for heat and power) and the use of biomass in CHP plants. China leads the world in the number of household biogas plants. |
| **Bio-fuels** | Liquid bio-fuels provided about 2.7% of global road transport in 2010. The global ethanol industry recovered in response to rising oil prices, with production increasing 17%. The US and Brazil account for 88% of the market; the US is now the world's leading ethanol exporter. Biodiesel production is centred in the EU. |
| **Geothermal** | At least 24 countries now have geothermal plants which generate some 11 GW. A significant acceleration in the rate of deployment is expected as advanced technologies allow for development in new countries. Use of geothermal energy for CHP is also on the rise. |
| **Ocean** | At least 25 countries are involved in ocean energy developments, and as a result wave and tidal technologies saw significant progress towards commercial generation in 2010. Some 2 MW of wave and 4 MW of tidal capacity have been installed, mostly in the EU. |

[1] Global Wind Energy Council.

*Source:* Renewable Energy Policy Network (2011), *REN21 Renewables 2011 Global Status Report.*

Continued strong growth is expected in all RES sectors in the coming years.

Close to 80 per cent of the world's energy supply could be met by renewables by mid-century if backed by the right enabling public policies a new report shows. The findings, from over 120 researchers working with the IPCC also indicate that the rising penetration of renewable energies could lead to cumulative GHG savings equivalent to 220 to 560 Gt of $CO_2$ ($GtCO_2eq$) between 2010 and 2050. The upper end of the scenarios assessed, representing a cut of around a third in GHG emissions from BAU projections, could assist in keeping concentrations of GHG at 450 ppm. The key findings, as follows, are contained in a summary for policy-makers of the *Special Report on Renewable Energy Sources and Climate Change Mitigation* (SRREN).

## SRREN findings

- Of the around 300 GW of new electricity-generating capacity added globally between 2008 and 2009, 140 GW came from renewable energy.

- Despite global financial challenges, renewable energy capacity grew in 2009 – wind by over 30 per cent; hydro-power by 3 per cent; grid-connected photovoltaics by over 50 per cent; geothermal by 4 per cent and solar water/heating by over 20 per cent. The annual production of ethanol increased to 1.6 Exajoules (76 billion litres) and bio-diesel by 0.6 Exajoules (17 billion litres) by the end of 2009. Meanwhile developing countries host more than 50 per cent of current global renewable energy capacity.

- Most of the reviewed scenarios estimate that renewables will contribute more to a low-carbon energy supply by 2050 than nuclear power or fossil fuels using carbon capture and storage.

- The technical potential of renewable energy technologies exceeds the current global energy demand by a considerable amount – globally and in respect of most regions of the world.

- Under the scenarios analysed in-depth, less than 2.5 per cent of the globally available technical potential for renewables is used – in other words over 97 per cent is untapped underlining that availability of renewable source will not be a limiting factor.

- Accelerating the deployment of renewable energies will present new technological and institutional challenges, in particular integrating them into existing energy supply systems and end-use sectors.

- According to the four scenarios analysed, the decadal global investments in the renewable power sector range from $1,360 million to $5,100 billion to 2020 and $1,490 to $7,180 billion for the decade 2021–2030. For the lower values, the average yearly investments are smaller than the renewable power sector investments reported for 2009.

- A combination of targeted public policies allied to research and development investments could reduce fuel and financing costs leading to lower additional costs for renewable energy technologies.

- Public policy-makers could draw on a range of existing experience in order to design and implement the most effective enabling policies – there is no one-size-fits-all policy for encouraging renewables.

The IPCC's assessment of the key RES sub-sectors is as follows:

**Bio-energy** technologies can generate electricity, heat and fuels from a range of 'feedstocks'. Most current bio-energy systems, including liquid bio-fuels, result in GHG emissions reductions. Others, such as advanced conversion systems, which for example convert woody wastes into liquid fuels, can deliver 80–90 per cent emission reductions compared to fossil fuels. Bio-energy, mainly for traditional cooking and heating in developing countries, currently represents over 10 per cent of global energy supply or around 50 Exajoules per year. While the share of bio-energy in the overall renewables mix is likely to decline over the coming decades, it could supply 100–300 Exajoules of energy by 2050.

**Direct solar energy** technologies including photovoltaics and concentrated solar power (CSP) can produce electricity, heat and light. Currently, direct solar contributes only a fraction of 1 per cent to total global energy supply. Potential deployment scenarios range from a marginal role of direct solar energy in 2050 to one of the major sources of energy supply. The actual deployment will depend on continued innovation, cost reductions and supportive public policies. In the most ambitious climate stabilisation scenarios solar primary energy supply by 2050 reaches up to 130 Exajoules per year, which can be attributed to a large extent to photovoltaic electricity generation. In some scenarios, its share in global electricity generation reaches up to a third by 2050, but in the majority of scenarios remains below one-tenth.

**Geothermal energy** utilises heat stored in the Earth's interior directly or to generate electricity, at a rate currently of about 0.7 Exajoule per year. By 2050, geothermal deployment could meet more than 3 per cent of global electricity demand and about 5 per cent of the global heat demand. However, geothermal energy does not reach the technical potential limit in any of the scenarios analysed, with the deployment rate remaining below 5 per cent for both the regional and global level.

**Hydropower** projects encompass dam projects with reservoirs, run-of-river and in-stream projects and range from small to large scale. The installed capacity by the end of 2008 contributed 16 per cent of worldwide electricity supply, making hydropower the largest RES in the electricity sector. According to long-term scenarios, hydropower's share in global electricity supply may decrease to 14 per cent.

**Ocean energy** technologies are diverse and use the kinetic, thermal, and chemical energy of seawater. Most are at the demonstration and pilot project phases. Due to its nascent stage of development, they are unlikely to contribute significantly to global energy supply before 2020. Ocean energy is currently only represented in very few scenarios. Projected deployments could result in energy delivery of up to 7 Exajoules per year by 2050.

**Wind energy's** primary application of relevance to climate change mitigation is to produce electricity from large wind turbines located on land or offshore. The wind power capacity installed by the end of 2009 met close to 2 per cent of worldwide electricity demand. The review shows a high expansion rate in Europe, North America and, more recently, in China and India. A greater geographical distribution of deployment is likely to be needed to achieve the higher deployments indicated by the scenario literature. Under the demand projection of some scenarios global wind power share could grow to more than 20 per cent by 2050.

## Global market trends: conclusions

- All reports reviewed demonstrated growth in the green economy market with significant growth expected in the coming decade.

- Rapid urbanisation and industrialisation is proving to be the major driver in the fast developing emerging economies of the east as they struggle to provide acceptable air and water quality. In the developed world, continuing compliance with environmental rules continues to drive investment in the sector. Over-arching all this at a global level is the 'decarbonisation' of society where the twin threats of oil and gas depletion and responding to climate change act as the biggest single driver in the sub-sectors of energy efficiency and renewable energy.

- Competition for resources and security of supply are becoming important issues for both raw materials and energy.

- Venture capital activity in Europe is relatively weak by comparison to the US and China. The vast amount of environmental venture capital is directed at cleantech/green energy sources. At a conventional level, investment appears to more conservative and directed at major utility and infrastructure developers and operators. Enterprise and job opportunities from this sector must consider the fact that these companies operate where the populations are located and the products and services investment opportunities are restricted by this fact. The only obvious exceptions are those companies making equipment and components in the renewable energy sub-sector.

- At a global and regional level, the recurring sub-sectors with the strongest growth potential are, without doubt, clean technologies and renewable energy technologies. Dwindling sources and availability of potable water throughout the world are also proving to be a factor aiding the development of the water/wastewater sub-sector.

- Many EU countries have attained 'first mover advantage' in niche areas and will seek to capitalise on this. For example, Germany (solar), Denmark (wind), Austria (energy efficiency), and the UK (marine pollution control).

- Some countries such as Germany and Austria that have a strong tradition in engineering and eco-innovation have been targeting export markets for environmental goods with strong government support for several years. On the services side, the UK has been successful in growing multi-disciplinary, publicly-quoted professional services with major European presence including RPS, Enviros, WYG and ERM.

## Market developments – Europe

*RES*

In its Alternative Policy Scenario, the IEA (2007) predicted that by 2030 renewable energy will remain at around 14 per cent of global energy consumption, but its share of the electricity mix will increase from 18 per cent to 25 per cent. A $1 trillion investment programme is needed to meet these targets.

The EU is the world leader in renewable energy with a €30 billion turnover and employing 350,000 people. However, China is expected to leapfrog all industrialised countries as the main producer of RES-E as it has a national target for renewable of 30 per cent by 2050. The market leaders are Brazil (bio-fuels); China (solar hot water); Germany (solar electricity); and Spain (wind power). In 2005, Germany was the world leader in wind power (with 18,430 MW of installed capacity), solar photovoltaics (1,400 MW of installed capacity), and in the production of bio-diesel (1.9 million litres).

The EU's Strategic Energy Technology Plan (SET-PLAN) was set up to accelerate development and deployment of cost-effective low-carbon technologies and complementary policies and measures to help the EU achieve its proposed 20 per cent reduction in GHG emissions by 2020. In addition, a study has been completed of the R&D energy capacity at EU level, which found that the volume of public investment has fallen, notwithstanding a broad recognition that R&D investment in the energy sector is crucial against the background of the EU's climate change/renewable package. Germany, France and Italy account for nearly 75 per cent of public R&D energy funding. A similar pattern is evident in relation to business R&D, with Germany, France, Sweden and Italy accounting for nearly 75 per cent of the total spend. The study also found that cross-EU cooperation is weak and assessed the way that energy R&D activity is organised at Member State level with reference to US and Japanese benchmarks.[330] Not one Irish company was listed among the 73 largest EU companies investing in the energy R&D sector.

In the energy sector, five types of support models exist: feed-in tariffs, quota obligations, fiscal incentives, tenders and green certificates. REFITs are a price-based policy that set the price to be paid for renewable energy per kWh generated (in the form of guarantee premium prices). This is often combined with a purchase obligation.

The following factors have lead to the relative success of the German RES-E sector:

- Feed-in tariffs

- Use of standards to set high technical performance levels

- Creation of social acceptance of renewable

- The use of industrial policy to promote indigenous enterprise

- Use of public procurement to drive demand for innovative goods.

Perhaps the most important driver will be the creation of an EU Offshore Supergrid to connect regional suppliers.

The fact that so many governments have recently changed their REFIT policy is a negative in what is otherwise a positive overall outlook for RES in Europe.

## Bio-fuels

Bio-diesel can be made from waste vegetable oil (via transesterification) or from plant oil (e.g. rape seed oil). Bio-ethanol is produced from fermentation of sugars found in crops (e.g. sugar cane) or from waste streams (e.g. whey from cheese production). Bio-ethanol and bio-diesel are the most common bio-fuels used in transport worldwide. Agriculture biomass in the EU is the dominant feedstock with rape seed being the main raw material for bio-diesel production while cereals and sugar beets are the main sources for bio-ethanol. Bio-ethanol production is currently based on a fermentation process of starch and/or sugar. It is considered that bi-ethanol and bio-diesel can be blended with petrol up to 10 per cent and 25 per cent respectively without significant changes on vehicle engines or operating infrastructure.

The use of second generation lingocellulosic materials as feedstock for bio-fuels production is the priority of the EU's Bio-fuels Technology Platform. Market entry for advanced bio-fuels production processes is foreseen around 2015–2020. The European Commission has forecast that bio-fuels will have a 14 per cent market share of transport fuels in 2020 rising to 20 per cent in 2030. The PREMIA project undertook a detailed analysis of support measures for bio-fuels.

Bio-fuels reached a share of about 1 per cent of all transport fuels sold in 2005. Only Sweden and Germany met the 2005 target set by the EU bio-fuels Directive and these two countries have advanced second generation demonstration plants. The US is the largest investor in bio-fuels R&D, with Sweden and Germany the highest spenders within the EU.

While there is an EU requirement that 10 per cent of transport fuel must come from bio-fuels, this is being reinterpreted as a 10 per cent requirement from renewables, softening the drive to bio-fuels. This distancing is in part driven by concerns that Europe will not be able to supply the bio-fuels;[331] that present production is unsustainable;[332] and allegations that food prices have been severely increased by fuel crops.[333]

At EU level the main barriers to the deployment of bio-fuels are:

- Cost competitiveness of bio-fuels with regard to conventional fuels
- Under-funding of R&D investment in feedstock and biomass supply logistics
- Too few demonstration projects at industrial scale
- Sustainability of biomass production.

## Solar

Very high growth – some 30 per cent over the past five years – has been recorded. Higher levels of production have led to significant price reductions, with an expectation that the cost of electricity from PV systems will be comparable to the retail price of electricity in 2015. Si-crystalline-based cells are a mature technology for a wide range of applications, whereas technologies as thin-film silicon cells, dye-sensitive cells, and polymer solar cells are not yet as competitively priced. High concentration devices are better suited for large grid-connected multi-MW systems, and compact concentrating PV systems for integration in buildings.

Installed capacity of PV systems in the EU (2006) was 3.4 GWp. The European Commission is predicting that by 2020 some 12 GWp will be installed, rising to 22 GWp in 2030. Germany (with the support of attractive long-term financial support in the form of feed-in tariffs), the Netherlands and Switzerland have invested most in this technology. Germany has 1,150 MWp installed; the EU total is 1,250 MWp. Germany's Conergy is the second largest solar energy producer in the world.

In the EU, production is carried out by many SME enterprises. It is forecast that new and emerging technologies will come to the market, including high concentration devices that are better suited for large-scale grid-connected multi-MW systems and compact concentrating PV systems for integration into buildings.

### Main barriers to the rapid deployment of PV technologies

- High production cost of electricity
- Lack of skilled professionals
- Usage of precious raw materials e.g. silver
- Under-funded research
- Requirement to have a generous feed-in tariff in the long term
- Poor awareness of potential within the building and construction sector.

The concentrated solar thermal power sector (CSP) is now reviving due to a favourable supporting framework in Spain and increasingly in the US. A CSP plant consists of a solar concentration system made of a receiver and collector to produce heat and a power block. The most mature large-scale technology is the parabolic trough/heat transfer medium system. Led by Spain, Europe has a market leadership in CSP technologies worldwide.

Solar-thermal systems installed in Europe are predominantly based on glazed flat plate and evacuated tube collectors, with the vast majority of capacity (90 per cent) comprised of single family house units used for the supply of domestic hot water. In addition, there are a few large-scale systems installed in Denmark, Sweden, Germany and Austria that deliver heat to district heating networks. Total installed capacity was 13 GW, which produced approximately 0.7Mtoe of useful heat. The potential of solar heating and cooling technology is large, however, with upwards of 135 GW in installed capacity forecast by 2030.

Solar Valley near Leipzig was built by German company UV and contains the largest series of solar modules in the world. It is reckoned that Germany is twenty years ahead of its global competitors. The critical success factor was the availability of feed-in tariffs: solar projects in Germany receive as much as €0.57 per kWh.[334]

It is easy to forget that photosynthesis – the process that ultimately underlies all plant growth on Earth – is a form of solar power. Further, since the days of the Roman Empire, mankind has used greenhouses and magnifying glasses to harness the energy of the sun in order to provide heat. However, it is only since the 1970s that development of large-scale projects to harness the sun's energy for conversion to electricity has gathered pace, with the twin incentives of higher fossil fuel prices and constantly improving technology.

## Ocean energy

There are several forms of ocean energy – marine current, wave and tidal – all of which are at a pre-commercial R&D stage. One of the largest units is the 240 MW tidal plant of La Rance in France. A large number of devices and designs are currently being studied and/or developed. Large-scale wave power demonstration facilities are currently being erected or planned, for example the Pelamis Wave Energy Converter. A 750 kW size unit is already in operation in Scotland. Nine wave energy systems based on different technologies developed by European investors are being tested under real sea conditions. Ireland, with the UK, Denmark, Sweden and Portugal, has invested modest sums to exploit ocean systems for power generation. The forecast installed capacity in 2020 is 0.9 GW and 1.7 GW in 2030; or just 1.1 per cent of projected EU-27 electricity consumption.

> **Main barriers to the deployment of ocean energy technologies**
>
> - Infancy state of development and its specific operating marine environment
> - Need for grid connections bearing in mind that offshore units will be quite some distance from onshore connection
> - Licensing and permitting
> - Maintenance and plant costs
> - Need for engineering capacity
> - Full development costs beyond range of SMEs.

In October 2006, the Carbon Trust in the UK launched a new technology acceleration project called the Marine Energy Accelerator. This aims to accelerate progress in cost reduction of marine energy (wave and tidal stream energy) technologies, to bring forward the time when marine energy becomes cost-competitive so that significant carbon-emission reductions are achieved. The project follows on from the Marine Energy Challenge and the Carbon Trust report published in January 2006, which highlighted that marine energy could supply up to 20 per cent of the UK's electricity needs.[335] The costs of marine energy are currently higher than conventional and other alternative energy sources, reflecting the early stage of technologies. However, the report found there is potential for costs to reduce considerably in future and for the technologies to become competitive with other generation forms. The reality is that ocean energy is a medium-term prospect.

## International benchmarks

### The US

There are some 1.8 million 'green collar' jobs in this $370 billion sector.[336] The sector has grown rapidly between 2007 and 2010 as Table 15 illustrates:

The American Recovery and Reinvestment Act 2009 (ARRA) facilitated the introduction of a $787 billion economic stimulus package. A significant amount of the promised funds have been

**Table 15: US climate change industry ($billion)**

|                              | 2007  | 2010  |
|------------------------------|-------|-------|
| Low-carbon power             | 113.1 | 131   |
| Carbon capture and storage   | 0     | 0.1   |
| Energy efficiency            | 46    | 62.3  |
| Energy storage               | 1.8   | 3     |
| Green buildings              | 44.7  | 54.5  |
| Transportation               | 68.6  | 74.8  |
| Carbon markets               | 0.2   | 0.2   |
| Adaptation                   | 0.2   | 0.5   |
| Consultancy                  | 0.5   | 0.9   |
| **TOTAL**                    | **274.9** | **327.4** |

*Source:* Environmental Business International (2011) Environmental Business International Inc (2010), *EBI Report: the Climate Change Industry*.

allocated. The 'green' elements of ARRA included the following measures.

- $4.5 billion for repair of federal buildings to increase energy efficiency
- $11 billion for smart grid activity
- $6.3 billion for energy-efficiency and conservation grants
- $2.5 billion for energy research
- $6 billion for loan guarantees to assist wind and solar projects.

The US market differs to that of the EU as it consists of large numbers of SMEs operating regionally compared with the EU market that is dominated by large firms, typically divisions of well-capitalised conglomerates.[337] The US domestic market for environmental technologies is of such scale that only a few firms are engaged in exporting internationally.

The fact that the US has not signed the Kyoto Protocol does not mean it is not facing up to the threat of climate change. The US is entrusting technology to point them towards a low-carbon future. This is most vividly demonstrated through their massive deployment of venture capital and federal funding into bio-fuels and solar energy. It also fits in with a stated Government policy to move away from dependency on oil imports from geo-politically unstable parts of the world. In the absence of increased oil production from domestic reserves, the US has focused on a range of alternative energies. Despite their reluctance to sign up to international climate change agreements, the scale of the US response has seen an extraordinary level of investment in a short time frame.

In summary, these are some of the key trends and developments.

**Renewable energy**: Investment in the renewables sector in the US is increasing rapidly from a low base. Renewable energy has been growing at an unprecedented rate, accounting for 22 per cent of new nameplate electricity capacity additions in the US in 2006, up from just 2 per cent in 2004. The Department of Energy (DOE) believes (optimistically) the US will reach a renewable target of 15 per cent by 2020; non-hydro accounts for some 5 per cent of the energy mix. There is a view that the ARRA will incentivise investment, and in particular the loan guarantee supports are expected to have a significant multiplier effect. However, the absence of REFIT tariffs is an inhibitor. This growth looks set to continue where the scaling of renewables will yield 4 GW of new installed wind energy and 3 GW of CSP projects. To put the 3 GW into perspective, it would be equivalent to building three Moneypoint generating stations (Ireland's largest power plant) in a year. The US cooperates with the EU under the auspices of the International Renewable Energy Agency.

**Wind**: This sector was until recently relatively underdeveloped in the US, with some exceptions (Texas). In 2006, the US surpassed Germany as the world leader in annual installed capacity of wind energy with the installation of an additional 2.4 GW.[338] In 2011, some 6.8 GW of installed capacity was built. Wind now represents 35 per cent of the new generation capacity (40 per cent in the EU) and forecasts suggest huge potential, with the wind resources of the states of Kansas, North Dakota and Texas capable of meeting all the country's electricity needs. The National Renewable Energy Laboratory and Gamesa Technology Corporation are testing a variety of components and systems that will guide developments of the next generation of wind turbines designed specifically for the US market.

**Bio-fuels**: In the area of bio-fuels, the US accounts for some 36 per cent of worldwide ethanol production.[339] The first of six US-funded commercial-scale cellulosic ethanol bio-refineries broke ground in November 2007, kick-starting production of 60 million gallons of cellulosic ethanol on-target to cost-competitive scaling by 2012. This is expected to ensure that the US Government meets its 'Twenty in Ten' target (of reducing motoring fuel use by 20 per cent in ten years). Some aspects of bio-fuels are losing their gloss as a form of alternative energy due to little net benefit in the energy balance equation and concerns over knock-on effects on global food prices. Cellulosic ethanol does offer the best prospect as a bio-fuel for the future with the energy balance equation showing a 1:2.36 step up versus the best case of 1:1.3 with corn ethanol. Cellulosic ethanol also offers a 91 per cent reduction in GHG emissions versus petrol compared with a 22 per cent reduction in GHG emissions versus petrol provided by corn ethanol.[340] A billion tonne biomass feedstock programme is part of an ambitious bio-energy strategy.[341]

**Solar**: It is estimated that as a consequence of the introduction of the Federal Investment Tax Credit in 2005, some $19 billion will be invested with the potential to create 115,000 jobs in the solar industry. The sector is now valued at some $325 billion and has grown rapidly despite the absence of feed-in tariffs. While Dow Corning's achievements are notable, the biggest force in the sector is Arizona-based First Solar. A site near the city of Phoenix has been identified that could produce one-fifth of the US's electricity needs.[342] On 22 October 2009, the House passed a Bill (HR 3585) that would authorise $2.25 billion over five years for the Energy Department to establish a committee tasked with identifying the country's solar power needs. The Bill also sets aside $300 million for demonstration grants for solar technology projects. In February 2012, and building on the SunShot Incubator Programme, the DOE announced more than $12 million in funding to speed solar energy innovation from the lab to the marketplace.

**Geothermal**: The US continues to lead the world in geothermal electricity generation with 2.9 GW of installed capacity, with a potential for conventional geothermal of 20 GW and for enhanced geothermal of 100 GW.[343] A new generation of enhanced geothermal technologies is being developed located in the western states, which could generate 100 GW.[344]

**Energy efficiency**: The US response to energy efficiency concentrates on the metric of energy-intensity reduction (energy consumption per dollar of GDP), which has reduced by 13 per cent since 2000. The US Government, the largest energy consumer in the US, has committed to a 30 per cent reduction in building energy intensity (energy per square foot) by 2015.[345] This is also a key ingredient with the EPA delivering many programmes, for example free energy audits. At least 28 states have adopted renewable energy standards requiring power utilities to get up to 25 per cent of their power from renewable sources. The US Action Plan for Energy Efficiency was published in November 2009. The Department of Energy is leading development and validation of cost-competitive zero-energy building technologies that will enable buildings to be secure and sustainable sources of distributed energy. The DOE is supporting advanced building codes that would decrease new building energy consumption by 30 per cent. On a domestic level, sales of compact fluorescent lighting (CFL) now account for 20 per cent of retail sales; with a similar level of activity observed in other domestic energy-efficiency measures.[346]

**Smart grid**: Unlike in the EU, the US electricity grid is out of date and in urgent need of upgrading. Three main generators dominate the market with some 30 local distribution companies also being key players. Trillions of dollars will be needed to modernise this infrastructure and to implement the smart grid programme. Investment in major interconnectors is a critical ingredient.

**R&D**: The scaling up of renewable energy and energy efficiency can be attributed to three main reasons: price signals from the rise in oil prices; strategic moves to address geo-political concerns; and a sustained investment programme undertaken by the US Government. For example, the Department of Energy funded $750 million for research, development and deployment of renewable energy and energy-efficiency technologies in 2006 with $350 million allocated towards energy efficiency, and $400 million in renewable energy applications. The Department's Solar America initiative doubled US investment in solar energy from $80 million to approximately $160 million per year, helping catalyse an increase in global market capitalisation for pure-play solar photovoltaic companies from $40 billion to over $160 billion.[347] Another prominent area in the deployment of funding has been the decision by the Department of Energy to invest $1.2 billion over five years to accelerate hydrogen and fuel cell technology. A Chatham House study argues that the cost of green technologies can come down rapidly if economies of scale are achieved through rapid and widespread use, provided issues about intellectual property are addressed. Chatham House makes a series of recommendations for the rapid diffusion of new technologies.[348]

**Funding**: Investment in solar looks set to continue; the battleground among the venture capital community will be picking the next generation thin-film materials that will replace crystalline technologies. Data presented by Greentech Media suggests that greentech venture capital investment in renewable and cleantech hit $3.4 billion in 2007 led by an investment of more than $1.05 billion in solar energy technology through more than 70 venture capital rounds. Battery technology was also well-supported by VCs at $33.9 million, followed by the energy-efficiency/smart grid sector at $419 million. Venture capital investment in renewable energy in 2007 was up 50 per cent over the previous year with more than 220 funding rounds across the entire spectrum of renewable energy. Notable recipients of venture capital investment were HelioVolt's $101 million for thin-film photovoltaics, Greatpoint Energy's $100 million for coal gasification, Amyris' $70 million for synthetic biology and bio-fuels, and A123 System's $70 million for innovative battery technology.[349] There is concern being expressed in some quarters that the hype surrounding bio-fuels could lead to excessive concentration of venture capital in this area and excessive valuations whereas other cleantech sub-sectors like carbon sequestration, water purification and energy storage are seeing a much slower inflow of capital.[350]

In the cleantech sector there were 60 deals in 2000 with an investment potential of $590 million. By 2007, the level of activity had increased to $2.6 billion with 168 deals concluded.[351] Since 2002, the percentage of total US venture capital invested in cleantech grew from less than 1 per cent to more than 23 per cent. Other statistics suggest that this is a growth sector with some $200 billion of global investment recorded in 2010; up 25 per cent on 2009.[352] The very latest assessment is that US-based venture capital investments in cleantech increased from $3.5 billion in 2009 to $5.1 billion in 2010, an increase of 45 per cent.

The bankruptcy of Solyndra, a California-based solar panel producer, has not only been spectacular but has raised much wider concerns about cleantech investment. The losers are the Virgin Green Fund ($1.1. billion) and US taxpayers' federal loan ($535 million). Volatility in the public markets has driven bearish valuations on cleantech stocks. UBS (2011) has valued publicly traded cleantech companies at $142 billion, down sharply from $475 billion in 2007. Advanced bio-fuels have largely been the only cleantech category for which the IPO window has stayed open. According to US analysts Cleantech Group, Solazyme is one of only 40 cleantech companies worldwide to go public; compared to 97 in 2010. Venture capitalists on both sides of the Atlantic still have confidence in solar (despite Germany's struggling Q-Cells). For example, VantagePoint, DFJ and Google have invested $2.2 billion in BrightSource, which is developing the Ivanpak solar thermal plant in the Mojave desert.[353]

**Transport**: Transport accounts for some 30 per cent of US GHG emissions. Therefore there is a rising awareness that investment in public transportation is among the key options available if the US is to meet its global climate change targets. One driver for action is the fact that an estimated $85 billion is wasted every year as a consequence of transport congestion. Also transport is hugely dependent on imported fossil fuels, accounting for 70 per cent of total consumption. A range of strategies is needed, with tougher vehicle emission standards a key element. On the other hand, only 50 per cent of Americans have access to public transport. In addition to loan guarantee and grant support, the development of electric vehicles is a key component of the state of Hawaii's Clean Energy Initiative. This is supported by the Department of Energy through the Energy Development/Deployment in Island Nations Initiative. The availability of some $187 million in funding for research into fuels cells is seen as a major development. The Department of Energy is the main driver promoting the deployment of electric vehicles. The programme is benefitting from significant grants under the US stimulus package, including incentives for the purchase of electric vehicles. President Obama wants 1 million electric vehicles on the market by 2015.

**Afforestation**: Forestry represents 31 per cent (5.9 Gt) of global abatement potential and 41 per cent of developing world potential. Deforestation accounts for one-fifth of global GHG emissions, which is more than the world's vehicle emissions and about on par with China's emissions. A key driver is a US proposal about limiting the deforestation of tropical products. It is envisaged that a $40 billion fund will be needed to reduce emissions by 1 billion tonnes. Indonesia and Brazil are the main culprits as they are clearing vast tracts of forests for palm oil and cattle production respectively. The US administration is impressed by evidence that for a modest investment of $5–15 billion, the US would be able to purchase project-based forest offsets while meeting wider environmental goals. Estimates suggest that additional planting could generate some 6 billion tonnes in offsets. The EU's position is that gross tropical deforestation should be reduced by at least 50 per cent by 2020 compared to current levels and to halt global forest cover loss by 2030 at the latest. Both the EU and the US support measures to reduce deforestation and forest degradation (REDD+).

**Jobs**: Job potential was cited by many in Washington as a major driver in securing political support for US climate change legislation, with analysts pointing out that renewable projects generate four times more jobs than other investments. While playing the 'jobs card' was a significant factor in trying to coax some senators to support the Kerry–Boxer Bill (an approach that did not work), there is growing evidence of the potential impact of the green economy, as the following examples illustrate:

- Revenues from the benchmark technologies of solar, wind and bio-fuels are forecast to grow from $116 billion in 2008 to some $325 billion within a decade.

- Some 2.3 millions are employed in the global renewable energy sector.354

- Venture capital activity is booming; jumping 78 per cent in North America since 2006 and now accounting for some 11 per cent of all venture capital activity.

- Solar has grown (2002–2007) by 41 per cent; wind energy by 24 per cent; and bio-fuels by 20 per cent.

**Clusters**: A recent trend in the US is the setting up of cleantech clusters. Some examples are as follows (Table 16).

### Table 16: US cleantech clusters

| Location |
| --- |
| East Bay Green Economy Industry Cluster launched in December 2007 |
| Colorado Cleantech; home of the National Renewable Energy Laboratory |
| San Diago Cluster with 800 cleantech companies |
| San Jose Environmental Business Cluster founded in 1994 |
| Washington Clean Technology Alliance founded in 2007 |

## Ireland–USA collaboration

On 19 March 2012 a memorandum of understanding was signed by the Minister for Communications, Energy and Natural Resources and the Department of Energy of the USA for cooperation in marine and hydrokinetic energy technologies. Thus a framework has been agreed for more intensive cooperation on wave and tidal energy for example involving SEAI, the Marine Institute and UCC's Hydraulics and Maritime Research Centre,

## Austria

Austria has long been considered a leading country regarding environmental protection and initiatives. It identified the environmental and economic benefits of environmental technologies and these benefits have been closely monitored as far back as 1993.[355] The Ernst & Young study of EU eco-industries indicated that Austrian turnover in that sector was about €10.1 billion, or eight times that of Ireland (€1.2 billion).[356]

Turnover of eco-industries per capita, again estimated by Ernst & Young, shows that Denmark and Austria are the European leaders with over €1,600 per capita in Denmark and over €1,200 per capita in Austria. Ireland's turnover per capita is just less than €300. With regard to turnover of eco-industries as a percentage of GDP the highest is Denmark, with Austria the second highest in the EU-25 at about 4.3 per cent, nearly double the EU average. In Austria, the development of environmental technologies is clearly a high strategic priority at government level. For example, the Austrian Federal Ministry for Economy and Labour has set up a website of such technologies. This comprises a searchable database of about 500 companies under region, name and keyword (services).

Companies in Austria have also set up national and regional associations of environmental technology suppliers. For example, Austrian Environment is an association of Austrian companies in all sectors of environmental technologies and waste management, which was set up in 1999 in the framework of the 'Austrian Export–Offensive'. According to this association there are 1,500 suppliers of environmental technologies and services in Austria. Regional clusters have also been developed.

For example, Eco World Styria comprises a comprehensive network of more than 500 companies in the field of energy and environmental technology in the state of Styria alone. The drivers of growth are particularly SMEs. From the total of 19,700 employees in the member companies, some 10,700 work in the field of renewable energy and environmental technology. This network provides a 24-hour answering service to its companies and potential clients and its website shows the diversity of companies and solutions provided in that province, with another searchable database of service providers. It provides a wide range of services to its constituent companies and has achieved a high level of branding for the green economy sector in this region, in all of Austria and abroad. It has published several publications and reports outlining the nature and advances of green economy services available in the region including a regular magazine and a product guide which categorises the companies and products under several categories for easy access (biomass/biogas/diesel; solar; water/wastewater; energy efficiency and other).

In 2007, the Austrian Government produced a Masterplan for Environmental Technologies.[357] This ten-year national strategy aims to put Austria in the leading position regarding the share of environmental technologies per GDP worldwide. It also aims to double the number of people employed in environmental and energy technologies and to aid Austria achieve its climate protection and other national environmental goals.

## Masterplan's four strategic fields of action

1. Promotion of exports – targeted initiatives on central export markets and further development of the existing export infrastructure for Austrian enterprises

2. Research and qualification – strengthening the technological competitive position and training the staff members of enterprises and research institutions

3. Financing – supplementing technological solutions and services with customer-specific financing offers

4. Making the domestic market more dynamic – safeguarding an innovative domestic market for products and services at a high technological level.

Environmental technologies are a strong economic sector in Austria and they continue to grow. This is due to long-term policies and programmes of support and legislation put in place over many years by the Austrian Government. Austrian businesses have also seen the economic potential in this sector and have moved quickly to innovate to take advantage of the drivers in place. The companies have also developed strong networks and industry support groups, providing joint services, a strong brand as well as joint business opportunities. The growth in environmental technologies has been qualitative as well as quantitative with more clean technologies and clean energy options being developed. This has greatly aided Austria's targets regarding the reduction of GHG emission targets as well as protecting the Austrian environment.

To achieve a similar success, Ireland also needs a long-term national strategy on environmental technologies with suitable policies, regulation and support mechanisms. The companies in this sector in Ireland also need to network better, develop support groups, avail of joint services and create a stronger brand.

## The UK

In November 2007, the report of the Commission on Environmental Markets and Economic Performance (CEMEP) was published. The CEMEP was established by the UK Government in light of the Stern Review on the Economics of Climate Change and drew together representatives of the business community, academia, trade unions and NGOs, with the Secretariat being jointly provided by the Departments for Environment, Food and Rural Affairs (DEFRA), and Business, Enterprise and Regulatory Reform (BERR).

The CEMEP report acknowledges that the transition to a low-carbon, resource-efficient economy is needed to meet the global challenges of climate change and sustainable development. The report noted: 'there will be winners and losers, but there are considerable opportunities for those countries and businesses with the foresight to seize them'.

The (then) UK Government committed to making the UK a global leader in low-carbon and environmental markets. The goal was to make the UK one of the best locations in the world to develop and introduce low-carbon and resource-efficient products, processes and services and, by doing so, attract the investment today that will help create tomorrow's prosperity and jobs, as well as contributing to a cleaner environment.

The UK Government has acknowledged that achieving this goal requires a policy framework that drives investment and enterprise in environmental markets and provides more effective support for the development and commercialisation of environmental innovations. In fact, the conclusions in the CEMEP report are mainly targeted at government because CEMEP believes that environmental market opportunities are heavily influenced and, in some cases, driven by the policy framework set by government.

Both the UK CEMEP and the UK Corporate Leaders Group on Climate Change underlined the fact that in order to stimulate private sector investment a strong policy framework is needed that creates a long-term value for carbon-emission reductions and consistently supports and incentivises the development of new technologies.[358] The CEMEP report also drew attention to the important role that sectoral deployment support can play. Such supports have been successful in stimulating the development of renewable energy, such as wind power and solar photovoltaics, and are used widely in the EU and elsewhere to build scale and reduce costs of a technology that is not currently cost competitive. It is clear that targeted sectoral initiatives will be necessary in many instances to stimulate the development and uptake of renewable energy technologies that would not otherwise be widely adopted. While there are inevitably costs associated with such support, they could prove the best option in the longer term. The CEMEP, however, noted that the choice of the appropriate policy measures will depend on the stage of the innovation process being supported. Policies to support investment in high-risk, early-stage options will be most effective if, in addition to providing revenue, they are designed to reduce or remove revenue risks associated with price volatility. Support should target those applications with significant potential for mass market rollout and should take into account areas of natural advantage for the UK, such as offshore renewables.

The report drew attention to the findings of the UK Energy Research Centre, which advocates a 'risk hierarchy' linking policy to technology maturity in the low-carbon and renewable energy generation sector.[359]

The CEMEP report also underlined the importance of support for R&D, particularly given the fact that market failure resulting in under-investment in R&D by the private sector is well established. Long lead times and high costs of technology development are significant factors in many environmental sectors, particularly energy. They are often compounded by the need to displace low-cost incumbent technologies. The CEMEP believed that targeted support would help to leverage private sector investment into the technologies required to meet future environmental objectives and the development of new products and services, building options to meet future environmental needs and potentially creating competitive advantages. To leverage best overall value for money from the funds available, the CEMEP recommended that existing capabilities and new initiatives in R&D across the public sector and industry should be better coordinated and that synergies should be sought between different strands of innovation support, including linking R&D support to procurement opportunities.

However, it warned that government should be careful not to 'pick winners' by focusing its attention and support on a single or small number of technologies to address environmental challenges. Therefore, the CEMEP recommended that a portfolio of candidate technologies should be supported. While it is acknowledged that few, if any, of these emerging technologies will at first be cost-effective compared with the technologies they are designed to replace, it would, however, be prudent to continue to invest in them to create an option for commercial deployment if the technology becomes economic in the future. The CEMEP report also drew attention to the fact that a commonly articulated barrier to the commercialisation of environmental technologies by the private sector is the perception of 'funding cliffs' i.e. the concern that government grant support is available for early stage R&D, but funding would not be forthcoming at the demonstration stage when technology and commercial risks are at their highest. To overcome this problem, the CEMEP recommended that government support should aim to be as consistent as possible through the life-cycle of a technology's development, to allow that technology to make progress towards commercial deployment.

In May 2008, the UK Government responded to the CEMEP report in its report Building a Low-Carbon Economy: Unlocking Innovation and Skills. This set out how the UK will become one of the best locations in the world to develop and introduce low-carbon and resource-efficient products, processes, services and business models.

The UK's Government is committed to being the greenest government ever and set up a Department of Energy and Climate Change (DECC) to establish its credentials. Prime Minister David Cameron wants to position the UK as a leading player in the new global carbon economy, creating significant new industries and jobs. He made this commitment in the following terms: 'the transition to a low-carbon economy is necessary, real and global. By stepping up, showing leadership and competing with the world, the UK can prove that there need not be a tension between green and growth.' It is taking action to cut carbon emissions (by 50 per cent in 2025 over 1990 levels), create the conditions for green growth, and improve resilience to climate change. In enacting the Climate Change Act 2008, the UK has become the first country to adopt binding GHG emission–reduction targets beyond 2020. In fact, in presenting the fourth carbon budget Chris Huhne, the Energy and Climate Change Secretary, said the UK is on course to cut emissions by at least 80 per cent by 2050. All these elements contribute to the development of a sustainable green economy. In order to deliver this, one of the priorities is to 'support a strong and sustainable green economy, resilient to climate change'.

A practical demonstration of the UK's leadership in the areas of climate change and the green economy is the Green Deal, provided for in the Energy Act 2011, which is intended to reduce carbon emissions cost-effectively by revolutionising the energy efficiency of UK properties. The Green Deal financial mechanism eliminates the need to pay upfront for energy-efficiency measures and instead provides reassurances that the cost of the measures should be covered by savings on the electricity bill. A new energy company obligation (ECO) is integrated with the Green Deal, allowing supplier subsidy and Green Deal finance to come together into one seamless offer to the customer. In addition, the UK has received EU state aid approval to roll out its £860 million Renewable Heat Incentive scheme, which will be open to householders. The scheme is expected to generate £4.5 billion in private investment.

In December 2011, DECC published a consultation document on electricity market reform. It comprises: a carbon price floor, which will be implemented by extending the climate change levy with the rate based on the particular fuel's carbon content; the replacement of the renewable obligation regime with a feed-in tariff with contract for difference (FiTCfD); a revised capacity payment mechanism; and emissions performance standards.

The UK Government believes the transition to a green economy is essential for delivering sustainable development and long-term growth. DECC's commitment will be met through leading by example in its own operations as well as working with business and consumers. The Department's policies on waste, valuing the natural environment and adapting to and mitigating climate change all play an important role in delivering a green economy; see the following links for more details:

- Sustainable development
- Sustainable public purchasing
- Sustainable business and resource efficiency
- Sustainable products and consumers
- Waste and recycling
- Natural environment and biodiversity
- Adapting to climate change
- Mitigating climate change.

## Northern Ireland

The UK Climate Change Act 2008 applies in Northern Ireland but does not specify particular targets or budgets. Informed by the (2010) Strategic Energy Framework, the Northern Ireland Executive has approved a target of 40 per cent of electricity consumption from renewables by 2020; it is currently 10.6 per cent. The Northern Ireland renewables obligation is the main supporting mechanism for increasing the level of electricity consumption from renewable sources. There are 29 wind farms with a total capacity of 400 MW connected with a further 20 (456 MW) in the pipeline.

In February 2011, the Executive approved a GHG Reduction Action Plan. The latest statistics (2009) suggest that Northern Ireland emissions are 19.5 Mt and are some 11 per cent lower than 1990. The target is to reduce emissions to 16.4 Mt by 2025.

Climate change is the responsibility of the Climate Change Unit of the Department of the Environment whose minister chairs a cross-department working group. The unit also develops and designs the CRC Energy Efficiency Scheme (formerly known as the Carbon Reduction Commitment scheme). NI's Green Deal will retrofit some 55,000 homes across Northern Ireland as part of its first phase of activity. A redesigned renewable heat incentive scheme (with a budget of £25 million) will be the main measure aimed at meeting the RES-H target of 10 per cent by 2020. A Bio-energy Action Plan (2010–2015) is being rolled out.

In December 2011, as part of the NI Offshore Renewable Energy Strategic Action Plan (2012–2020), the Crown Estate announced two offshore renewable energy leasing rounds: an offshore wind area off the east coast for one developer to deliver up to 600 MW of generating capacity and a tidal stream area off the north east coast around Rathlin/Torr Head of up to 200 MW.[360]

The NI Department of Enterprise, Trade and Investment is working with the UK's DECC on proposals for the reform of the electricity market and with HM Treasury on the UK-wide carbon price floor tax.

There is ongoing north–south cooperation in the sector under the auspices of a Joint Steering Group (JSG) established in July 2003. The JSG comprises of senior officials from the DCENR and the Northern Ireland Department of Enterprise, Trade and Investment and the offices of the two regulatory authorities (Commission for Energy Regulation (CER) and the Northern Ireland Authority for Utility Regulation (NIAER)). In 2005, the Minister for Enterprise, Trade and Investment, Northern Ireland and the Minister for Communications, Marine and Natural Resources, started a period of consultation on how the future energy needs for the island can be achieved in a sustainable manner. The two ministers agreed that this process should be initiated with the publication of a joint high level consultation paper that seeks to map out a possible '2020 Vision' for policy cooperation on the development of sustainable energy supplies for the island of Ireland. Their agreement is set within the framework of the All Island Energy Market Development Framework and the need to bring long-term and mutual economic and social benefits to consumers, north and south. The Sustainable Energy Working Group (SEWG) of the JSG for the all island energy market is mandated to develop policy in relation to electricity supply to 2020 and beyond and will also be dealing with heat supply, energy efficiency and combined heat and power (CHP).[361]

In January 2008, a report on an all-island grid examined:[362]

- A range of generation portfolios for Ireland
- The ability of our power system to handle various amounts of electricity from renewable sources
- The investment levels required
- The climate change and security of supply benefits that would accrue.

The Climate Change Risk Assessment for Northern Ireland (January 2012) has considered the main opportunities and threats for Northern Ireland that may result from changes to the local climate.[363] Its key findings were as follows:

- Hotter summers and warmer temperatures may boost tourism and extend the tourist season.
- Less summer rainfall may lead to a reduction in river flows, affecting public water supplies and increasing the risk of pollution.
- Flooding may pose an increasing threat to people, property, critical infrastructure and natural habitats. This is seen as the biggest risk for business.
- The ability of industry to abstract water may be affected.
- There is a potential disruption to supply routes.
- There may be increased container traffic if Arctic shipping routes open up.
- Wheat yields and grass growth may increase.

These findings will now be considered and a Northern Ireland adaptation programme will be presented to the Assembly in 2013.

A survey of public and political opinion found a high degree of consensus that climate change is already having an impact in Northern Ireland and that modifying behaviour will make a difference. Awareness about climate change impacts is the responsibility of Climate Northern Ireland.

## Conclusions

This chapter has examined the green economy sector in a number of diverse markets: the US, Austria, the UK and Northern Ireland. The analysis concentrated on a number of factors including market mechanisms, domestic regulations and key sub-sectors. Each of these markets possesses characteristics that, individually or collectively, provide Ireland with key pointers to the successful development of its green economy sector.

Looking at market focus, the contrast between the US and Austria is particularly evident; the US has established a system of supports and enablers that has resulted in a rapid inflow of capital providing a huge impetus to the renewable energy sub-sector; whereas in Austria renewable energy forms part of an integrated master plan across a number of sub-sectors. The UK has adopted a more broad-based strategic approach avoiding the 'picking of winners'.

Common to all three markets is the need for a regulatory environment that provides clear, consistent and long-term signals.

The lead-time behind commercialisation of some of the technologies and the capital construction costs require a long-term approach to attract capital. These serve to act as a spur to domestic markets and, building on that knowledge position, countries like Austria have become very export focused. In the US, the scale of the domestic market and availability of capital has allowed US green economy companies to focus internally.

The over-arching message is clear; allied to implementation of EU environmental and energy Directives, Ireland should have an ambitious strategic policy framework that will stimulate the development of the green economy as enterprises respond to the rigorous implementation of legislation in areas such as water quality, energy efficiency, renewable energy etc.

## Chapter 11

# Overview of the green economy in Ireland

Our mission is to play a leading role in transforming Ireland into a society based on sustainable energy, structures, technologies and products.

SEAI, 2011

## The Irish green economy sector

There are no published national statistics on the value of output of the green economy sector in Ireland. Despite data collection problems, Forfás estimated that the environmental goods and services sector in Ireland (which excludes building and construction materials) is valued at €2.8 billion, with Northern Ireland accounting for a further €790 million, and employs 6,500 people directly.[364] The Expert Group on Future Skills Needs estimated the market size at €3 billion with 18,500 employed in the sector.

An Ernst & Young report for the European Commission on the size of the European green economy sector put the value of the Irish green economy sector at €1.2 million in 2004.[365] However, following examination of and consultation with the sub-sectors it would appear that previous estimates of the sector have significantly under-estimated its true scale. The size of the Irish green economy sector is in the region of €4.3–5.2 billion. The basis of this estimate is set out in Table 17.

**Table 17: Value of the green economy sector in Ireland (€m)**

| | |
|---|---|
| Air Pollution Control | 4–5 |
| Clean Technology | 350–700 |
| Environmental Consultancy | 60–75 (island)[1] |
| Environmental Monitoring | n/a |
| Energy Management | 20[2] |
| Marine Pollution Control | 3–5 (island)[3] |
| Noise | n/a |
| Remediation of Land | 46–58 (island)[4] |
| RES | 600–700[5] |
| Waste Management | 1,200–1,600[6] |
| Water/Waste Water | >2,000[7] |
| **TOTAL** | 4,280–5,160 |

[1] Industry estimate.
[2] Industry estimate. This is likely to be an under-estimate given the success of SEAI's schemes including the Better Energy Workplace Scheme 2012.
[3] Industry estimate.
[4] Industry estimate
[5] EPS Consulting estimate
[6] Industry estimate
[7] Department of Environment, Community and Local Government, *Water Services Investment Programme 2007 – 2009*, capital costs only.

*Source:* EPS Consulting (2008), *Business Opportunities for the Environmental Goods and Services*, Report for Forfas/InterTrade Ireland.

In addition to these sectors, it is estimated that the potential value per annum of the emerging market for energy efficiency in the building and house construction sector could be in the region of €620 million per annum on the assumption that some 40,000 houses are retrofitted each year, at an average cost of €15,500 per unit.

Moreover, it is important to note that the estimate of the size of the Irish green economy market under-estimates the quantum of business as companies are increasingly:

- Addressing the environmental impacts of products throughout their lifecycle [366]

- Investing in energy efficiency (through SEAI's LIEN programme and the energy agreements programme)

- Beginning to embed low-carbon and cleaner technologies in process and product development
- Using recycled material on a more systematic basis367
- Re-engineering processes to cut costs and improve environmental impacts[368]
- Incorporating environmental factors (such as packaging) into initial design[369]
- Actively seeking to reduce or offset their (or their suppliers') carbon footprint.[370]

The sector comprises companies of all size categories. With the exception of some major players the Irish green economy market is dominated by SMEs who have established a substantial business presence over the past ten years. This has largely been associated with the significant increase in public investment in environmental services and infrastructure. It is important to note, however, that key sectors such as renewables, environmental consultancy and waste and water are dominated by subsidiaries of UK and EU parent companies. This may have the effect of limiting the export opportunities of their Irish operations as the parent typically is responsible for new emerging export market business development.

To a very large extent, with a few notable exceptions, the sector is playing catch-up with the technologies in greatest demand (RES-E and waste management) that are deployed and exploited by European companies of scale. This has implications for the prospect of an Irish company breaking in to the market for PV (solar technology), for example, without the setting up of a joint venture with an existing manufacturer.

On the other hand, many markets are starting from a low base of activity so it should be possible to gain market share in niche areas.

### Enterprise Ireland's Top 5 Cleantech Exporters

Ecocem Materials
FLI International
Green Biofuels Ireland
Mainstream Renewable Power
Nualight

## Investment in the Irish green economy sector

While international investment in the green economy sector has increased dramatically there is little evidence yet that the Irish venture capital community has woken up to the commercial opportunities within the Irish marketplace. A review of the Irish Venture Capitalist Association's (IVCA's) Techpulse report for 2007 shows approximately 50 Irish venture capital deals concluded deals worth €225 million across all sectors; none of the deals listed could be defined as being in the green economy sector. There is little evidence that the situation has changed much in the intervening years.

Consultation with the Irish venture capital industry indicates that the green economy sector is viewed as one driven by legislation and as being primarily subsidy led.[371] The absence of Irish legislation and the deferring of policy decisions on climate change to 2013 has not helped matters. A key issue for the venture capitalists is the level of capital expenditure required in products and technologies that are not yet proven. They view the renewable energy sector, mainly wind and biomass, as entering a mature phase and a number of other technologies as being too early in their development to attract the interest of the venture capital community. The good R&D infrastructure existing in Ireland was commented upon but overall the lack of a track record in the sector is predicating against its future development.[372] This attitude is consistent with findings contained in an OECD briefing, where it was stated that technology and market risks were issues that may create barriers to investors.[373]

At a more traditional level, the emergence of 'green funds' in the investment community has been a distinctive feature of activity over the last number years. Sustainable banking is a growing area with key investment banks such as Merrill Lynch and Citigroup investing in the area of environmental risk management. KBC Asset Management, for example, has been the leader in this area with a suite of alternative energy, water and climate change funds and Al Gore launched a similar environment fund on behalf of Merrion Capital. However, closer examination of these funds reveal that they are generally made up of composites from S&P indices for water, clean energy and other commodities. In an offering from Merrion Capital, none of the companies listed in the prospectus had a presence in

Ireland. One success for Merrion Capital is Green Biofuels Ireland, the country's largest bio-diesel plant (based in New Ross). However, despite this, green investments and investing particularly in alternative energy and climate change strategies are at the top of the agenda in terms of being flagged as major growth themes over the next five years.[374] The pillar banks were active in this area. For example, in February 2009, Bank of Ireland launched a €100 million fund for renewable energy projects in Ireland, and said this amount would be doubled (which has not happened).

Funding provided through business expansion schemes (BES) activity has tended to concentrate on asset-backed investments such as wind farms.

## Irish success stories

There have been some notable successes. ESB's Novusmodus, with a €200 million investment fund, has assisted Nualight (high efficient LED lighting for retail food displays), Wind Energy Direct (developer of on-site wind projects in Ireland), and SELC (high efficiency digital controls for external lighting). Enterprise Ireland clients who are actively looking for venture capital include Aer Sustainable Energy (a UCD-based bio-fuel technology developer), SolarPrint (wireless sensors), Red-T (flow batteries) and Ikon Semiconductor (LED technology). Ireland's world leading wave energy technology company Wavebob has closed an investment round with GREinvest Management. Perhaps Ireland biggest success story is Mainstream Renewable Power, a global player in the on- and offshore wind development market.

The announcement of the establishment of the Emerald Fund by the New York Pension Funds (retirement fund of the city employees) is significant as this fund has been established as a vehicle to invest $150 million in a range of projects, the majority of which will be located in Northern Ireland. The categories of investment include public infrastructure, real estate, waste management and renewable energy.

The Government's Innovation Fund is seeking to attract global venture capital presence in Ireland with a budget of €250 million available. To date, the fund (which is managed by Enterprise Ireland and the National Pension Fund Reserve) has made investments in Polaris and DFJ and Sofinnova Ventures. Enterprise Ireland's Competitive Start Fund is also supporting cleantech companies and in the latest round assisted Activation Energy DSU (smartgrid demand response and energy demand-side management) and BYO Responsible Water Solutions (water filtration membrane technology).

In summary, the cleantech area is being viewed as one with huge promise by the international venture capital community and it is expected that investment will continue to flow as long as there are suitable projects and technologies. The challenge in Ireland will be to get the venture capital community to move away from the staples of bio-technology and software that pre-occupy most of the funding activity and, ultimately, result in an Irish equivalent of Q-Cells launching on the ISEQ and beyond.

## Skills and jobs

Companies view the supply of appropriate skills and talent as crucial for their long-term productivity and competitiveness. Therefore the publication of an assessment of the future skills requirements of enterprises engaged with the green economy will help companies to gear up.[375] The study assessed employment prospects under two scenarios (Figure 31) and predicted a potential 10,000 additional jobs may be created within six years

**Figure 31: Green economy jobs potential**

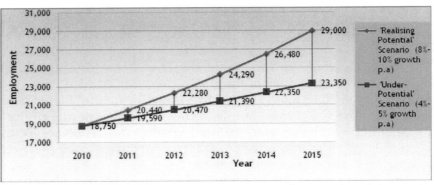

*Source:* Government of Ireland, Department of Enterprise, Jobs, and Innovation (2011), *Progress Report on the implementation of the recommendations of the Report of the High Level Group on Green Enterprise.*

(2010–2015). Given the slow progress in the rolling out of promised 'green' investments this modest forecast for an increase in employment is probably realistic at least as a short-term prediction. It is anticipated that the green economy growth transition will be an important driver of structural labour market changes with a potentially large impact on job skill requirements.[376] Job opportunities are anticipated from company start-ups in the cleantech area; from an expansion of environmentally related businesses; and from companies 'going green'. There will be job opportunities for engineers, scientists and technicians in particular. The Expert Group does not anticipate any major problems as some €30 million per annum is being spent on 91 higher education courses underway or planned in relation to 'green skills'. The Group called for a more coordinated approach and a higher priority (and more funding) for the enhancement of business, engineering and ICT skills and capacity.

The Action Plan for Jobs (February 2012) did not add much to the debate as most of the thirteen actions on the green economy are already in the pipeline. The decision to proceed with the development by Dublin City University of the vacant Enterprise Ireland site at Glasnevin into an Innovation Campus is to be welcomed. However, announcing the publication of another green economy plan (see below) is a disappointment as there is nothing wrong with the current plan other than it is

**Table 18: Forecast sustainable energy jobs**

| | Current Employment | Jobs Potential | Assumption |
|---|---|---|---|
| Wind | 1,300 | 3,490 | Total installed capacity increases to 4.65 GW in 2020 (4.1 GW onshore and 550 MW offshore) |
| Ocean | 230 | 2,770 | 500 MW installed capacity by 2020 |
| Biomass | 900 | 2,410 | 700 MW of installed capacity for biomass heating and biogas |
| Other RES | 1,060 | 3,340 | By 2020, CHP grows to 150 MW; solar thermal grows from 100 MW to 500 MW; and heat pumps grow from 120 MW installed capacity to 560 MW. |
| R&D | 550 | 1,100 | Ocean energy and smart grid activity |
| Energy Efficiency (residential) | 4,820 | 6,890 | 100,000 homes upgraded per annum |
| Energy Efficiency (commercial) | 1,020 | 2,110 | Higher uptake of SEAI programmes |
| Smart Grid | 30 | 1,000 | Smart meter deployment (with some technology development in Ireland) |

*Source:* SEAI (2012), 'Sustainable Energy Sector to Treble by 2020', Media Release.

taking much longer to implement the agreed recommendations. The sub-sectors where Ireland has competitive advantages are well-known.

> SEAI's analysis of the economic and enterprise benefits of the sustainable energy sector suggests that over 20,000 jobs can be created in the period to 2020; some 7,700 of this total is assumed to come from secondary competitiveness effects.[377]

## Support structures in Ireland

Policy instruments as well as regulatory measures have been put in place in support of all of the green economy sub-sectors. Substantial time, effort and resources have been invested in several areas to support the uptake of environmental technologies by government departments, state agencies and private organisations through grant aids, research etc.

**Table 19: Agencies/departments providing green economy support**

| | |
|---|---|
| • Environmental Protection Agency | • Science Foundation Ireland |
| • Enterprise Ireland | • Marine Institute |
| • IDA Ireland | • Higher Education Authority |
| • Shannon Development | • Department of Transport, Tourism and Sport |
| • Údarás na Gaeltachta | • Teagasc |
| • Sustainable Energy Authority of Ireland | • Forfás |
| • The Green Way | • Department of Communications, Energy and Natural Resources (DCENR) |
| • InterTrade Ireland | • Department of Environment, Community and Local Government (DECLG) |
| • Invest Northern Ireland | • Department of Jobs, Enterprise and Innovation (DJEI) |
| | • Department of Agriculture, Food and the Marine (DAFM) |

Many of the instruments and incentives implemented by these agencies are listed in the Irish National Roadmap for the implementation of The Environmental Technology Action Programme.[378] Two studies, funded under the 2005 ERTDI Environmental Technologies research programme, also identified other specific support and research programmes in Ireland.[379, 380] More recently, the main agencies published a guide for potential project promoters in the green economy.

A key service for Ireland's growing cleantech sector is Enterprise Ireland's EnviroCentre information portal. It contains a directory of the agency's 240 client companies in the energy efficiency, renewable energy, waste, waste to energy, water and environmental services sectors. The emphasis is on enhancing environmental awareness and improved performance for indigenous SMEs in particular.

Ireland's €500 million budget for state spending on scientific research will be spent on 14 specific sectors of greatest opportunity as identified by the Prioritisation Action Group; these include marine renewable energy and smart grids.[381] In addition, industry-led innovation partnerships supported by Enterprise Ireland and projects assisted by the Commercialisation Fund will continue to have an impact as will the competency centres for bio-energy and bio-refining, energy efficiency and the Irish Centre for Manufacturing Research.

## Business and trade associations

Irish Bioenergy Association
Irish CHP Association
Irish Wind Energy Association
Marine Renewables Industry Association
National Offshore Wind Association of Ireland
Irish Waste Management Association

## The key drivers

There are four key drivers and anyone contemplating getting involved in the sector in Ireland should be fully aware of these issues, as quite different risk profiles are emerging.

First, there is the regulatory and compliance agenda. Central to this is the EU's and Ireland's legally binding requirement to reduce its GHG emissions by at least 20 per cent by 2020, and possibly by a further 10 per cent depending on the outcome of international negotiations within the UNFCCC. Ireland has signed up to an EU political commitment to reduce GHG emissions by at least 80 per cent by 2050. In addition, Ireland must comply with the Water Framework Directive, and implement a wide range of EU Directives on waste.

Second, there is the phenomenon of what is called peak oil. This thesis – supported by the IEA – holds that fossil fuel production has peaked and that alternative sources will have to be found as the law of supply and demand will force energy prices ever higher. The debate on peak oil is about *when,* not *if,* prices will start to rise. The cost of energy in Ireland is very much centre stage of the debate about enterprise competitiveness.

Third, even during the current economic turmoil, investors have an appetite for green economy projects ('cleantech', 'greentech'), in particular where project promoters have a strong balance sheet.

Finally, energy security is a key factor from an Irish Government perspective as we import all our coal and oil and over 90 per cent of gas requirements.[382]

## Business opportunities – overview

As the following diagram shows, there are a wide range of business opportunities, short- to long-term possibilities; cheap and more costly alternatives; all involving the deployment of new and old technologies.

**Figure 32: Green economy business opportunities**

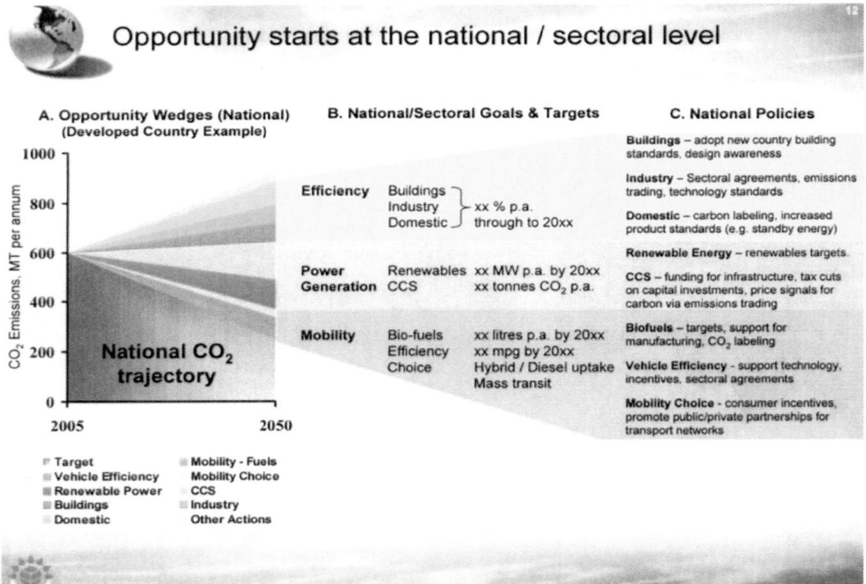

*Source:* World Business Council for Sustainable Development (2010).

In summary, and based on announcements already made, here are the key elements of Ireland's green economy investment programme. Each sector is discussed in more detail in subsequent chapters.

## Eirgrid

*Grid25*, Eirgrid's €4 billion investment programme, is intended to future-proof Ireland's electricity transmission network.[383] It is predicated on a scenario of strong economic growth over the period to 2025. Some 5,300 MW of electricity is generated at present and the forecast is for at least 8,000 MW of capacity by 2020. Some 4,750 MW of renewable capacity will be required to deliver Ireland's 2020 renewable energy target. In 2010, some 500 MW of wind energy, involving some €750 million in investment, was added to the grid. The €600 million EU cofinanced 45 km sub-sea 500 MW-capacity east–west interconnector (which runs from Rush North Beach in Dublin to Barkby Beach in North Wales) opens in 2012. Eirgrid is also progressing plans for a 80km 400kV power line between Kingscourt (Co. Cavan) and Turleenan (Co. Tyrone) and a 58km 400kV power line between Woodland (Co. Meath) and Kingscourt. Without a significant level of investment, including interconnectors with the UK and the rest of Europe, Ireland will struggle to meet its renewable energy targets. There are, however, serious problems with securing the necessary planning for this infrastructure. Another crucial question that is often overlooked is aligning investment in grid capacity with Ireland's domestic electricity needs (in the absence of additional interconnector capacity). It makes little economic or financial sense to over-supply or front load grid capacity, especially given more modest economic growth scenarios.

## ESB

The company's (2008) strategic framework to 2020 commits the ESB to a €22 billion investment programme that will transform this commercial semi-state into a global renewables company and in so doing will halve its carbon emissions within that period to become carbon neutral by 2035. As part of a €4 billion investment programme, the ESB will derive one-third of its electricity from renewable sources, including 1,400 MW of wind generation, in addition to wave, tidal and biomass. Some €11 billion will be spent on its network so as to facilitate up to 6,000 MW of wind on the island. In addition, some €6.5 billion will be spent on smart metering and smart networks. The CER has completed a large-scale technical and behavioural trial of smart meters to ascertain the costs and benefits of this project and to inform the technologies chosen and has concluded a public consultation (November 2011) on the national roll-out of smart meters.[384]

## Bord Gáis

A five-year investment programme of €5 billion will see BGE moving into the renewable space. Some €1.2 billion is earmarked for wind; a 445 MW power production plant has been completed at Whitegate (€400 million); and €300 million is earmarked for electricity peaking plants. Private sector energy companies such as Airtricity are also investing in renewables.

## Wind

By the end of 2011, Ireland had 1,900 MW of renewable generation on the grid, including 1,630 MW of wind connected; 234 MW of hydro; and 46 MW from other sources. Meeting the 2020 renewable target will require an estimated 4.5 GW of installed wind capacity.[385] By 2030, a further 2 GW of wind capacity is expected to be installed. The CER estimates that some €16 billion of investment in on- and offshore wind is in the pipeline. Bear in mind that one-third of Europe's offshore wind potential is located on Ireland's continental shelf and we are using less than 2 per cent of its potential.

In the UK, some €100 billion of investment is planned in offshore wind farms within the next decade, including a huge 4,200 MW facility in the Irish Sea. In terms of the scale of construction activity, this is the equivalent of building ten Channel Tunnels with some 70,000 jobs expected to be created.

In addition, significant grid interconnector capacity will have to be built as part of the EU's 'Supergrids' project. To date, the Moyle link capacity is 500 MW, with a similar capacity interconnector coming on stream with the commissioning of the new east–west interconnector in 2012. A further 2,000 MW of capacity is the minimum forecast requirement rising to 5,000 MW should a high penetration of renewables come on stream and, critically, that export markets can be secured.

## Tidal and wave

This is another area with huge potential. For example, AEA Technologies has forecast that the global market for wave energy is worth €200 billion with one projection suggesting wave power could produce five times the current global consumption of electricity. Significant capital investment will be needed if the Government's target to generate 500 MW 'in the water' from ocean energy by 2020 is to be achieved. By 2030, the net present value of wave energy could be as high as €10 billion and tidal energy's NPV could be €2.75 billion.[386]

## Electric vehicles

In addition to a step change in investment in public transport, Ireland has the potential to become the first country in the world where the use of electric vehicles could be the preferred mode of transport. By virtue of the fact that we are an island means we could turn this dream into reality far quicker than many people might imagine. To date, over 550 EV charge-points have been installed rationally. With potential carbon savings of some 8 Mt per annum, such an electric vehicle programme has the potential to be the largest low-carbon technology programme in the country. In this regard, a far more ambitious approach needs to be taken, and a national electric vehicle champion (in partnership with the ESB) appointed to drive investment, R&D and public awareness of the benefits of driving electric vehicles. Battery and other technologies are developing fast, but R&D is not based in Ireland. The strategic question is whether Ireland will be a technology taker or technology maker? The Oireachtas Joint Committee on Climate Change and Energy Security recommended a comprehensive framework strategy whereby all newly registered private vehicles would be electric vehicles by 2020. This suggests that the vast majority of cars could be electric vehicles by 2030. Potential investment, excluding cars, has been estimated at €500 million (battery exchange stations and residential recharging).[387] Arguably, the current electric vehicle plan being driven by ESB eCars is not ambitious enough when benchmarked against what is happening in other jurisdictions.[388] Kilkenny company Gaeltec Utilities won the ESB tender competition to install electric car home-charging points. Irish company JTM Power has developed the world's first innovative portable charging station for electric cars.

## Smart(er) transport

*Smarter Travel* is the national strategy for a sustainable transport future.[389] Its starting point is that transport and travel trends are unsustainable, which they clearly are. While *Smarter Travel* sets the scene and identifies high-level goals and targets, it is arguably not ambitious enough given the GHG emission-reduction targets set for the transport sector. Taking account of the projected surplus of wind energy, it is not unreasonable to suggest the entire inter-city and inter-urban fleet be electrified in the medium term. There is no reason why all buses cannot be electric vehicles within a decade. There are also opportunities for Ireland to apply intelligent transport systems.[390]

## Retrofitting

It is cheaper to save energy than to buy it. This is the fundamental idea behind investing in energy efficiency. The opportunities for the residential sector have been identified and are as follows:

- Upgrade energy efficiency in approximately 1 million homes
- Bring Irish housing stock to a minimum C1 Building Energy Rating within 15 years
- Overall cost of €14 billion over ten years
- 5,000 jobs
- Mitigate up to 2.3 Mt of GHG reductions annually.391

However, unless and until the energy utility companies are required to cofinance this type of investment, as they are in other countries, the take-up of retrofitting will continue to remain low. The signs are positive with nine energy companies having reached a (voluntary) agreement with SEAI to deliver energy savings to their customers.[392] Bear in mind the export opportunity if Ireland's eco-building industry ever got off the ground. McKinsey has estimated (2009) that global energy-efficiency investment opportunities could be worth €130 billion. In addition, investment (as yet unquantified) will be needed to improve the energy efficiency of public buildings.

## Water

Ireland's 34 local authorities are spending nearly a €1.2 billion a year to provide water and wastewater facilities. Arguably, we cannot achieve value for money with dispersed responsibility, given the local authority funding crisis. Significant additional investment is required. As an example of the scale of this investment, the Greater Dublin Strategic Drainage project will cost €2.5 billion. The only way we are going to get the required level of investment is to outsource the entire water and wastewater services and set up a national regulator along the lines of the UK's Ofwat – hence the Government's decision to set up Irish Water as a new utility.[393] There is arguably a case for issuing a competitive tender for a single supplier, or a few regional suppliers, for the installation of domestic water meters. The sector is not at all export oriented, with limited R&D activity. With suitable enterprise supports Irish companies should be encouraged to take advantage of the UK's (Ofwat) €27 billion five-year (2010–2015) water investment programme.[394]

## Waste

Government policy on waste is in a state of flux. Until there is a clear policy framework investors will not commit to the Irish market. Based on the Eunomia report, the Department of the Environment, Community and Local Government has invited comments on a *Statement on Waste* that is intended to inform policy, legislative reform and investment decisions.[395] Ireland does not have a national waste electrical and electronic equipment treatment and recovery facility; nor glass, plastics or paper recycling plants. Incineration seems to be the preferred solution. Engineers Ireland has estimated that over €2 billion in investment is needed if targets set in regional waste management plans are to be met.

## The tally

Over the next decade some €80 billion in potential investments have been announced or are committed by virtue of government having to implement EU Directives. The construction element of these projects is quite high. In summary the figures are as follows (Table 20):

**Table 20: Potential investment in Ireland's green economy**

| | |
|---|---|
| ESB | €22 billion |
| BGE | €5 billion |
| Eirgrid | €4 billion |
| Wind | €16 billion |
| Other RES | €1.5 billion |
| EVs | €0.5 billion |
| Retrofitting | €14 billion |
| Smart Transport | €2 billion |
| Forestry | €0.7 billion |
| Water | €12 billion |
| Waste | €2 billion |
| R&D | €1 billion |
| **TOTAL** | €80.7 billion |

*Source:* EPS Consulting (2010), Presentation to the Construction Industry Federation.

In addition, the UK has announced significant investments, as follows, which dwarf, for example, the construction costs of the 2012 Olympics. All of these projects will be put out to open tender, thereby giving Irish companies with the requisite expertise an opportunity to pitch for this work.

**Table 21: Potential Investment Opportunity UK**

| Sector | Investment Value | Source |
|---|---|---|
| Offshore wind | £100 billion (to 2020) | The Crown Estate |
| Onshore wind | £60 billion (9.6 GW in planning) | www.bwea.com |
| Water | £27 billion (to 2015) | www.ofwat.gov.uk |
| Waste | £11 billion (to 2020) | DEFRA |
| Energy efficiency | £70 billion (to 2020) | DECC |
| Smart meters | £0.54 billion | DECC |
| **TOTAL** | **£268.5 billion (€324 billion)** | |

*Source:* Author's calculations.

The UK Government's green economy strategy estimates that the UK share of the global £3.2 trillion low-carbon market was £116 billion (2010) and should be much larger.[396] Therefore between the Irish and UK Governments and private investors a working assumption is that at least €500 billion will be spent on green economy investments over the next decade or so.

## The Green Way

Set up in 2010, The Green Way (*an tSlí Ghlas*) is a collaborative venture established by industry, academic institutions and the public sector in the North Dublin region. The partners include the Dublin Airport Authority, Fingal County Council, Dublin City Council, Ballymun Regeneration Ltd, Dublin City University, Dublin Institute of Technology and the North Dublin Chamber of Commerce. The shared vision is to create jobs and trade opportunities by activating and developing an internationally recognised cleantech cluster modelled on successful clusters in other jurisdictions. The Green Way, a member of the Global Cleantech Cluster Association, represents the largest green economy cluster on the island. This is a welcomed initiative as hitherto cluster policy was at national level only. The overall ambition is that by 2013 Ireland will be internationally renowned for the excellence of its research, and will be to the forefront in generating and using new technology for economic and social progress, with an embedded eco-innovation culture. However, we have perhaps a long way to go as only 0.34 per cent of the workforce is employed in eco-industries and only 0.14 per cent of exports come from this sector. There is a view that a cluster such as The Green Way is not strong enough (yet) to push the creation of the national cleantech sector, but has the potential to leverage eco-innovation (an ill-defined concept in Ireland) in specific sub-sectors.[397]

## Global Green Interchange

The Government is supportive of a proposition – the Global Green Interchange – that will position Ireland as a centre of excellence in green finance and carbon management. This green IFSC initiative emerged from a workshop on the future of the IFSC, chaired by the Department of the Taoiseach, in February 2009. A few months later, in November 2009, a Green IFSC Steering Group was set up to examine green finance opportunities. A feasibility study determined the scale and shape of the green finance opportunity and concluded that considerable opportunities do exist as new green financial products are developed.398 A marketing and business plan, including the establishment of a government-supported carbon markets initiative, was reviewed by an independent cross-departmental evaluation group during 2011. One of the key projects being developed is an international carbon standard and an associated Dublin Voluntary Offset Registry.

## SWOT

The strengths, weaknesses, opportunities and threats of Ireland's green economy sector can be summarised as follows.

### Table 22: SWOT of Ireland's green economy

| Strengths | Opportunities |
|---|---|
| • Large public sector investment<br>• Government commitment to use fiscal and other incentives<br>• Commitment to regulatory enforcement<br>• Open economy facilitates imported know-how<br>• Access to natural energy sources<br>• Vibrant domestic economy and rising population<br>• Good project engineering capacity in Ireland<br>• Clear government policy in RES and energy efficiency<br>• All Island energy market<br>• SEAI<br>• State agency adaptability (strong experience in FDI) | • Rapidly growing global market<br>• Potential emerging markets in Eastern and Central Europe<br>• Business opportunity generated though public procurement<br>• North/south alignment on infrastructure investment<br>• Adjacency to growing UK market<br>• Regulatory compliance<br>• Transition to carbon neutral economy<br>• WRAP and Carbon Trust models could drive innovation<br>• Benchmarks could offer best practice examples<br>• Growing environmental awareness in public and business<br>• Potential synergies between sectors (e.g. ICT and sensors) |
| **Weaknesses** | **Threats** |
| • Low starting base (playing 'catch up')<br>• Weak R&D<br>• Uneven knowledge base<br>• Risk averse public procurement which embeds old technology<br>• Poor spatial planning with diffuse pollution sources<br>• Lack of scale and fragmented market (lack of networks)<br>• Diffuse state support to the sector<br>• Lack of investor interest<br>• Lack of identity for the sector<br>• Lack of FDI presence<br>• Difficulties due to two jurisdictions<br>• Low history of innovation | • Rising energy and raw material costs<br>• Security of supply of energy and raw materials<br>• Climate change<br>• Cost of not meeting RES targets<br>• Non compliance costs<br>• Lack of government driver<br>• Infrastructural investment<br>• Weak buy in from enterprise sector regarding climate change<br>• Conflicts of interest between regulator and regulated sectors |

*Source:* EPS Consulting (2008), *Business Opportunities for the Environmental Goods and Services*, Report for Forfas/InterTrade Ireland.

## High Level Group on Green Enterprise

In its framework for sustainable economic renewal (*Building Ireland's Smart Economy*) the Government committed to establishing a High Level Group on Green Enterprise. In May 2009, the group was formed by the Tánaiste and mandated with developing an action plan within four months to foster the growth of the green economy in Ireland. The group's terms of reference emanated from previous Forfás and InterTradeIreland research (carried out by EPS Consulting) assessing enterprise opportunities in the environmental goods and services sector, and included the obligation to identify areas where Ireland could succeed in the green economy, with a focus on job creation.

The group's report *Developing the Green Economy in Ireland* (November 2009) contained 55 policy recommendations which are at various stages of implementation.[399]

**Key recommendations**

1. Promote the following key sectors that can drive exports and job creation:
   - Renewable energy (particularly wind and wave energy)
   - Efficient energy use and management, including eco-construction
   - Waste management, recovery and recycling
   - Water and wastewater treatment
2. Deliver 'green zones' and a green IFSC, to take advantage of economies of scale and scope that can be delivered from grouping cleantech organisations geographically close to each other
3. Create world class research centres
4. Remove basic hurdles to the development of the green economy, including
   - Planning barriers
   - Access to finance
   - Ireland's 'brand'
5. Appoint a minister/minister of state to oversee the green economy, and establish a cabinet committee to ensure inter-departmental coordination of these goals.

The progress report on the implementation of the High Level Group on Green Enterprise emphasised the intensity of international competition for investment in the sector and the need for urgency in addressing barriers if Ireland is not to lose out to competitors.

Equally sobering, the group said the green economy sector in Ireland would not achieve its potential unless the following outstanding barriers were immediately addressed:

- Developing a coherent national approach to the 'common good' message in electricity grid development
- Continuing to market Ireland's 'green' image internationally
- Developing an integrated efficiency programme
- Addressing the key issues for the waste sector
- Pooling research expertise
- Addressing barriers to micro-generation of renewable energy
- Accelerating foreshore licensing for offshore energy projects
- Developing and marketing Ireland's potential of a green IFSC.

## Conclusions

### Preliminary conclusions

- The green economy sector in Ireland is valued at some €4.3–5.2 billion, with Northern Ireland accounting for approximately £624 million.

- In common with European trends the overall sector is growing, with the sustainable energy sub-sector having the potential to generate some 20,000 additional jobs by 2020.

- The largest sub-sectors, and indeed those with the greatest potential, are renewables, energy efficiency, waste management, and water.

- Many companies do not rely on the state development agencies for core funding. They use their own resources, or those of investors, to develop their business.

- The most active of the largest green economy companies are subsidiaries of non-Irish parents who either acquired capacity through mergers and acquisitions or grew their businesses organically.

- Green economy companies are, however, generally not aware of export market opportunities. The majority of small companies show no interest in expanding outside their niche area of expertise in the domestic market.

- An all-island 'one-stop shop' providing market intelligence at sub-sector level may be needed as the service offerings of the state agencies north and south are not coordinated.

- The venture capital community is generally risk adverse to investments in green economy companies, with few exceptions. To this end, the relevant state agencies need to enter into a more intensive dialogue with the venture capital community to brief them about the political importance now attached to the sector.

- Supports to incentivise the green economy, which work successfully in other Member States (and that are compatible with EU state aid rules), should be introduced in Ireland provided a business case can be made.

A determined focus to exploit Ireland's natural competitive advantages in every area of the green economy has the potential to generate significant investments, which will contribute to economic growth and provide sustainable employment to tens of thousands of people in every region of the country. However, the reality is that project promoters have been frustrated for years as the public sector, with some notable exceptions, has not yet grasped the challenge of this investment opportunity. Some areas such as renewables have a clear strategy and supporting regulatory framework. In other areas, water and waste for example, investors will not be attracted as reform proposals to leverage the huge investment that is needed have not been implemented.

Who is in overall charge of this €80 billion plus investment opportunity? Who is the champion of this agenda? 'Nobody' is the short answer. The resources, such as they are, are scattered across 14 departments and agencies. Unless perhaps upwards of 1,000 public servants are redeployed under one NRA/SEAI-type agency to facilitate project promoters, Ireland will continue to be at the bottom of the class in the green economy as our competitors step up their efforts to take advantage of what is a multi-billion euro opportunity.

## Chapter 12

# Sustainable development and carbon sustainability

> Sustainability is the single biggest business opportunity of the 21st century and will be the next source of competitive advantage.
>
> Lee Scott, CEO, WalMart

## Introduction

The Treaties of the European Union refer, in the preamble, to the principle of sustainable development. In addition, the Union has among its objectives the achieving of 'balanced and sustainable development'. This is reflected in the Treaties by a requirement to promote 'harmonious activities'. Specific reference is made to the need to provide that 'environmental protection requirements must be integrated into the definition and implementation of other community policies'.

The EU Treaties therefore reflect a worldwide process that is based on sustainable development. Equally it is fair to state that, while the Treaties reflect a history of development since the establishment of the Common Coal and Steel Community in the 1950s, sustainable development has only been recognised at EU level since the adoption of the Single European Act (1987). It was made a core task of the EU in the Amsterdam Treaty (1997).

Nonetheless, sustainable development as a concept is not new. There are examples of the linking of economic and environmental considerations with those of societal considerations during the age of enlightenment in the middle ages, the industrial revolution of the eighteenth and nineteenth centuries and more recently in the movement towards public health policies in the Victorian age. Indeed sustainable development as a concept has existed since the advent of civilisation with the move of man from hunter-gatherer to farmer-fisherman, to industrialist, to informationist. Sustainable development is marked therefore, not by its historical base but rather by the process of change associated with the development of mankind and his relationship with the Earth's resources around him.

## Origins of sustainable development

The origins of late twentieth century concepts of sustainable development are to be found in the stress associated with the environment in western Europe and North America in the 1950s and 1960s. The London smog of 1952, in which more than 4,000 people died, brought home to the UK authorities the need to begin to move towards regulation of the private citizen and the industrial sector. This experience was replicated throughout the advanced economies of the world including the US and Germany. In these experiences the recognition was created, among the general population, as well as the body politic, of the relationship between economic activity, its inputs, and the environment and economic outputs. Thus the need to regulate water and air quality forced a new recognition of the principle of sustainable development. Prior to the 1950s the idea of development was based on the creation of a constant growth pattern using resources that at the time were seen as unlimited.

The key difference between the recognition of the need for sustainable development in the 1960s, and earlier experience is based upon the systematic approach adopted at that time. In addition is the fact that the level of economic development in the west was such that large sections of the population were affected by the pollution difficulties and therefore a political demand for systematic action was created. Against this background came the publication of *The Limits to Growth* in 1972.[400] This study predicted the collapse, ecologically, of the Earth within a century. The report, although now considered to be dated (given its underestimations of the link between technological development and economic development) is important in that it identified for the first time a relationship between:

- Population
- Industrial production
- Food output
- Raw material reserves
- Pollution.

It also, for the first time, sought to analyse future scenarios for economic growth. The thinking set out in the study was also reflected in the UN's resolution to engage with the issues of economic development, the Earth's natural resources and the development of the world's population.

This resolution let to the first UN conference on the human environment in Stockholm in 1972. The conference was important in three ways:

- It recognised the cross-border impact of pollution.

- It recognised the need for positive developmental action based on the relationship between the advanced economies of the north with the less advanced economies of the south.

- It formally recognised the relationship between environment and economy.

The conference led to the adoption of the Action Plan for the Human Environment, which included:

- Measures to deal with environmental recording

- Internationally agreed actions on the protection of the environment

- Support for flanking measures to create the infrastructure to support international action.

The UN Environment Programme (UNEP), with its headquarters in Kenya, was established as a result. The worldwide response was, as one would expect, varied, with the EU taking the lead through the establishment of an Environment Action Programme to deal with the specific issues of pollution. This first, and indeed subsequent programmes were based upon the necessity to deal with the major air and water quality issues associated with the level of national development in the Common Market, as it was then called.[401]

A feature of the worldwide response was therefore its concentration on 'end-of-pipe solutions' rather than the taking of a strategic view on the relationship between the use of the Earth's resources and the need for ongoing economic development. This failure to recognise the need for a strategic framework for economic development was reflected in the oil crises of the 1970s, the debt crisis of the third world and increasing levels of unemployment and poverty in the west. In 1982, at the ten-year review conference, held in Nairobi, it became clear that something further was required i.e. a recognised, internationally accepted strategic process that would relate the need for economic growth with the maintenance of the world's environment and more significantly its natural resource stock. The Nairobi Conference was to lead to the establishment of the UN's World Commission on Environment and Development, which became known as the Brundtland Commission after its chairperson, former Norwegian Prime Minister Gro Harlem Brundtland.

## The Brundtland Report – *Our Common Future*

The Brundtland Report (1987) is now generally regarded as the basis for the principles of sustainable development for the twenty-first century, including Agenda 21 (see below).[402]

Sustainable development was defined by Brundtland as: 'Development that meets the needs of the present without compromising the ability for future generations to meet their own needs.'

There are two central themes to the report and the over-arching principle:

- In order to ensure the long-term development of the world economy and to meet the political and environmental crises associated with that development, behavioural changes, particularly in the more advanced economies, are necessary.

- To achieve these changes in behaviour a new definition of growth is necessary. In other words to ensure ongoing economic growth, the growth must be based upon a process that integrates social, environmental and economic aspects rather than simply concentrating on short- or medium-term economic gain that is non-equitable.

The report formed the basis for the UN conference in Rio de Janeiro in 1992, also known as the Earth Summit, which was attended by 178 governments, including over 100 heads of state and government. Five documents were agreed to at the conference, as follows:

- **The Rio Declaration:** This provides the 27 principles for the pursuit of development and social well being.

- **Agenda 21:** This 900-page document describes the processes, including Local Agenda 21, which, it was felt, are necessary to assure ongoing growth and development.

- **The Climate Convention:** This legally binding document sought to stabilise GHGs at 1990 levels. However, no time frame was provided. This was only achieved at a conference held in Kyoto (Japan) in 1997.

- **The Biodiversity Convention:** Another legally binding convention (but not accepted by the US), which provides for the conservation of living species and the management of biodiversity, including provision of genetic engineering programmes.

- **The Forest Principles:** This provides for the protection of the world's forests, particularly the rain forests and provides a guidance process to the management and conservation of forests.

These documents have shaped and guided sustainable development policies and actions at international, regional, national and local levels for the past two decades.

If the Brundtland Commission provided the definition of sustainable development, it is the Agenda 21 document that provided the action plan for implementing the principle. Agenda 21 is not simply a process associated with maintaining the environment. It is a process of integrated socio-economic planning that recognises resource stock and the process of collaborative planning. The importance of sustainable development and the Agenda 21 process is that the latter moves economic thinking from the focus on units of output to a focus on the life-cycle of production and the equity associated with such a life-cycle.

One of the principal problems with the application of the principle of sustainable development is that while the Brundtland

Commission's definition may seem clear and readily usable from a policy-making position, the reality is somewhat different. The key difficulty is that the nation state signatories to the Rio process can actually create their own interpretations of the principle and therefore they tend to reflect nationally based ideologies rather than the genuine need to provide for greater equity, more efficient use of resources and general responsibility towards the long-term development of the Earth. This is particularly the case with countries such as the US, which seeks to protect its world leadership in economic activity, and China and India, countries that are at a given level of development and thus refuse to adopt western levels of regulation.

The Rio process identified the key challenges to sustainability as:

- Difficulties with the definition and application of equity

- Difficulties due to personal, local and national and international perspectives on sustainable development

- The different scientific and sectoral disciplines involved in socio-economic development

- Differences in definition of renewable/non-renewable Earth resources.

The UN Conference on Environment and Development (UNCED) argued that the key to the successful implementation of sustainable development is the creation of integrated processes of vertical and horizontal public policy-making using collaborative planning models. Horizontal integration would cover the process of public policy development between the key socio-economic sectors at a particular level. Vertical integration would cover the process of public policy-making between the hierarchical levels of governance and economy.

Sustainable development is clearly an extremely difficult objective to achieve given the potential for conflict within the different levels of governance and more specifically between the levels of governance. It is a process that is intensely political and requires a clear vision that may not always be available at the local level of governance, let alone national or international levels of government.

## Implementation of sustainable development

One of the ongoing features of sustainability is the question of implementation. It has been argued that much of the policy output associated with the Rio process has been ineffectual. If anything it has done nothing but generate lots of hot air and waste paper; hardly sustainable! This is particularly important given the increasing globalisation of the world markets and the impact of the fall of the old bi-polar world into a multi-polar series of economic blocks. The net effect is that levels of economic inequality have increased while government remains centralised in most of the developed world and virtually non-functioning in much of the most under-developed states that were signatories to the Rio agreements.

This has had the impact of rendering void many of the Rio principles. The impact of this void is reinforced in continued environmental degradation, social exclusion, increasing levels of poverty and social inequality across the globe. In recognition of this paralysis world leaders issued what is known as the Millennium Declaration, which essentially restated the commitment to the Rio process and put in train the preparation of work for the Johannesburg Conference in 2002.

The following six policy principles that should guide policy development at all levels of governance were identified:

* Strengthening institutions and governance
* Making environmental sustainability central to all sector policies
* Improving markets and removing damaging subsidies
* Bolstering international mechanisms for public management
* Investing in science and technology
* Increasing efforts to conserve critical ecosystems.

The effect of a sustainable development led policy environment is that:

Authoritarian, interventionist, usually top-down approaches (power emanating from a central authority) are being pushed out by (vertical, horizontal and spatial) contractual collaboration among both public-sector and private-sector actors within less homogeneous and sometimes more fragmented areas whose borders are becoming ever more amorphous.[403]

So the use of separated models of spatial planning, public policy development and organisational theory are no longer appropriate to applying an understanding of the dynamics created within such a framework. What is required is a new model that bridges the gap between these three traditional perspectives on how the governance of a community, local or national, works.

## Institutional reform and sustainable development

Good governance, as should now be clear, is essential for proper planning and sustainable development.

In this context, the (2002) Johannesburg Conference called on all countries to:

- Continue to promote coherent and coordinated approaches to institutional frameworks for sustainable development at all national levels, including through, as appropriate, the establishment or strengthening of existing authorities and mechanisms necessary for policy-making, coordination and implementation and enforcement of laws.

- Take immediate steps to make progress in the formulation and elaboration of national strategies for sustainable development and begin their implementation by 2005. To this end, as appropriate, strategies should be supported through international cooperation, taking into account the special needs of development countries, in particular the LDCs. Such strategies, which were applicable, could be formulated as poverty-reduction strategies that integrate economic, social and environmental aspects of sustainable development, and (critically) should be pursued in accordance with each country's national priorities.

In recognition of the principle of subsidiarity every country has a primary responsibility for its own sustainable development. All countries, including Ireland, are expected to promote sustainable development at the national level by enacting and enforcing clear and effective laws that support it. In addition, the strengthening of governmental institutions remains a core part of the move to sustainable development, including the provision of necessary infrastructure and the promotion of transparency, accountability and fair administrative and judicial institutions.

Public participation, including thorough measures that provide access to information regarding legislation, regulations, activities, policies and programmes, remain at the heart of what may now be styled *the Johannesburg process*. Most critically, the Johannesburg process now includes promoting cross-sectoral approaches in the formulation of strategies and plans for sustainable development, such as, where applicable, poverty-reduction strategies, aid coordination, encouraging participatory approaches and enhancing policy analysis, management capacity and implementation capacity, including mainstreaming a gender perspective in all those activities.

Following the adoption of the Millennium Development Goals at the Johannesburg conference sound economic policies, solid democratic institutions responsive to the needs of local communities and improved infrastructure are seen as the basis for sustained economic growth, poverty eradication, and employment creation. In addition, the conference held that freedom, peace and security, domestic stability, respect for human rights, including the right to development, and the rule of law, gender equality, market-oriented policies, and an overall commitment to just and democratic societies are also essential and mutually reinforcing.

Sustainable development is no longer solely about (if it ever was at all) the environment but about the way the environment underpins human activity and the competitive world we now live in.

There is therefore broad political acceptance, internationally, of the measures required to strengthen institutional arrangements on sustainable development. If the Irish Government and others are to apply this in Ireland and elsewhere in policy terms it should lead to the achievement of an integrated public management process based upon a spatial dimension that is multi-tiered with clearly defined competencies set out within an agreed framework for governance.

## Sustainability in action

An increasing number of companies from all parts of the world have made sustainability a major component of their business strategy. To achieve this objective, senior managers have had to find ways of instilling a culture of sustainability, often across a globally dispersed workforce. Sustainability translates into different kinds of actions depending on the regions or industries in which they operate. For example, energy utilities may focus on providing affordable access to low-income households in one market while worrying about energy conservation in another. Consumer goods companies might focus on labour conditions within their supply chains and recycling efforts with their consumers.

Evidence suggests that very few executives (18 per cent globally) had their remuneration determined on hitting sustainability targets.[404] Sustainability efforts are typically guided by the need to address areas of immediate or potential vulnerability, for example ethical trading and sourcing issues feature well above such activities such as charitable donations, employee volunteering etc. In a significant number of cases, it is the CEO and/or chairman that takes the lead. The disjuncture between the aims and reality, although narrowing, is still apparent.

Launched in 1999, the Dow Jones Sustainability Indexes are the first global indexes tracking the financial performance of the leading sustainability-driven companies worldwide. They provide asset managers with reliable and objective benchmarks to manage sustainability portfolios. The Index, representing some $8 billion in assets under management, has become the gold standard in recognising the world's corporate sustainability leaders.

Comhar, Ireland's (former) Sustainable Development Council, conducted research and provided guidance to the Government on measures to move Ireland to a sustainable, equal and low-carbon society. Measuring Ireland's performance using a set of indicators is an important part of that process. The sustainable development role performed by Comhar has been transferred to the National Economic and Social Council. Examples of best practice in Ireland include BT Ireland, the Smurfit Kappa Group plc and CODEMA (Dublin City Council).

In addition, Enterprise Ireland conducts environmental assessments of its 600+ client companies to ensure that they comply with regulation and good environmental practice. Of particular note are the reports on sustainable practices in the Irish beef, pig and sheep-meat processing sectors where significant reductions in GHG emissions, lower energy usage and more efficient use of resources, especially water, have been achieved. In addition, Enterprise Ireland carries out environmental

312

compliance into important sectors such as engineering and generally finds high standards of sustainable practices.

At European level, Eurostat monitors the EU's 100+ sustainable development indicators.[405]

## Sustainability and competitiveness

The importance of maintaining Ireland's competitiveness is underlined in a number of published policy documents, which seek to outline the steps Ireland needs to take. For instance, the current National Climate Change Strategy sets out a revised framework for achieving the necessary GHG emission reductions to ensure that Ireland complies with the Kyoto Protocol.

Through innovation, energy efficiency and more sustainability in our personal choices, we can achieve the necessary lowering of the carbon intensity of our economy without sacrificing competitiveness, economic performance or quality of life.[406]

The White Paper on the Government's Energy Policy Framework 2007–2020 seeks to deliver a sustainable energy future for Ireland. It is set firmly in the global and European context that has put energy security and climate change among the most urgent international challenges.

Sustained economic growth and population growth also add to the challenges for Irish energy policy. We have, however, major opportunities to be realised in harnessing the full potential of our renewable and bio-energy resources.[407]

Ireland's strong economic performance and growth through the so-called Celtic Tiger years is well documented. During this period, Ireland's good economic and competitiveness performance placed pressure on the environment. It is evident that industry's contribution to aggregate $CO_2$ emissions is far less substantial than emissions from the agriculture, energy and transport sectors. This is because the industry sector has changed from being a manufacturing-based sector to one that is now dominated by low-carbon industries primarily in the services sector.

It is important to bear in mind the factors lying behind the increase in Irish GHG emissions since 1990. There have been significant increases in population, national income, industrial output, car ownership, house completions, tourist numbers, etc. This leads to the question whether it is possible to grow an economy and increase the nation's population while simultaneously reducing GHG emissions i.e. to decouple these variables. Evidence suggests that Ireland has done well in managing to increase national income at a far greater rate than the increase in GHG emissions, but it remains an ongoing issue of key strategic national importance that more is achieved in this regard so that we can reduce pressures on the environment, achieve our binding environmental commitments without damaging economic growth.

A realistic way of looking at Ireland's present position in relation to environmental sustainability is to benchmark our performance against other developed economies.

**Proportion of energy from renewable sources and per capita energy consumption**: Data on OECD countries shows that Ireland generates a small proportion of its energy needs from renewable sources and, although improving, still lags well behind other developed countries, and far behind the EU average. The percentage of renewable-sourced electricity has risen to about 14.4 per cent.[408] Energy consumption per capita is high in Ireland relative to many other EU countries with only Sweden, Finland and the Netherlands consuming more energy on a per capita basis. The reasons for this are manifold but include: Ireland's large household size; relatively poor thermal standards in the domestic sector; heavy reliance on private motor transport together with an underdeveloped public transport system; and a continued heavy reliance on energy-intensive agricultural processes.

**Energy intensity**: Energy intensity is a measure of the energy efficiency of a nation's economy. It is normally calculated as units of energy per unit of GDP. High energy intensities indicate a high price or cost of converting energy into GDP. Low energy intensity indicates a lower price or cost of converting energy into GDP. Ireland's overall energy-intensity rating has improved significantly. Industrial energy intensity between 1990 and 2005 reduced by 54 per cent. The overall energy intensity of the services sector was 17 per cent lower in 2005 than 1990. The intensity of primary, final energy and electricity requirements have been falling since 1990. This is due to technological efficiency, choice of fuel mix, economies of scale and changes in the structure of the economy. However, there is further scope for significant improvement and the critical challenge is to ensure that the energy intensity trend remains downward and that energy use is as efficient as possible across all the economic sectors and in all Irish households.

The challenge is to address these problems while maintaining or improving our competitiveness position. Linking cost reductions to reduced resource use has the potential to become a significant competitiveness differentiator.

## The banks and sustainable finance[409]

Financial institutions are under pressure to react to the challenges of climate change. They are in a powerful position to encourage their customers and clients to invest in more sustainable and environmentally friendly products and standards. Banks play an important role in society in providing capital and funding for investment projects. To move to a low-carbon economy, banks need to be able to measure and manage the risk of climate change to their business model and respond to this challenge with adequate policies and planning. Banks are the main providers of capital in the economy and their investment is therefore essential to achieving a low-carbon society.

The Stern Review maintained that the international financial community has an 'important role to play...the establishment of a clean energy investment framework by the World Bank and other multilateral development banks offers significant potential for catalysing and scaling up investment flows'.

Governments and the private sector are looking to mobilise the debt capital markets to help meet the gap in funding for clean energy projects not through project financing but through corporate loans and bonds through which financing is achieved.[410]

Banks, given their experience with developing risk-management policies, can play an influential role in developing climate change mitigation tools and encouraging investments in sustainable projects. To become more effective lenders, they will need to incorporate levels of risk premium associated with high concentration carbon projects and price these projects accordingly. Green investment projects are unlike financing for normal projects as both the likely returns and the societal benefits must be calculated. These investments are unique in that the return derived from the investment and the social and environmental benefits of the project must both be measured.

It is clear the financial austerity measures in place in many countries will have an impact on the level of public funding available for investment in low-carbon technology and infra-structure. The constraints on public finances have changed the viability of many projects worldwide. This has also moved environmental risk issues to a lower risk ranking as perceived by companies.[411]

Therefore capital markets must play a stronger role in financing low-carbon technologies. Considerable progress has been made in promoting low-carbon projects in recent years but, similarly with public investments, it will become increasingly difficult in times of financial constraint. As the number of projects decreases, decisions become more focused on the potential profit.

New approaches are needed to create large-scale flows for investment in low-carbon development paths. The private sector needs to act as governments cannot promote and advance the green economy at the pace that is required.

There are a number of ways to finance green projects in an environmentally conscious manner. One of these is funding through green or climate bonds. The bond market is currently underutilised when it comes to financing green projects but this is expected to change. A climate bond initiative was set up to encourage large-scale investment in carbon-efficient investments. The World Bank has come out in support of climate bonds and stated that they are important for the development of green debt capital markets.[412] Climate bonds are usually bonds linked to the performance of carbon credit projects.[413] The climate bond initiative also involves a Climate Bond Standard that provides assurance as to the relevance of the particular bond issuance in delivering a low-carbon economy.

Green bonds are a similar type of product. The World Bank has launched a green bond product that since 2008 has issued around $3 billion in green bonds. State Street Global Advisors expect the green bond market to grow to $1.4 trillion by 2020.[414] The proceeds of green bonds are used for climate change mitigation and adaptation.

Green funds are used by a large number of financial institutions whereby an investor can invest in a portfolio of environmentally sustainable stocks. Alternative energy investments have increased in recent years and were expected to increase further. For example, in 2012 the UK-funded Green Investment Bank will begin operations and will inevitably look to the bond market to fund projects. This may increase interest in these bonds from institutional investors.

HSBC research *Sizing the Climate Economy* has shown that even in its most negative scenario, this global financial institution expects the world low-carbon energy market to double by 2020.[415] The research also shows that Europe holds the largest share of the low-carbon market (33 per cent) followed by the US (21 per cent) and China (17 per cent). This indicates the potential benefits for Ireland if it becomes a centre for green finance.

A report of 100 banks highlighted a number of institutions, including Westpac, Santander UBS and HBOS, to be among the forerunners in integrating climate change into their lending approvals process. These banks request higher risk premiums for clients with high levels of carbon exposure. Clients are also advised on aspects such as implementing a climate strategy, climate change risk management and carbon market transactions.[416]

The Irish Banking Federation's *Climate Change Principles for the Financial Sector* (May 2009) have been adopted by over 30 of Ireland's leading domestic and international financial institutions. They were produced through a collaborative effort by a working group of financial institutions to promote environmental sustainability and mitigate climate change risk. The principles cover the areas of energy financing, waste management, customer services and operations management.

Banks face the same challenge as other sectors in reducing their carbon footprint and costs by becoming more energy and resource efficient. The right balance needs to be achieved between the business activities of the institutions and how these activities are affecting the environment.

There is a high level of awareness of the risks of climate change in the banking sector in Ireland. More transparency and forward thinking will be needed to advance the transition to a low-carbon economy. It is likely the more successful financial institutions in the future will be those who responded to the challenge of climate change in a timely manner.

## Do investors care?[417]

The *Global Investor Survey on Climate Change* is the first global survey of investment practices coordinated by the three investor networks on climate change – the International Investors' Group on Climate Change, based in Europe, INCR based in North America, and the Australia/New Zealand IIGCC.[418] This study confirmed that investors identify climate change as being a serious risk, especially in the long term, and they realise the need to address the associated risks.

### Key highlights from the report

- 87 per cent of asset managers and 98 per cent of asset owners view climate change issues as a material investment risk/opportunity across their organisation's entire investment portfolio.

- Over 80 per cent of asset managers and 57 per cent of asset owners make specific reference to climate change in their investment policy.

- More than 90 per cent of investors maintain a dialogue with their investee companies around climate change risk and opportunity.

- As a result of stronger climate policy in the EU, there is greater integration of climate change across the portfolio from European investors.

The study also highlighted the importance of companies completing a full and complete risk management process. This would begin with a risk assessment that typically consists of companies considering first- and second-order risks. First-order risks are those that flow from the direct impact on companies of changes in the climate system due to carbon emissions caused by human activity – for example a farmer suffering crop damage due to an extreme weather event. It is generally assumed that first-order risks represent the biggest threat to businesses, but second-order risks create substantially more challenges in terms both of their scale and the range of industries affected. Second-order carbon risks flow from changes to a company's business landscape resulting from key stakeholders employing strategies to manage their own carbon risks and expectations.

An example would be a food business suffering earnings volatility as the underlying crops of the supplying farmers have failed.

In a PwC survey of FTSE 350 sustainability reports for the period April 2009 to March 2010, it was noted that of the 125 companies reviewed, sustainability risks were linked to company strategy by only 20 per cent of companies (with 9 per cent linking opportunities to strategy).[419] Just under a third of companies (30 per cent) linked their sustainability objectives to the core business strategy. PWC observed:

Many companies invest significant resources in their sustainability activities. The results of our survey suggest that they are not effectively communicating return on this investment and therefore missing an opportunity to demonstrate how sustainability activities enhance the value of the company, rather than being seen by some investors as a drain on the company's resources.

Examining this from the opposite perspective, the *Global Investor Survey on Climate Change* also highlighted that investors still struggle with how to translate currently available climate change related data and research into investment practices and decisions. Many investors still lack the knowledge and resources to address climate change related risks and opportunities across their portfolios. To counteract this, the majority of investors support research on climate change and join collaborative initiatives to engage with policy-makers and/or investee companies to address climate change.

When investors review a company's sustainability approach do they act on this review? Funding opportunities based on a company demonstrating itself as being 'green' may take on a number of forms, such as access to green funds, green bonds, carbon funds or impact funds.

## Challenges identified with the growth of green funds

- The availability of comprehensive and comparable data on carbon emissions, emission reductions and energy-efficiency cost savings associated with assets
- Lack of confidence in the materiality of climate change among portfolio managers. This is partly due to the

longer-term nature of some climate change related issues, but also a lack of experience in interpreting and analysing data on climate change impacts

- Lack of disclosure around how companies are managing climate change-related risks and capitalising on opportunities. Regulators have sought to address this. For example the Securities Exchange Commission in the US has provided guidance on certain existing disclosure rules that may require a company to disclose the impact that business or legal developments related to climate change may have on its business.

The growing recognition of climate change as a source of material risk for businesses has not escaped the attention of the global equity research community and the regulatory environment.[420] Equity research teams at some leading investment banks have already created metrics based on the Carbon Disclosure Project response data that are used to translate a company's carbon performance into its financial results. Goldman Sachs, Citigroup, JP Morgan and Morgan Stanley have all issued research reports that quantify material carbon risks and evaluate their likely impact on financial performance. The concept of carbon risk is being integrated into decision-making processes across the entire financial value chain, including credit-rating agencies. It is likely, too, that the leading credit-rating companies will soon begin downgrading the outlook and ratings of companies considered to be failing to manage climate change-related risks. In the face of such evidence, it would seem that even those companies not targeting carbon finance as a source of funding may still need to disclose their assessment of sustainability risks and opportunities in order not to dissuade general investors.

## Do consumers care?[421]

Along with funding, the other main lifeline for business is its customers. Organisations place great importance on marketing and advertising, ensuring that consumers know the merits of their products.

A number of retail examples are used because this is a sector that can provide consumers with choice based on information about the carbon footprint of a product and the results of that choice can be clearly measured (one product is favoured over another).

Around the world demographic shifts, such as a growing middle class and growing urban population, are driving an ever-increasing demand for convenience. The World Bank expects the global middle class to soar from 430 million in 2000 to 1.15 billion by 2030. It is expected that these new middle-class consumers are particularly interested in products that meet the needs of their busy, urban, on-the-go lifestyles, but without compromise on quality, safety, or sustainability.

The 2011 *Green Brands Survey* covers eight countries, including the US.[422] Among the key findings was that concern over the state of the environment has rebounded to pre-recession levels, with consumers wanting to buy green, but price being a factor. Some 73 per cent of respondents said that it was important to buy from green companies; 65 per cent believe that green products cost 10 per cent more, but only 22 per cent are willing to pay that premium; and 45 per cent of consumers look for a specific certification mark to determine if the product is green. Another study of US consumers by Mintel showed that 35 per cent of respondents would pay more for environmentally friendly products.[423]

A Tesco survey of 5,000 UK consumers found that 97 per cent of them would actively seek low-carbon products if they were available at the same cost as current items. As with the Mintel survey, some 35 per cent of the consumers surveyed would seek low-carbon products, even if they were more expensive. PwC commissioned independent research of 4,000 UK consumers and the results clearly demonstrate the existence of mainstream public awareness and concern about sustainability issues.[424] Over 60 per cent of consumers stated that sustainability issues (climate change, poverty, food and water shortages) were the most important issues facing the world. When asked about climate change, 80 per cent said they were worried. The research also identified a number of barriers to buying sustainable goods. For example, 48 per cent of consumers were either unwilling or unable to pay the premium associated with more sustainable goods; almost 20 per cent of consumers said the lack of available alternative sustainable products was the key reason why they did not buy more. The research indicates that around 60 per cent of basic grocery products have sustainable alternatives available in store. While consumers are witnessing some changes in packaging, the study indicates that they want more rapid action. They continue to be bombarded with messages about reducing their carbon footprint, but lack the mechanisms to differentiate products on the basis of their relative impact. Carbon labelling has begun to appear on some products. This could be a source of competitive advantage going forward.

An Irish study [425] found that only 24 per cent of the general public are aware of companies taking action to limit their environmental impact. When asked should the Government make it part of legislation for public companies to issue an annual and environmental/sustainability report similar to the annual (financial) report that they currently issue, 61 per cent responded 'yes' (up from 50 per cent in 2006). Some 86 per cent said they currently buy green products and services. These findings would suggest that, like their UK and US counterparts, Irish consumers are interested in companies that are offering sustainable products and services, and are also keen to have further information in this area.

Consumers may not yet demand detailed carbon data, but carbon-management performance is rapidly becoming an issue of brand trust. Consumer goods firms and retailers in particular recognise the importance of action on climate change to their brand image. Business customers increasingly ask for carbon footprint data. Tesco (Ireland's largest retailer) and M&S tried to differentiate themselves with a sustainable strategy unlike Dunnes Stores and SuperValu. This may indicate that the Irish market is not as mature in this area as the UK, which could be related to the fact that UK businesses have been encouraged (by the Carbon Trust) by binding UK legislation in relation to GHG emission-reduction targets.

## Reporting standards

When reporting carbon, GHGs or sustainability more generally, a company has a number of options open to them. A number of frameworks have been developed, some more widely used that others. A sample of some of the standards companies may base their reporting on are as follows:

**Greenhouse Gas Protocol Corporate Standard**: This was developed by the World Resources Institute and the World Business Council for Sustainable Development. Rather than being a practical guide on how to measure emissions, it is a framework for considering the problem. The protocol frames the process for measuring carbon emissions by using a series of 'scopes'. Scope 1 is concerned with direct emissions such as those from a factory; scope 2 is indirect but concerned with products and services bought by the company, for example purchased electricity; and scope 3 is focused on indirect sources such as outsourced services.

**Global Reporting Initiative (GRI)**: This framework makes use of the GHG Protocol framework and is supported by the OECD. While the GHG Protocol focuses on what the scope of a company's activities are, the GRI framework focuses on providing a common set of measures for the company to report on. In 2009, the Sustainable Investment Research Analyst Network noted that, since 2004, the number of companies making reference to the GRI in their sustainability reports had more than doubled from 24 to 55 of the S&P 100.

**ISO 14064**: The International Organisation for Standardisation has developed a standard, ISO 14064, which provides a specification (at the organisation level) for quantification and reporting of GHG emissions and removals. The ISO standard makes the GHG Protocol more precise by removing any of the commentary. However, this also makes it less accessible to a typical business user than the GHG Protocol itself and for that reason is seen as a document written for the specialist analyst.

**Carbon Trust Standard**: This UK standard uses the GHG Protocol as the basis for its work in providing companies with a certification scheme for organisations looking to measure and reduce emissions. To encourage companies to join and comply with the Carbon Trust Standard, the organisation provides a carrot in terms of a certification mark in a similar way to organic or Fairtrade schemes. It specifies requirements in three key areas: carbon footprint measurement; carbon management; and carbon-reduction performance. Those companies looking to lead in the sustainability reporting area have taken the next step by having independent assurance completed over specified parts of their sustainability reports, for example their carbon numbers. Even within this grouping, there is a wide range from those that are completed using an accepted assurance standard and those that are not.

The **Carbon Disclosure Project** (CDP) regularly surveys companies using the GHG Protocol as a basis for its methodology to collect emission data. The latest CDP results show that, compared to the UK, fewer Irish companies are completing sustainability reports, although the trend is upwards.

There is a demand from both investors and consumers for more information in the area of sustainability reporting. On the investor side, the growth of Irish-domiciled green/SRI funds is a clear indicator that investors do consider more than absolute return. In addition, the Global Investor Survey on Climate Change provided evidence that although investors may not always be clear on how to use the information, they are seeking more transparency from companies around their sustainability agenda and their risk-assessment process. On the consumer side, both Irish and international studies show that consumers are interested in buying what are perceived as 'green' products, although they may not always be willing to pay a price premium to do so. There would seem to be some real opportunities for Irish companies to gain some element of first-mover advantage, while trying to catch up with their international competitors.

The new Irish framework for sustainable development will no doubt attach a high priority to the setting of sustainable development indicators.[426]

## Adaptation[427]

Mitigation action involves measures to reduce GHG levels. Adaptation action deals with the unavoidable impacts.

At EU level, the Commission published a white paper (policy statement) on adapting to climate change and encouraged Ireland along with other Member States to reduce their vulnerability to the impacts of climate change.[428] Papers were also published about the agriculture, health, water and marine sectors.

The UK Government is already taking clear and firm action to ensure its processes and organisations are adapting to climate change. This is because the Government believes that climate change is one of the most serious threats that the world faces. The Environment Agency has taken on a new role as the Government's delivery agent in England and it is providing advice and support to key sectors to help them build resilience to climate change. The UK's Climate Change Act 2008 set up an adaptation sub-committee under the independent Committee on Climate Change. One of its main tasks is to prepare a climate change risk assessment for the UK.

Forfás has issued clear guidelines to the Irish business community about climate change risks and the need for companies to adopt sustainable practices arguing that competitive advantage will only be realised if the following risks are managed in a systematic way:

**Adaptation risks**

- **Markets:** climate change could change demand for goods and services.

- **Logistics:** climate change could increase vulnerability of supply chains, utilities (in particular water and energy), transport arrangements and communications.

- **Premises:** climate change (such as more frequent flooding events, storms, coastal erosion, etc.) could impact on location, materials, building design, construction, maintenance and facilities management.

- **Finance:** climate change could have implications for investments, insurances and stakeholder reputation.

- **People:** climate change could have implications for workforce, customers and changing lifestyles.

- **Processes:** climate change could have impacts on production processes (in particular cooling requirements) and service delivery.

Despite a call for a clear policy framework to provide certainty for business adaptation planning, nothing has been forthcoming to date from Government. However, in 2012 a national climate change adaptation framework and a national adaptive capacity assessment are to be published.

## Next steps

Two decades after the first Earth Summit in 1992, although good progress has been made as regards poverty eradication and environmental degradation, considerable global challenges remain. Several of the Millennium Development Goals are severely off-track. Roughly 1.4 billion people still live in extreme poverty and one-sixth of the world's population is undernourished. Natural resources are depleting while global GHG emissions continue to rise. Against that backdrop world leaders met in Rio de Janeiro from 4–6 June 2012 for the fourth Earth Summit to mark the 20th anniversary of the 1992 Rio UN conference on Environment and Development and the 10th anniversary of the 2002 Johannesburg World Summit on Sustainable Development.[429]

The goal of Rio+20 is to take stock, promote what works, adopt concrete goals and targets and lay a foundation for a future of prosperity, peace and sustainability.

The European Commission adopted a Communication preparing the ground for the EU's position at the Rio+20 Conference.[430] The Communication outlined objectives and specific actions on the two inter-linked themes of the conference: enabling the transition to a green economy in the context of sustainable development and poverty eradication, and ensuring better governance for sustainable development.

The selection of the green economy as a headline theme for Rio+20 reflects the current global effort to promote the 'green economy' concept i.e. 'an economy that results in improved human well-being and social equity, while significantly reducing environmental risks and ecological scarcities'. While there is no agreed definition of the green economy, this UNEP definition aligns with the goals of sustainable development and the current drive away from the 'brown economy' model that is heavily dependent on fossil fuel energy.

Environment Commissioner Janez Potocnik and Development Commissioner Andris Piebalgs presented the Communication jointly, marking an important link between environment and development. Janez Potocnik said:

The sustainable management of resources and natural capital is essential, for countries in all stages of development – and it can be particular opportunity for developing countries as resources and natural capital are fundamentally linked to the efforts to eradicate poverty. To make this happen at a global level we have to start putting in place the right market and regulatory conditions globally. Rio+20 can mark the start of a world-wide transition towards a global green economy.

Andris Piebalgs added:

Developing countries are the first affected by climate change and degradation of the environment. Floods, drought, and earthquakes are the most visible effects. They put at risk the economic and social development we strive to trigger through our assistance. Rio+20 is the opportunity to secure political commitment to improve the well-being of millions of people. We need to shift towards a green economy that will help us achieve sustainable growth which benefit to all citizens.

The Communication maps out the 'what, how and who' of a transition to a green economy, proposing specific actions that could be implemented at the international, national and regional levels.

**Key themes**

- **Investing in key resources and natural capital** ('what'): these are: water, renewable energy, marine resources, biodiversity and ecosystem services, sustainable agriculture, forests, waste and recycling. These areas underpin millions of livelihoods and can help alleviate poverty. They could become areas for future economic growth and global markets.

- **Combining market and regulatory instruments** ('how'): eco-taxes, removing environmentally harmful subsidies, mobilising public and private financial resources, investing in skills and green jobs. Indicators that reflect a wider sense of progress (both environmental and social), and that can work alongside GDP, need to be developed.

- **Improving governance and encouraging private sector involvement** ('who'): reinforcing and streamlining the existing international governance structures for example by upgrading the UNEP. The much greater involvement and engagement of businesses and civil society is also essential.

The Communication laid the basis for dialogue between the Commission, the Council (i.e. Member States) and the European Parliament, civil society, business, and countries in the lead up to Rio+20.[431] EU environment ministers support the adoption of clear operational targets and actions with agreed timeframes to promote the transition towards an inclusive green economy as a vehicle for sustainable development. The EU's strategy is that once agreement is reached at global level on the development of the green economy this will provide the EU and the Member States with a framework within which to advance national priorities. For certain, the EU's Seventh Environment Action Programme will have as an over-arching theme the promotion of a resource efficiency, greener and more competitive European economy.

## Resource efficiency

One of the EU's flagship initiatives under the over-arching *Europe 2020* strategy covers resource efficiency.[432] This was a key driver for advancing the EU's sustainable development objectives at Rio. The Commission supports the shift towards a resource-efficient, low-carbon economy to achieve sustainable growth because natural resources and quality of life underpin the EU's economy and that of its Member States. Against the background that the current patterns of resource use is not an option, increasing resource efficiency is therefore a key to securing growth and jobs for Europe. The key messages (with reference to many practical examples) are as follows.

Increased resource efficiency can offer competitive benefits to industry. While it does of course require additional investment, it also offers new opportunities that EU companies will want to harness. A number of key sectors have already embarked on a resource-efficient strategy.

In the cement industry for example, significant costs arise from high levels of carbon emissions (60 per cent of which result from the decomposition of raw material and limestone) and high energy costs. 'Co-processing' uses alternative fuels and alternative raw materials in a combined process that includes the use of waste-derived material and can reduce $CO_2$ emissions, energy costs and waste.

Potential input savings to UK firms from unexploited resource-efficiency savings with a payback period of less than one year were estimated at €6.4 billion per year in 2006, with further research indicating that savings from investment with a longer payback period would be four times greater from, among others, actions improving industrial processes and light-weighting.

In the food and drinks industry, resource efficiency is vital to cut input costs. This is mainly achieved through full use of material in production, including energy and water, through reduction and recovery programmes, recycling and reuse of material. For example, one UK food manufacturer carried out a water investigation in 2008 and found anomalies. An analysis using detailed sub-metering of water usage found potential savings of 73,000 cubic meters of water (42 per cent reduction per tonne of product).

In the Netherlands, a large chemical firm has, since 2007, secured a long-term, cost-effective, reliable supply of water by taking the local community's wastewater, and reusing it twice – firstly for steam production in manufacturing plants and then again in cooling towers, taking more than 9.9 million litres of household wastewater every day and cutting freshwater use. It has also reduced resource use in purifying salt water that was used in the past, using 65 per cent less energy and 500 tonnes fewer chemicals per year, and consequently 5,000 tonnes less $CO_2$.

The EU's core environmental industries active in the fields of pollution management and control, waste collection and treatment, renewable energy and recycling have a combined turnover of over €300 billion; provide nearly 3.5 million jobs, and have impressive global market shares of 30–40 per cent. This sector is growing at annual rates of more than 8 per cent in a global market predicted to reach €4 trillion by the middle of the decade and is offering many new and skilled green jobs.

Analysis suggests that for consumer goods makers, high-tech players, and other manufacturers, between 40 and 60 per cent of a company's carbon footprint resides upstream in its supply chain from raw materials, transport, and packaging to the energy consumed in manufacturing processes. For retailers, the figure can be as high as 80 per cent. For example, one large international industrial company requires the supply chain to meet minimum standards in sustainability. They look at the whole life-cycle of their products: from design, development, manufacture and use to end-of-life treatment, and acknowledge that in many cases there are synergies between economic and environmental advantages.

Resource efficiency is also a key issue for indigenous Irish industry as Enterprise Ireland's report on the dairy processing sector clearly demonstrates; energy intensity has fallen by 20 per cent and water use has dropped by 200 million litres per annum. Proving the sustainability and green credentials of this €20 billion industry – Ireland's most important indigenous sector – is assisting with marketing efforts to grow exports.

One issue that Ireland needs to address more seriously is the recognition and quantification of life-cycle costs and reflecting this sustainable principle in public tenders. This is a potential win–win for Government as achieving better resource efficiency is highly rated in the McKinsey MACC.

## Ireland's position

Much progress has been achieved in embedding the principles of sustainable development across all policy areas in the years since the publication of *Sustainable Development: a Strategy for Ireland.*[433] While progress has been achieved under Local Agenda 21, there is still a need for greater awareness raising and capacity building to further advance sustainable development issues in Ireland. Sustainable development is an over-arching objective for government and must be integrated across all policy areas where the sustainability of the Exchequer's finances are an issue.

In the context of the Rio Conference and reflecting a stakeholder consultation, Ireland (through the DECLG) will prepare a revised National Sustainable Development Strategy (rNSDS). It is the intention that the rNSDS will set a framework that integrates sustainable development into key areas of policy, put in place effective implementation mechanisms and deliver concrete measures to advance sustainable development in Ireland. Drawing on the model established by the EU's Sustainable Development Strategy and the Europe 2020 Strategy, the rNSDS will concentrate on gaps where limited progress has been made and that still present formidable challenges, not least among those being the need to decouple natural resource use and economic growth. The rNSDS will elaborate on those themes and outline a coherent series of practical measures (including the gradual introduction of green public procurement) aimed at tackling these challenges from a medium to longer-term perspective. Once adopted, the rNSDS will be reflected in the National Reform Programme which is part of the EU-IMF Programme.

The rNSDS will only work if it includes a comprehensive implementation plan with a resource budget for all priority actions. In addition, there is a need to reduce the plethora of bodies that are responsible for sustainable development.

## Chapter 13

# Renewable energy

The benefits in jobs and economic recovery from investment in energy efficiency and renewables will far outweigh the up-front costs.

Professor Owen Lewis, CEO of SEAI

## Introduction

Under the EU's Renewable Energy Directive Ireland is committed to meeting a 16 per cent share of renewable energy demand in gross final consumption by 2020. This will be quite a challenge as the contribution in 2010 was just 5.5 per cent.[434] In May 2012, announcing a stategy for renewable energy, the Minister for Communications, Energy and Natural Resources set a 40 per cent target for electricity generation from renewable sources (RES-E) before 2020.[435] The Minister believes that wind energy will form the bulk of Ireland's commitment to reaching these targets.[436] Thus the development of renewables is at the heart of the Government's energy policy.

The SEAI's estimate of current share and future targets in the three sub-categories can be summarised as follows:[437]

In addition to what is already connected, there is around 1,000 MW from Gate 1 and Gate 2, which has been contracted with the system operator and are scheduled to be built out and connected. Around 4,000 MW of additional renewable capacity is provided for in Gate 3.

Some 4,000 MW of renewable generation will be required to deliver the 40 per cent RES target by 2020. By the end of 2011,

## Table 23: Meeting Ireland's RES targets

|  | 1990 | 2010 | 2020 | Comment |
|---|---|---|---|---|
| **RES-E** | 5.3 | 14.8 | 40 | 40% renewable electricity is required to contribute to meeting the EU's overall 16% target; the current contribution is 12.9%. |
| **RES-T** | 0 | 2.4 | 10 | There has been a significant increase in the share of transport energy from bio-fuels since 2006. |
| **RES-H** | 2.6 | 4.4 | 12 | The growth in thermal energy (dominated by biomass) is mostly due to increased use of wood waste as an energy source. |

*Source:* SEAI (2011), *Energy in Ireland 1990–2010.*

Ireland had 1,900 MW of renewable generation on the grid, including 1,630 MW of wind connected; 234 MW of hydro; and 46 MW from other sources. An average of at least 200 MW of new renewable generation will have to be connected per annum to ensure that Ireland can deliver this target. The estimated amount of $CO_2$ avoided from RES increased by 267 per cent between 1990 and 2010, reaching 2.88Mt, with wind (1.3Mt) the biggest contributor.

As a consequence of RES (and energy efficiency and a restructuring of the economy) there has been a gradual but noticeable decoupling of total primary energy requirement from economic growth.

There are two important truths in relation to Ireland's current energy mix: First, Ireland is over-dependent on fuel imports for energy production.[438] Second, a massive change is required in order for Ireland to meet its renewable commitments by 2020. This change will come about to some degree through a process of technological innovation – whether in Ireland or abroad – as well as a policy shift that encourages the development of non-fossil-fuel energy through subsidies, grants, education and/or legislative intrusion.[439]

The NREAP sets out the Government's strategic approach and concrete measures to deliver on Ireland's 16 per cent target under the EU Renewable Energy Directive 2009/28/EC. Renewable energy reduces dependence on fossil fuels, improves security of supply, and reduces GHG emissions creating environmental benefits while delivering green jobs to the economy, thus contributing to national competitiveness.

Grid capacity, access conditions and the availability of REFIT tariffs influence investors' decisions. Clearly the correct policies are in place as the CER had applications for 7,000 MW of additional capacity prior to its Gate 3 announcement.[440]

Irish companies are using renewable energy, for example in the panel board and sawmilling industries; the meat-processing sector used tallow as a fuel substitute and is exploring anaerobic digestion as a viable proposition; the dairy sector has invested in natural gas CHP and is assessing biomass energy alternatives.

The Government's commitment to accelerating the development of renewable energy was set out in the Government's energy policy *'Delivering a sustainable energy future for Ireland – The Energy Policy Framework 2007–2020'*;[441] and in the strategy *'Building Ireland's Smart Economy – A Framework for Sustainable Economic Renewal'*.[442]

The Government's ambitions for renewable energy and the related national targets are fully commensurate with the EU's energy policy objectives and the targets addressed to Ireland under the Renewable Energy Directive. Ireland's energy-efficiency ambitions (20 per cent by 2020) as set out in the NEEAP are duly reflected in the NREAP.

In terms of both policy and technology the focus at the moment is on onshore wind farms. Other technologies – at various stages of development – must also be considered, and each is analysed briefly below. Bear in mind when considering opportunities in Ireland that over $211 billion was invested in this sector globally in 2010.

## Energy forecasts

Perhaps the most accurate, and certainly the most recent, forecast of future energy provision and requirements is SEAI's Energy Forecasts for Ireland to 2020, as it is a orward-looking modelling exercise that projects renewable energy, GHG emissions and other energy sector outcomes in 2020 using the ESRI's HERMES economic modelling tool. SEAI uses two distinct scenarios in its analysis *Energy White Paper Plus* and *Exploratory*, comparing them to a baseline scenario and each represents a different path towards Ireland meeting its energy-mix and carbon-abatement obligations by 2020.[443] Under the *White Paper Plus* scenario, Ireland would narrowly miss its obligation to have 16 per cent of final energy consumption derived from renewable sources (the figure would be 15.4 per cent) by achieving figures of 40 per cent, 12 per cent and 10 per cent in electricity generation, heating and transport, respectively; Ireland would also become a net exporter of electricity. The report notes that with the increased wind capacity planned as part of Gate 3, which does not form part of this scenario, Ireland could easily meet its EU obligation by 2020 if the White Paper is implemented. Under the *Exploratory* scenario all of the wind-derived energy in the Gate 3 process is completed. Ireland would exceed its 40 per cent target of renewables in electricity generation, instead deriving 52 per cent of electricity from renewable sources, and 17.5 per cent of final energy demand.

The two scenarios represent the poles of a range of options that can be met based on the degree to which the Gate 3 process is implemented. It is interesting, given the critique of the east–west interconnector plans from the Irish Academy of Engineering that SEAI concluded 'increased interconnector capacity goes hand in hand with increased wind deployment', assuming that Ireland would import energy from the UK/Europe when wind generation is low (i.e. when it is not windy). The modelled scenarios are predicated on a policy-determined future electricity plant mix and interconnector capacity. Failure to meet these policy targets would make it very difficult for Ireland to meet its renewable energy commitments by 2020.

**Figure 33: Electricity generation by fuel 1990–2020 in the SEAI Modelling Framework under three scenarios: Baseline (top), White Paper Plus (middle) and Exploratory (bottom)**

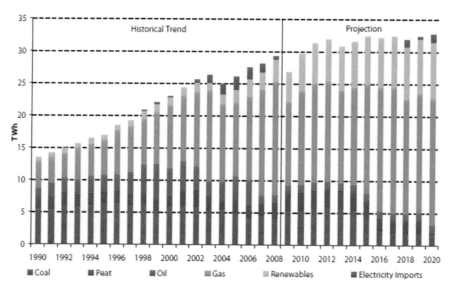

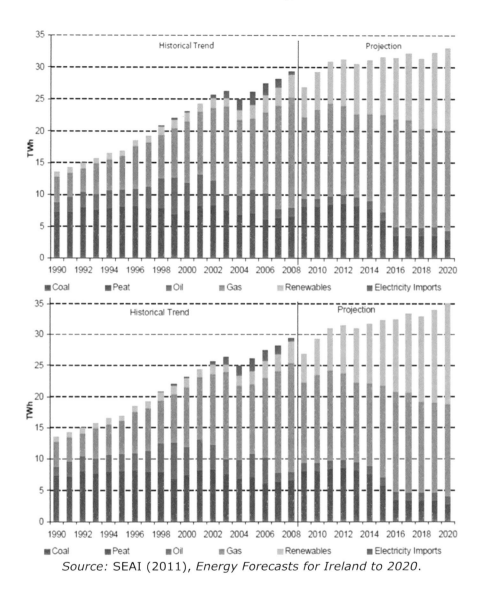

Source: SEAI (2011), *Energy Forecasts for Ireland to 2020*.

Therefore, the Government's commitment to develop commer-cial large-scale electricity storage and infrastructure to deliver the export of (renewable) electricity to the UK is noteworthy.

## Drivers

The requirement for renewable energy is being driven by the world's needs to reduce GHG emissions in conjunction with increasing global energy demands. While policy is less important a driver in energy than in other sectors (notably waste) nonetheless there are a range of issues that are key to the development of renewable energy in Ireland:

- We have a significant ocean resource.
- Ireland has commitments under the Kyoto Protocol.
- Global warming resulting in climate change is having a fundamental impact on business and is having a positive impact on growth in the sector.
- Depletion of fossil fuels has reached the point where some observers claim we have already reached 'peak oil'.
- Security of supply of fuel imports (oil, gas and coal) is influencing government policy towards greater self-sufficiency in energy generation.
- There have been significant price rises in gas and oil in the last five years as a consequence of increasing demand.
- Social influences, including customer and shareholder expectations, are influencing corporate social responsibility (CSR), which also impacts on investment decisions.

## Barriers

Not having a tradition in heavy engineering makes it unlikely that Ireland will become a significant centre for wave and/or wind turbine manufacture. Small population and market and low population density (outside of the Dublin conurbation) is not attractive for large-scale CHP/district heating. Maturity of the technology in some renewable subsectors (e.g. wind, anaerobic digestion, bio-ethanol fermentation etc.) leaves Ireland with some catching-up to do to develop a manufacturing base. There is no history of recent vehicle manufacturing, which means electric vehicle innovation is more likely to happen elsewhere. Small electricity generators have had difficulty in selling to the national grid and the situation of larger facilities in remote areas has also presented problems with limited capacity/availability of high voltage transmission lines.

## NREAP

On 30 June 2010, Ireland's draft NREAP was sent by the Government to the European Commission. The NREAP, which was the subject of wide consultation with stakeholders, is based on the Government's White Paper *Delivering a Sustainable Energy Future for Ireland (2007–2020)*. The main targets are as follows:

- Overall renewables in 2011 was 6.7 per cent and will be at least 16 per cent by 2020

- 40 per cent electricity consumption from renewable sources by 2020 (RES-E)

- 10 per cent electric vehicles (EVs and PHEVs) by 2020; this represents some 220,000 cars

- Initial penetration rate of bio-fuels of 4 per cent per annum rising to 10.5 per cent by volume from 2019 (8.4 per cent by energy) (RES-T)

- 12 per cent renewable heat by 2020 (RES-H).

The NREAP summarised the situation as follows.[444]

**Electricity**: The Government has set a target of 40 per cent electricity consumption from renewable sources by 2020. In the last five years in particular, Ireland has made big strides in accelerating renewable generation. In the 2001 European RES-E Directive, Ireland was set a target of moving from 3.6 per cent RES-E to 13.2 per cent RES-E by 2010. Ireland achieved 14.4 per cent RES-E in 2009 and is on track to exceed the national target of 15 per cent in 2010. All key national entities, including the CER, the distribution and transmission system operators and the renewable energy sector are working with the Government to deliver the 2020 target through grid connection and grid development strategies. The significant growth in electricity from renewable sources in recent years is largely attributable to onshore wind. As Ireland moves towards achieving circa 40 per cent RES-E by 2020, the Irish grid is increasingly have to cope with the challenges posed by large amounts of intermittent power. As outlined in the NREAP, the Irish Transmission System Operator, EirGrid, is involved in detailed examination of the issues and is pioneering several renewables facilitation studies with a view to ensuring the appropriate management of the grid and stability of the electricity system during this transition.

The all-island single electricity market, overseen by the regulatory authorities north and south, is evolving continuously to take account of the growth in renewable energy. Together with the significant contribution of large-scale generation, the introduction of a robust framework for the development of a vibrant micro-generation sector is an important component of building societal acceptance of energy infrastructure and ownership of the national renewable energy targets. The micro-generation area has the potential to create employment and enable participation by a wide section of the community. The Government is committed to developing a comprehensive micro-generation framework that will be taken forward up to 2020.

**Transport**: A two-pronged strategy has been put in place that combines significant increases in the use of bio-fuels with the accelerated development and use of electric vehicles in Ireland. The national Bio-fuel Obligation Scheme 2010 obliges all road transport fuel suppliers to use bio-fuel in the fuel mix to ensure that they represent a certain percentage of their annual fuel sales. The initial penetration rate will be 4 per cent per annum, to be increased over time. The bio-fuel obligation will ensure that Irish consumers have access to appropriately priced, sustainable and reliable sources of bio-fuels over the coming years, and, in doing so, this will give an important incentive to domestic bio-fuel production.

The Government has set a target of 10 per cent electric vehicles by 2020. The Government is taking a broad-ranging series of initiatives around electric vehicles, including signing memoranda of understanding with a number of motor manufacturers, committing to a large-scale national roll-out of electric vehicle infrastructure and appropriate supports for the customer. The size and geography of Ireland make the country uniquely suitable for electric vehicles, and the Government is ensuring that Ireland becomes an early test bed for this technology, and that it takes full advantage of the potential benefits associated with using electricity from renewable sources in transport. Ireland is uniquely placed through the interrelationship between the national 40 per cent target for electricity from renewable sources and the national target for the electrification of transport to deliver a fully holistic and mutually reinforcing energy system.

**Heat**: The Government has set a target of 12 per cent renewable heat by 2020. A series of related and complementary support programmes have been put in place to address the delivery of this target already aimed at supporting both demand and supply sides. For historical, geographical and demographic reasons, renewable heat poses considerable challenges for Ireland, challenges that the Government is determined to address. To that end, work is nearing completion on a new framework to ensure delivery of these targets using the full range of resources available, with an initial focus on the biomass sector but also including geothermal resources in due course.

**Energy planning**: In energy planning terms, 2020 is rapidly approaching. The Government is also looking beyond 2020 in terms of the significant opportunities to develop Ireland's abundant offshore renewable energy resources, including offshore wind, wave and tidal energy, recognising that these offer rich potential over the coming decades.

Implementing and delivering on this NREAP will be a challenge and will require enhanced coordination and collaboration between all relevant government departments and state bodies. A fully joined-up and integrated approach, involving all appropriate public sector bodies at national, regional and local level will be critical for delivery over the next decade. The European Commission (DG Energy) approves every NREAP and monitors Member States' progress in meeting the RES targets and provides details about all national NREAPs. The Oireachtas has assessed the NREAP and concluded that while it is an *adequate* response there is a risk of under-performance through to 2020 as measures to be taken before 2015 are too ambitious in scope and scale to be delivered in such a short time frame. The Oireachtas also questioned the methodology used to select some measures.[445]

## Onshore wind

The sun heats the Earth unevenly, causing flows of air as nature attempts to equalise temperatures in different regions. As an island next to a large ocean, Ireland is exposed to some of the strongest winds in Europe, and is thus well-positioned for the development and deployment of wind energy technology (Figure 34).

SEAI points out that 'wind turbines produce no pollutants, no harmful gas emissions, no effluent, no waste products and no radioactivity'. They are also far less polluting to install and decommission, with the majority of decommissioned materials available for reuse. Concerns exist that wind farms can negatively affect local scenery, wildlife, property values and tourism,

**Figure 34: European wind atlas**

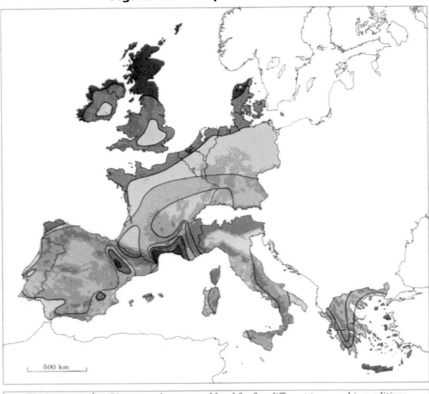

| Wind resources[1] at 50 metres above ground level for five different topographic conditions | | | | | | | | | |
|---|---|---|---|---|---|---|---|---|---|
| Sheltered terrain[2] | | Open plain[3] | | At a sea coast[4] | | Open sea[5] | | Hills and ridges[6] | |
| m s$^{-1}$ | Wm$^{-2}$ | m s$^{-1}$ | Wm$^{-2}$ | m s$^{-1}$ | Wm$^{-2}$ | m s$^{-1}$ | Wm$^{-2}$ | m s$^{-1}$ | Wm$^{-2}$ |
| > 6.0 | > 250 | > 7.5 | > 500 | > 8.5 | > 700 | > 9.0 | > 800 | > 11.5 | > 1800 |
| 5.0-6.0 | 150-250 | 6.5-7.5 | 300-500 | 7.0-8.5 | 400-700 | 8.0-9.0 | 600-800 | 10.0-11.5 | 1200-1800 |
| 4.5-5.0 | 100-150 | 5.5-6.5 | 200-300 | 6.0-7.0 | 250-400 | 7.0-8.0 | 400-600 | 8.5-10.0 | 700-1200 |
| 3.5-4.5 | 50-100 | 4.5-5.5 | 100-200 | 5.0-6.0 | 150-250 | 5.5-7.0 | 200-400 | 7.0- 8.5 | 400- 700 |
| < 3.5 | < 50 | < 4.5 | < 100 | < 5.0 | < 150 | < 5.5 | < 200 | < 7.0 | < 400 |

*Source:* http://www.windatlas.dk/Europe/About.html

but each of these factors can be largely negated in the planning and development stages, according to the SEAI.[446]

Wind farms can only produce electricity when it is windy (generally considered to be speeds above 16–18 kph), and will shut down for safety reasons if it is too windy (over 80 kph). Optimal efficiency is at around 40 kph. Thus wind is an inconsistent source of energy and, on its own, unsuitable for base load energy. However, wind farms can be combined with facilities that store energy, such as batteries (which are expensive, dirty and inefficient, particularly for anything above the scale of micro-generation), pumped-storage hydroelectric stations (such as at Turlough Hill), compressed air energy storage, hydrogen energy storage or thermal energy storage. This combination process to convert renewable wind energy into base load energy – in order to deal with changing demand throughout the day ('load-levelling') – increases the cost of wind energy projects.

The first wind farm opened in Ireland in 1992 at Bellacorrick in County Mayo. Since then, production of energy from wind farms (both onshore and offshore) has increased steadily. SEAI claims that 'it is envisaged that wind power will make the most significant contribution to the achievement of national and international targets for green electricity, due to its environmental benefits, technological maturity and increasing competitiveness'.

Wind energy's contribution to gross electricity consumption has risen sharply over the past decade and was 9.7 per cent in 2010. Installed capacity is 1,630 MW (December 2011). The peak recorded wind power output was 1,412 MW delivered on 2 November 2011, or some 45 per cent of national energy demand, with no issues reported by Eirgrid. According to Eirgrid, there were 471 MW of wind contracted for connection before the end of 2012. There are an additional 729 contracted, approximately 3,600 MW of live offers and a further 13,202 MW in the queue as part of the CER's Gate 3 process.[447] Once completed, these projects will boost Ireland's wind-generated energy capacity to 17,822 MW out of a national total of 33,063 MW (or 53.9 per cent).[448] The total installed energy capacity in Ireland is 6,317 MW,[449] with 2,262 accounted for by installed renewable generation. While wind energy counts for approximately 20 per cent of Ireland's installed capacity, the actual energy derived from these farms is far below capacity due to the intermittent use of wind.

Eigrid is confident that the island of Ireland will reach a level of installed wind generation in 2020 that will be enough to meet around 37 per cent of electricity demand and that technical solutions can be found to the operational challenges of having high levels of variable renewable generation on the power system.[450]

In January 2012, the European Commission approved the Government's proposals for the REFIT 2 scheme to support onshore wind under EU state aid rules. While this was a welcome development, the CER single electricity market's unexpected decision to change the rules on curtailment has drawn huge criticism from the wind sector. The rule requires some wind farms to close down when there is surplus capacity on the grid than can be met by fossil fuel plants and some wind farms. A strict curtailment rule will affect investor's appetite for new renewable investment projects.

## Offshore wind

Ireland is ideally suited to take advantage of its comparatively large area of windy coastal waters (Figure 35).

**Figure 35: Wind conditions off the Irish coast**

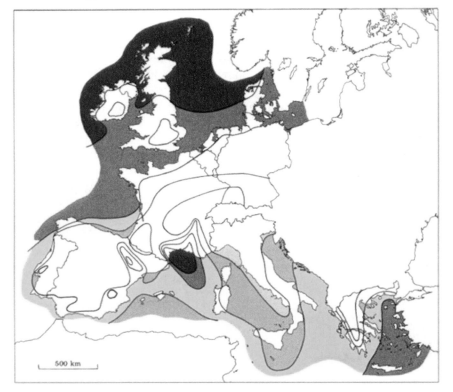

| Wind resources over open sea (more than 10 km offshore) for five standard heights | | | | | | | | | |
|---|---|---|---|---|---|---|---|---|---|
| 10 m | | 25 m | | 50 m | | 100 m | | 200 m | |
| $ms^{-1}$ | $Wm^{-2}$ | $ms^{-1}$ | $Wm^{-2}$ | $ms^{-1}$ | $Wm^{-2}$ | $ms^{-1}$ | $Wm^{-2}$ | $ms^{-1}$ | $Wm^{-2}$ |
| > 8.0 | > 600 | > 8.5 | > 700 | > 9.0 | > 800 | > 10.0 | > 1100 | > 11.0 | > 1500 |
| 7.0-8.0 | 350-600 | 7.5-8.5 | 450-700 | 8.0-9.0 | 600-800 | 8.5-10.0 | 650-1100 | 9.5-11.0 | 900-1500 |
| 6.0-7.0 | 250-300 | 6.5-7.5 | 300-450 | 7.0-8.0 | 400-600 | 7.5- 8.5 | 450- 650 | 8.0- 9.5 | 600- 900 |
| 4.5-6.0 | 100-250 | 5.0-6.5 | 150-300 | 5.5-7.0 | 200-400 | 6.0- 7.5 | 250- 450 | 6.5- 8.0 | 300- 600 |
| < 4.5 | < 100 | < 5.0 | < 150 | < 5.5 | < 200 | < 6.0 | < 250 | < 6.5 | < 300 |

*Source:* http://www.windatlas.dk/Europe/About.html

Although it would be imagined that producing energy from offshore wind is very similar to producing energy from onshore wind, offshore wind technology has more in common with oil platform technology than onshore wind farms. It is thus a much more expensive method of producing energy. However, according to NOW Ireland, by situating wind turbines away from the coast, one can overcome many of the problems associated with onshore wind farms that were noted above. For example, such projects are unlikely to interfere with tourism, property prices or scenery. Even the problem of inconsistency of supply is reduced (but not eliminated) by basing wind farms offshore, where wind is generally greater and more constant.

Offshore wind is a rapidly maturing technology around the world. According to the European Wind Energy Association, there are currently 830 offshore wind turbines installed and grid connected in nine European countries, totalling 2,063 MW in 39 wind farms. In 2010, a further 1,000 MW of offshore wind was installed. Currently there are 16 offshore wind farms under construction, totalling over 3,500 MW and a further 52 wind farms have been fully consented, totalling more than 16,000 MW.

In terms of full load-hour potential, Ireland has one of the best offshore wind energy climates in Europe. The potential offshore wind resource in Ireland is large scale and much greater than the capacity of our electricity system to absorb it all for domestic use.

To date, foreshore leases have been granted for the operation of two sites – a 520 MW wind farm on the Arklow Bank and a 1,100 MW wind farm on the Codling Bank, both in the Irish Sea. Seven turbines totalling 25.2 MW have been installed on the Arklow Bank. The remainder of the two consented sites currently have no grid connection offers.

Approximately 800 MW of offshore wind projects in Gate 3 were due to receive an offer of a grid connection in 2011. Offshore wind projects included in Gate 3 are the Dublin Array (off Bray Head, Co. Wicklow – in the Irish Sea) (364 MW); Oriel (Dundalk Bay, Co. Louth – in the Irish Sea) (320 MW) and Doolick (Outer Galway Bay, Atlantic coast) (100 MW). These projects have applied for foreshore leases which are being processed by the DECLG.

Ireland is actively involved in the development of on an offshore grid for offshore wind, wave and tidal energy potential and is involved in a number of initiatives and developments in the EU context.

**North Sea Countries' Offshore Grid initiative**: Following a political declaration by the ministers concerned at the December 2009 Energy Council in Brussels, the North Seas Countries' Offshore Grid initiative, which consists of nine Member States and Norway, was established and Ireland is one of the participants. The ministers declared their interest in discussing the development of an offshore grid in a common and coordinated way. The North Seas Countries' Offshore Grid initiative adds a political dimension to other work being carried out in the EU on the development of offshore grids. The commission has identified the North Sea area as one of the EU's electricity highways of the future and, as a consequence, the project will probably receive access to EU funding under the EU's 'Connecting Europe' finance programme (2014–2020). The House of Commons Energy and Climate Change Committee said (September 2011) that as an energy island the UK needs a drastically improved grid. The committee's chairman, Tim Yeo, said that better connection would give the UK's energy industry access to better markets. It would also enable the country to make more use of wind power domestically by ensuring that imported power would be available in calm weather. Being realistic, this project will take decades to complete.

**ISLES project**: The Irish–Scottish Links on Energy Study (ISLES) is a collaborative EU Interreg-funded feasibility project between the DCENR (Ireland), the Scottish Government and the Department of Enterprise, Trade and Investment (Northern Ireland). The main findings are that, assuming an appropriate regulatory framework is in place, a cross-jurisdictional integrated network is economically viable and technologically achievable. The initial maximum resource potential is 16.4 GW, including 12.4 GW of offshore wind. There is sufficient UK network capacity for the connection of the ISLES on the scale and within the time frame envisaged i.e. by 2020.

**European Network of Transmission System Operators in Electricity**: EirGrid actively participates in the European Network of Transmission System Operators in Electricity (ENTSO-E), which is now fully established. For the purpose of system development ENTSO-E is organised in a number of regional groupings. EirGrid participates in the North Sea Regional Group, which will in due course be an important contributor to the development of proposals for an offshore grid in this region.

**Offshore Grid Connection Study**: EirGrid has carried out a study on how significant offshore wind resources (beyond the 800 MW in Gate 3) off the east coast of Ireland could be integrated into the Irish transmission system, if developed. The research considered the implications and merits of how an offshore and onshore grid would work together. Early indications from the study suggest that there are positive synergies between onshore and offshore systems. Of course, any decision regarding the development of an offshore grid is dependent on assumptions relating to cost and reliability performance of the offshore assets.[451]

Ireland's offshore wind potential is identified in the (draft) Offshore Renewable Energy Development Plan.[452] Once implemented, the OREDP and the general scheme of a Bill to reform the foreshore consenting arrangements should provide for improved strategic decision-making and greater policy cohesion in the marine renewable energy area.

Of the 6,000 MW potential only 2,680 MW of capacity is currently in planning and development. NOW Ireland estimate a further 5,000 MW is possible on the basis that the electricity is exported via interconnectors.

By way of comparison, it is interesting to note the UK Government's recent decision to grant rights to energy companies willing to spend £75 billion installing 6,400 offshore wind turbines at ten wind farms, and creating as many as 20,000 jobs by 2020. This is the biggest expansion of wind energy ever seen in the world according to the British Government, whose Keynesian approach to economic reform will also see it exceed the UK's target of a 20 per cent use of renewables in its energy mix by 2020 as a result of this massive expansion in wind energy deployment.

## Opportunities – wind energy

The largest growth in renewable energy contribution in Ireland in recent years has come in the form of electricity generated from wind power. Wind energy has been touted as one of the big sources of 'green collar' jobs in a number of countries over the last few years. The wind sector currently employs around 64,000 people in Germany, around 21,000 in Denmark and 35,000 in

Spain according to national statistics.[453] As a rule of thumb, employment can be gauged by twelve individuals employed per MW installed. Employment projections for the EU-25 for the year 2020 are 153,400 direct and indirect employees for manufacturing.

It is arguable that there is an enterprise opportunity currently being missed in the absence of any direct wind energy manufacturing facilities on the island of Ireland. According to IDA Ireland, Ireland has no more than 18 months left to secure a large-scale manufacturing plant. There is a sense that Ireland is 'closed for business' because of a distinct lack of joined-up thinking.[454] On the other hand, companies such as Wind Energy Direct, Windturbines.ie and C&F Green Energy are good examples of Irish entrepreneurship in this sub-sector.

The global value of turbine sales is approximately €18 billion; there cannot be too many other hi-tech sectors of this scale where Ireland has such a negligible presence. It also comes at a time when the order books for some wind turbine manufacturers are filled with lead times in the region of four years. What is also certain is the fact that demand is not going to diminish anytime soon. There are expectations of some consolidation among the manufacturers, which could result in a positive disruption to the supply chain network, providing enterprise opportunities.

The challenge for Ireland is to examine the wind turbine supply chain and carve out areas where sustainable jobs can be provided. Ireland should use existing networks to approach the turbine manufacturers and, given the long lead times being experienced, offer a fast-tracked manufacturing plant close to sea routes where capacity bottlenecks could be relieved extremely rapidly. At the same time, the individual components making up the tier 2 and tier 3 supply chain should be reviewed for suitability to establish manufacturing operations in Ireland. Enterprise Ireland should also review these components and provide introductions for indigenous firms to bid for supply contracts among the tier 1 suppliers, a very successful policy adopted to service the computer industry in the 1980s and 1990s. In addition, Ireland has the opportunity to become a recognised world leader in the testing of the next generation of offshore renewable energy equipment.

Another major factor emerging is the fact that much of planned generating capacity will be installed in areas with a poor grid network. SEAI has estimated that 6,565 kms of new transmission lines for wind energy alone will be required. This is effectively double the existing capacity of 6,800 kms; we are looking at a scenario not faced since the electrification of the state in the 1930s. The transmission network and successfully attracting manufacturing or services work with the turbines themselves offer huge sustainable employment potential in the coming decades.

There are many in the sector who argue that Gate 3 has run its course and it is time for a Gate 4 (while preserving acquired rights). A new approvals process must be linked to Eirgrid's capacity to deliver on its strategy on and offshore; on the export targets for electricity from renewable sources; on plans to accelerate the introduction of electric vehicles and a gradual electrification of the public transport system; on a long-term REFIT agreement; and on the mix of renewables best suited to Ireland's much changed economy having regard to the fall in costs of solar PV for example. To get a debate going it would be helpful if the CER sought views on the basis of a wide-ranging consultation paper.

As the Minister for Communications, Energy and Natural Resources does not intend to make an EU state aid application in respect of offshore wind on the grounds that it is twice as expensive as onshore wind (at €3 million per MW) and because Ireland can meet its renewable energy targets from onshore capacity, biomass and related technologies, the question could well be asked as to whether the sector has any prospects at least in the short term. The Minister is also on record as saying that it is possible to conclude an intergovernmental arrangement with the UK for the export of surplus energy capacity, but this investment should not be supported by a REFIT and the cost-benefit analysis must be positive.[455]

The consensus, informed by lower than previously projected energy demand, is that Ireland will meet its targets for wind.[456]

## Micro-generation

Micro-generation is a catch-all term for small-scale energy production that allows customers to generate their own electricity; a small generator is powered by a renewable source.[457] Individuals, businesses or communities can derive energy from a wind turbine, small hydro plant, solar power, domestic-scale combined heat and power (DCHP) equipment, or some combination of these technologies in a hybrid system. The majority of micro-generation plants are in remote areas, or temporary structures.

The process for connecting a micro-generation plant to the electricity network involves a single-page application to ESB Networks. Indeed, the planning process for wind turbines and solar panels receives a general exemption for projects generating up to 11 kV, though there are location-specific exceptions to this exemption. The European standard EN 50438 sets out the requirements for the connection of micro-generators.

Although there are a number of government-sponsored grant schemes to assist homeowners and businesses to consume less energy, there is currently no equivalent scheme in place to encourage micro-generation.[458] In other jurisdictions such schemes are commonplace and again it is enlightening to look at the situation in the UK, where in April 2006 the Department of Trade and Industry (DTI) launched the Low Carbon Buildings Programme to provide grants for micro-generation schemes. In that year's budget, it was declared that income derived from selling surplus electricity to the national grid from micro-generation plants was not liable for UK income tax.

ESB Networks plans to make it easier for generation units of up to 50 kW to connect to the network as at the moment these projects face the same stringent tests as much larger power plants.

The SEAI monitors activity in this sub-sector on a regular basis.

## Bio-energy

Bio-energy can be exploited primarily through:

**Combustion**: Biomass (e.g. wood chips) can be burned to provide process and/or space heating. The combustion of biomass can also be used to raise steam to drive engines/turbines that are coupled to generators producing electricity.

**Anaerobic digestion**: Biomass (e.g. animal manure) can be transformed to biogas by anaerobic digestion and the biogas can be used to fuel a gas engine or gas turbine, or burned in a boiler to provide heat or to raise steam.

Other technologies for the exploitation of bio-energy include gasification and pyrolysis but these are not as commercially developed as combustion and anaerobic digestion.

## Types of biomass

Biomass is all organic material, an example being plant matter. It is either:

- the direct product of photosynthesis (for example plant matter – leaves, stems, etc.);

  or

- the indirect product of photosynthesis (for example animal mass resulting from the consumption of plant matter).

Types of biomass that are used to provide bio-energy include:
- waste streams, including residues from forestry and related industries

- recycled wood

- agricultural residues and agri-food effluents

- manures

- the organic fraction of municipal solid waste

- separated household waste and sewage sludge

- purpose-grown energy crops including short-rotation forestry, miscanthus grass etc.

Biomass energy production covers a wide array of technologies, but two broad categories are distinguishable from the literature on biomass energy conversion. Organic material such as short-rotation forestry, organic waste, agricultural residue, manures or purpose-grown crops (such as rape seed or sugar cane for producing bio-ethanol and bio-diesel) can be combusted in the same manner as fossil fuels in order to produce energy. The emissions from this process are offset to a large degree by the $CO_2$ absorbed by the fuel when it is being grown. Bio-ethanol (produced by fermenting sugary and starchy crops) can be used as a partial substitute (up to 5 per cent) in regular petrol combustion engines for transport vehicles.[459] Similarly, bio-diesel (produced primarily from rape seed oil) can be used as a partial substitute for diesel in the extant vehicle/home heating stock.

The European bio-fuels Directive entered into force in May 2003 and set targets for bio-fuels, including 5.75 per cent bio-fuels penetration by 2010.[460] These targets were repeated in Ireland's Bio-energy Action Plan (2007), which outlined the framework for Ireland to develop its bio-energy resources to generate electricity, for use as transport fuels, for use in heating and cooling buildings and for conversion to bio-chemicals as industrial raw materials. Grants were provided in the 2007 budget for growing willow and miscanthus, both of which are short-rotation forestry crops.[461] However, the Directive was shelved in 2008 over concerns that the production of bio-fuels had unintended social and environmental side-effects.[462] As such, liquid bio-fuels are currently only a potential replacement for distilled fossil fuels such as petrol and diesel, until such time as technical and agricultural developments permit yield to be improved.

Gasses emitted by organic or waste material as it decomposes can be utilised in a similar manner to 'natural' gas for energy production. This gas can be produced anaerobically (in sealed chambers where oxygen is not allowed to interfere with the production of other gasses) or aerobically (where oxygen – itself a combustible gas – is part of the process as the biomass is open to the air). The by-products of these processes are often usable as compost for agriculture, or as a coal substitute for cement production.

The Council for Forest Research and Development (COFORD) convened and facilitated a strategic group formed from the saw milling and forestry sectors, which appointed Electrowatt-Ekono, an international consultancy specialising in biomass and energy, to carry out a strategic study in the area of wood use for energy in Ireland.[463] The report *Maximising the Potential of Wood Use for Energy Generation in Ireland* includes an outline of the potential sectors where wood fuel could be used to substitute existing fuels in solid fuel power plants and heat only plants in the domestic, commercial, public and industrial sectors.

On 8 December 2011, the Minister for Agriculture, Food and the Marine announced the reopening of the Bio-energy Scheme for 2012 for the planting of miscanthus and willow. The contentious condition that participants had to maintain the crop for seven years has been dropped.

Phase 2 bio-fuels (using enzymes to breakdown the cellulosic content of feedstock) is an area where existing research should be further supported. Gasification of wood pellets can result in an increase of up to 30 per cent in calorific output and should be promoted as a more efficient heat energy technology (over conventional biomass boilers).

Despite the roll back on its increased production, it produces over 150 million litres of liquid bio-fuels for heating and transport, equivalent to 2 per cent of transport fuels.

Based on a German plant, a 500kWe biogas plant running on a single feedstock (maize) on a farm costs €2–4.7 million for gas grid connected plants. The most economically attractive size of bio-methane plant is a production capacity of between 1 and 2 million Nm3 bio-methane per annum.[464] While economies of scale are important so is the REFIT for the electricity component of biogas CHP, which has been estimated at €0.12 per kWh.[465]

SEAI's bio-energy roadmap, based on a detailed bio-energy analysis model, sets out the growth potential for the sector until 2050 and as such is a major planning tool for potential investors. The roadmap will inform the forthcoming comprehensive National Bio-energy Strategy.

## Key findings

- Bio-energy has the potential to be an indigenously-derived cornerstone of national energy requirements to 2050 across transport, electricity generation and heat.

- Over 3,500ktoe of indigenous resources are available for the bio-energy supply chain by 2050.

- Some 11 Mt of GHG can be abated annually.

- High-yield demand-driven crops are capable of being grown in Ireland.

It has been estimated that almost €1.5 billion in direct investment in biomass-processing infrastructure and equipment will be required over the period to 2020 to deliver the output needed to meet Ireland's renewable energy targets.[466]

The REfiT 3 scheme for biomass technologies marks an important step in providing certainty for the sector.

## Anaerobic digestion

There are over 9,000 anaerobic digestion (AD) plants in Europe; the technology and the financial model are proven.

As far back as January 2005 the EPA earmarked AD as a viable policy option to address national commitments in the areas of global warming (and) renewable energy.[467]

Biogas from AD can be used in electricity generation. Sources available for digestion are agricultural slurries, sewage sludge, food and catering wastes, the biodegradable fraction of municipal solid waste (MSW), industrial sludges and landfill gas.[468] Some 132 million wet tonnes of agricultural slurries, wastewaters, effluent and sludge are generated in Ireland annually, while the primary food-processing and catering sectors also generate substantial waste flows. At present the majority of these wastes are either spread on land, rendered, or disposed to landfill, but with additional processing these waste flows can be more beneficially exploited.

AD technology is in competition with composting for feed stocks. It has had a chequered operational history in Ireland in terms of reliability and there may be a prejudice against the technology here as a consequence. However, under controlled conditions it is now a proven technology and has its place in the Irish market. On-farm AD plants are considered viable in the Irish context but centralised plant feasibility is dependent on gate-fee prices for sludges, slurries and other feed stocks (and to a lesser extent on the electricity price payable). The EPA consultation document on AD concluded by saying that:

AD has the potential to deliver multiple environmental benefits, including reduced water pollution potential, lower greenhouse gas emissions, and reduced odours from agricultural slurries. In places that have high concentrations of animal waste threatening water quality, centralised AD can play a significant role in managing the problem. AD is also unique among policy instruments as it can deliver positive outcomes for multiple policy objectives with respect to global warming, renewable energy and water pollution.

A 380kW digester typically requires 380 acres of land, 8,000 tonnes of grass silage plus 1,300 tonnes of maize silage, along with 4,000 tonnes of slurry. The cost of the feedstock is around €250,000. Capital expenditure is around €1.5 million, or some €4,000 per kW. Therefore AD plants could be built by a farmer or a farmers' cooperative.[469]

The major stumbling block for AD is that its financial return is (at present) insufficient to repay the investment outlay, but financial analyses ignore the environmental benefits. Government support for AD can be justified on the basis of its environmental benefits, which without government support would not be realised.

Biomass is currently only contributing in the form of micro-generation plants in Ireland. Greenstar has two sites producing energy (c. 750 kW) from aerobic digestion gasses.[470] One of these, at Knockharley landfill in Meath, changed from flaring off excess gas to converting this gas to energy in January 2010. The Greenstar site in Meath is located very close to a Panda Waste facility that will produce both gas and solid fuel from 'black bin' (i.e. unrecyclable contaminated) waste in order to produce electricity (1.3 MW). Energy derived from this facility will be as a result of AD, as described above.

## Bio-fuels

Some $10 billion is spent on liquid fuels every day. Hence there is significant interest in technologies that can generate fuels to be blended with petrol. Driven by new fuel standards, in the US for example, their market is expected to grow to some $50 billion by 2022.[471]

The Energy (Bio-fuel Obligation and Miscellaneous Provisions) Act 2010 implements the Renewable Energy Directive (2009/28/EC) that requires 10 per cent of the energy used in transport in Member States to be derived from renewable sources by 2020. The Act's explanatory memorandum noted that 'bio-fuels have a central role to play in the delivery of this target'. The legislation requires all petrol and diesel sold in the state to contain at least 4.116 per cent bio-fuel, the portion rising in the period to 2020. This is to ensure a vibrant Irish market for the production of bio-fuels, which will provide some level of energy security.

### Problems with this proposition

- There is evidence that even with favourable tax breaks it will be difficult for indigenously produced ethanol to compete against cheaper sources of imported ethanol.[472] The delivery of a significant penetration of indigenous ethanol into the market would require either higher compulsory take-off obligation or considerable financial supports to feedstock and ethanol producers.[473] This suggests that incentives should be better targeted at the purchaser of the vehicle than the producer of the fuel.

- The existing market for bio-fuels has developed in the absence of draft legislation. Indeed, from a base of zero in 2006, 6,497 flexi-fuel vehicles have been purchased, accounting for over 3 per cent of all new car registrations in Ireland in 2010.[474] However, the penetration rate of flexi-fuel vehicles is too small to generate the necessary economies of scale needed to ensure that the provision of E85 and other bio-fuels can be delivered on a commercial basis by fuel distributors.

- The success of Government support for flexi-fuel vehicles has created industries in other areas. Thanks largely to the efforts of Maxol, E85 fuel is now available in 34 petrol stations nationwide. Basic principles of economics tell us that the continually increasing availability of E85 fuel is a reflection of the demand for this fuel from vehicle owners who have purchased their cars under the Government's VRT scheme.

Meanwhile, the carbon tax that also formed part of the Finance Act 2010 (section 64) has been in effect since May 2010. This provision applied an initial tax of €34.38 per 1,000 litres of petrol, or just under 3.5 cent per litre; this was increased in budget 2012. However, the Act specifies that bio-fuels – or the bio-fuel portion of a fuel comprised of a blend of bio-fuel and fossil fuel (provided it is greater than 10 per cent) – are exempt from the carbon tax.

This target is part of a much wider strategy to decarbonise the EU's transport sector, and specifically to reduce $CO_2$ emissions for road vehicles, by promoting new clean car technologies.[475] These ambitions were explained in some detail in the European strategy on clean and energy efficient vehicles, which acknowledged the role that flexi-fuel vehicles can play. Among the measures envisaged are the publication of guidelines on financial incentives to consumers to buy green vehicles and better coordination of Member State' taxation legislation to promote green vehicles.[476]

The national strategy for reducing emissions in the transport sector is twofold. Firstly, the NREAP includes a significant increase in the use of bio-fuel in the fuel mix; 4 per cent initially, 6 per cent by 2012 and an unspecified increase in subsequent years, bearing in mind that Ireland must achieve a 10 per cent penetration of renewable energy in transport by 2020. Secondly, a target of 10 per cent has been set for the penetration of electric vehicles by 2020.

In summary, if Ireland wishes to meet the 10 per cent bio-fuels target the greater use of E85 and other bio-fuels will have to be encouraged. The choice for policy-makers is to incentiv-ise the producers of bio-fuels, or the motorist wishing to buy a green car, or a combination of both.

A regulatory impact assessment was completed prior to the publication of the legislation on the introduction of a bio-fuel obligation.[477] It concluded, inter alia, that mineral oil tax relief (MOTR) schemes are not effective in terms of changing behaviour to meet national bio-fuels targets. In other words tax measures targeted at bio-fuels do not work (unless there is a very significant price differential at the pumps).

The regulatory impact statement concluded in relation to the VRT scheme:

Such a scheme can have positive results and it is impor-tant that vehicles be taxed by carbon emissions performance rather than any particular technology so that the best vehicle performance is incentivised and there is no market distor-tion. This policy of VRT relief does reward more fuel efficient cars but does not encourage the use of bio-fuels in cars per se. Therefore to meet the 2020 goals for renewable energy in transport some support for the industry itself is required.

It is Government policy that the VRT scheme would encourage the purchase of flexi-fuel vehicles and that the purpose of these reliefs is to encourage the development of new technologies and thereby contribute to reducing the $CO_2$ emissions arising from the transport sector to below what it would otherwise be.[478]

The Minister for Communications, Energy and Natural Resources has stated that:

...bio-fuels remain a fundamentally good idea, given that we need alternative sources of fuel. The era of cheap oil is over and Ireland requires new methods of fuelling our trans-port fleet. Bio-fuels also remain necessary for Ireland terms of energy security. We need access to a certain percentage of non-fossil fuel to run essential services, in the event of a global oil shortage. This is prudent planning in an uncertain energy world.

The (former) Minister for Transport was also a strong proponent of bio-fuels vehicles and is on the record as follows:

I have no doubt that opportunities in the transport sector are growing for those who have a commitment to sustainable energy. In fact, I'm convinced that the bio-fuel industry will be a major growth area that can deliver significant and multiple benefits. My vision of a sustainable travel and transport system in this country by 2020 will, among other things, provide additional momentum for increased reliance on bio-fuels.

The Commission on Taxation also supported favourable VRT treatment for flexi-fuel cars because these fiscal measures help the environment by leading to the purchase of newer, cleaner cars.[479]

Ireland will have around 2 million private cars by 2020.[480] A 10 per cent bio-fuel penetration could be achieved by reaching an 11.8 per cent penetration of E85 by 2020. If this is achieved by 100 per cent of flexi-fuel vehicles running on E85 all of the time, this implies that 235,294 flexi-fuel cars will need to be in use by 2020. Given a ten-year lead-in period, this implies average flexi-fuel vehicle sales of 23,000 per year between 2010 and 2020.

The critical question is whether the withdrawal of the VRT scheme supporting flexi-fuel vehicles along with a carbon tax that does not significantly encourage the use of bio-fuels will encourage the penetration of 10–20 per cent of flexi-fuel vehicles in the Irish market by 2020.

Green Biofuels Ireland, the New Ross-based bio-diesel company, has grown to become the largest bio-fuels plant in Ireland with sales in 2011 rising to €28 million.

## Geothermal

The Earth is heated by the sun, and in hot seasons the Earth's crust absorbs some of this heat that it emits during colder months. In addition, and since the formation of this planet, the Earth's core has been emitting heat; the core of the Earth is estimated at approximately 4,200°C. As such, two forms of 'geothermal' heat energy exist that can be exploited to produce energy that is sustainable, if not theoretically renewable.[481]

Firstly, 'deep' geothermal energy derives heat by drilling very deep into the Earth's surface in order to tap into some of the heat produced at the Earth's core. Traditionally, this was only possible along the fault lines between tectonic plates (where heat penetrates closer to the surface), but recent developments in plant and drilling have led to tests further away from fault lines. One such test in Switzerland was halted after only a few days when it was found to have triggered earthquakes. Secondly, 'shallow' geothermal energy derives energy from heat stored in the ground close to the surface of the Earth. This heat can be extracted from the ground using geothermal heat pumps, and is sufficient to heat a household. However, the higher temperatures required for large-scale industrial geothermal energy exploitation can only be derived from much deeper excavation/drilling.

It should be noted that, as well as heat, deep geothermal wells release GHG trapped deep within the Earth, but these emissions are much lower per energy unit than those of fossil fuels. Deep geothermal energy is thus not a 'zero-emission' sustainable energy source, but is far less damaging than the combustion of fossil fuels.

Globally, nearly 60 GWh of geothermal energy is converted to power for human use each year, but this is exclusively in countries that are close to the fault lines in tectonic plates.

In Ireland 154 MW of energy for the purpose of home heating is derived from single-unit pumps in approximately 2,000 homes throughout the country, and a further 100 MW is derived from slightly deeper projects for the purpose of heating colleges and office blocks.[482] Much of this uptake has been on the back of the Government-sponsored 'Greener Homes Scheme' initiative, which provided grants for the installation of such technology. In 2004, the CSA Group completed a study commissioned by SEAI, which aimed at identifying the potential resources of geothermal energy in Ireland. One of the outcomes of the project was to create a series of geothermal resource maps.

The initial capital cost of installing a geothermal heat pump system is usually higher than other conventional central heating systems. However, under the Greener Homes Scheme, grants were available to reduce these costs significantly. A large proportion of the outlay will be for the purchase and installation of the ground collector. The system is among the most energy-efficient and cost-effective heating and cooling systems available. Typically, four units of heat are generated for every unit of electricity used by the heat pump to deliver it and the payback is typically about eight to ten years. The life expectancy of the system is around twenty years.

There are some geothermal spring sources (e.g. Blackwater Valley between Mallow and Fermoy) that could be further utilised on a local basis for space heating. Deep excavation is probably more than a decade away at least for Ireland, but a pilot bore hole in Newcastle, Co. Dublin, drilled by GT Energy has gone to a depth of 1.4 km to find water of 42°C, with plans to dig deeper in the future.

One barrier to the development of this renewable resource is legal: is geothermal a mining or a ground resource? There are precedents for both approaches. As a result of pressure from the industry the DCENR carried out a consultation about the sector's potential and subsequently, in July 2010, the Government approved a draft general scheme for the Geothermal Energy Development Bill along with a regulatory impact statement.

ESB Novusmodus is one of several shareholders who have invested in Geothermal International, Europe's largest designer and installer of ground source heat pump systems.

## Combined heat and power (CHP/cogeneration)

Many forms of energy production produce heat as a by-product that is allowed to dissipate into the atmosphere via cooling towers or chimneys. CHP generation plants recycle this heat to be used in another generation process or to heat neighbouring buildings or communities. A power plant in New York uses excess steam to heat much of Manhattan.

Whether CHP is a 'renewable' form of energy production really depends on the fuel used in the initial generating process, but it is certainly a more efficient use of the gross energy generated than allowing the heat by-product to dissipate. Using bio-fuels, for example, would allow a CHP plant to generate both heat and power more efficiently than mere combustion of these fuels.

The use of some of the electricity or heat produced to operate a cooling system is often referred to as 'tri-generation'.

The majority of CHP generation in Ireland is at a domestic level (DCHP or 'MicroCHP') or at a level that serves a large office block, college or shopping centre ('MiniCHP'). Only a few of these plants are of a scale to provide electricity to the national grid, and only one of those is of a scale that it is connected to the transmission network.[483] As well as the 130 MW capacity of this facility, fourteen CHP generation plants are either contracted to be connected to the national grid, or have permission to do so. Once completed, the combined contribution of 29 CHP generation units to Ireland's energy capacity will be 327 MW, which is less than 1 per cent of projected capacity.

The vast majority of CHP users in Ireland qualify as auto-producers i.e. they produce electricity for use on one single premise only. Only a small number hold a licence to supply electricity. Therefore, for the majority of CHP users, although the CHP unit is connected to and synchronised with the electricity system, payment is made for any additional electricity units imported, but no payment is given for any surplus units exported.

Due to Exchequer constraints SEAI's CHP Deployment Programme has been closed.

## Ocean energy

Ocean energy contained in the world's waves and marine tidal currents provides an untapped source of renewable energy with a €230 billion potential by 2050.[484]

Ireland is located at the centre of one of the most favourable climates for ocean wave energy in the world. With a significant percentage of Europe's coastline (but only 1 per cent of its population) this is a major renewable energy resource waiting to be tapped. In fact, Ireland has one-third of all of north-west Europe's renewable energy resources, including the world's most energy intensive waves and Europe's high wind speeds.[485] It has been estimated that the total wave energy resource could yield 48 TWh if all of the Irish coastline alone were developed. The Irish Marine Institute has identified the medium-term practical resource as around 800 MW of installed capacity. The 2005 Bacon/ESBI study calculated that 1,900 jobs would be created by 2020 if Ireland invested in ocean energy technology. A more recent forecast suggests that the figure could be as high as 2,770; on the assumption that 500 MW of installed capacity is in place by 2020.[486]

Ireland has third-level research expertise in the areas of turbine design at University of Limerick, wave tank model testing at the Hydraulics and Maritime Research Centre of University College Cork and wave energy modelling at Queen's University Belfast. In terms of prototype development there are currently several tidal and wave energy developers in Ireland.

## The main players

OpenHydro: Set up in 2004 and now employs 70 based in Greenore. Owns the worldwide rights to its open-centre turbine technology. In November 2009, deployed the first commercial scale in-stream tidal turbine in the Bay of Fundy, Canada, for Nova Scotia Power. Currently testing at the European Marine Energy Centre (EMCE) in Orkney. Will install an array of grid-connected units as part of the EDF Paimpol-Bréhat project in Brittany during 2012. Selected by Snohomish PUD for showcase tidal project in the US. Awarded UK licence for 200 MW joint venture with SSE Renewables (Airtricity). It won an award at the prestigious Global Cleantech Cluster Association in November 2011.

Wavebob is also active in proving its technology as being commercially viable with two PTO onshore test rigs. Closed a funding round with GREinvest Management. Wavebob has also secured deals with Vattenfall, Chevron and Abengoa.

On 5 February 2010, Ocean Energy, a wave energy R&D company based in Cork, announced a strategic development deal with Dresser-Rand, a US energy company seeking first-mover advantage in the commercialisation of wave energy. At pre-commercial stage of development and testing in Galway Bay.

Aquamarine Power has an 800kW demonstration device (Oyster 800) being tested at the EMCE and expects a grid connection during 2012. Some €76 million in investment has been raised to date.

Sea Power, based in Galway since 2007, is testing a 4 metre test rig with a view to having a full-scale device by 2017.

Westwave, a consortium comprising four leading technology developers, expects to become Ireland's first wave-energy project with a 5 MW device operational by 2015.

## Revenue incentives (2012)[487]

Scotland 5 ROCs plus wholesale price (£270/MWh total)
Rest of UK 5 ROCs proposed, plus wholesale price (£270/MWh total)
Portugal REFIT (€260/MWh)
France REFIT (€150 MWh)
Spain REFIT (€70/MWh)
Ireland Capped REFIT tbc

The establishment in 2006 of the National Strategy for Ocean Energy as a joint venture of SEAI and the Marine Institute has led to the Government announcing an Ocean Energy Strategy, the Ocean Energy Development Unit and its associated Prototype Development Fund. This has the specified targets of nurturing and developing tidal and wave energy projects to a commercial stage, such that 75 MW of energy will be derived from these sources by 2012, and 500 MW by 2020. In January 2008, a major programme of activity, grants and supports to develop ocean energy in Ireland was announced by the Minister for Communications, Energy and Natural Resources. Over €26 million in targeted funding will go to the sector. The initiative announced by the Minister included:

- €1 million towards a world-class, state-of-the-art national ocean energy facility in UCC. The facility will now have an advanced wave basin for the development and testing of early ocean energy devices.
- €2 million to support the development of a grid-connected wave energy test site at Annagh/French Point near Belmullet, Co. Mayo.
- €2 million in grants in 2008 under the Ocean Energy Prototype Fund. This will help developers to make their devices commercial.
- €500,000 to establish an Ocean Energy Development Unit as part of SEIA.

Most importantly, and more recently, SEAI published its Ocean Energy Roadmap, with the following key findings.

- Some 29 GW of ocean energy capacity can be installed without likely significant environmental effects.
- The job potential for the sector is 70,000.
- The cumulative economic benefits by 2030 could be €12 billion and €120 billion by 2050.
- The projected carbon abatement by 2050 amounted to 94 Mt.
- National energy security significantly enhanced.

In addition, the SEAI/Eirgrid have also commissioned reports on:

- Irish ports and shipping requirements for a marine renewable energy industry
- The industrial development potential of offshore wind in Ireland
- Offshore grid study (August 2011)
- An economic study of ocean-energy development in Ireland
- (Forthcoming) A study on the viability and cost benefit analysis for Ireland exporting renewable electricity using the cooperation mechanisms in Directive 2009/28/EC.

SEAI is very active in this area but with limited resources that are in no way commensurate to the sector's potential. Ireland has a lot of catching up to do with Scotland, the location of choice in Europe.

Despite the 2009 announcement of a REFIT of €220 MWh for ocean energy, it appears an EU state aid application has not been sent to the European Commission and that the Minister for Communications, Energy and Natural Resources is not supportive of such a high subsidy.

## Solar energy

Ireland is poorly situated geographically for large-scale energy production from solar power. Unsurprisingly, southern Spain and Portugal are the sites for much of Europe's solar photovoltaic energy development and production.[488]

### Three forms of solar power technology

- **Passive solar:** Architectural methods that seek to maximise the light and heat provided by the sun, while at the same time insulating against energy loss
- **Active solar heating:** The use of solar collectors to heat water for domestic use. In Ireland, active solar heating can provide 50–60 per cent of a household's hot water needs
- **Photovoltaic systems:** Photovoltaic systems use daylight (not necessarily direct sunlight) to convert solar radiation to electric current. Such systems are common in watches and calculators, but on a much larger scale – and in the

right location – can produce renewable energy to feed into national/regional grids. Similar to wind power however, solar power can only be produced during hours of daylight, and is thus unsuitable for base-load energy, unless it is combined with a method of energy storage such as a pumped-storage hydroelectric plant. A research body in Germany has successfully piloted a system that combines photovoltaics with wind, biogas and hydro-storage to produce reliable base-load electricity entirely from renewable sources. Photovoltaic solar power is a comparatively expensive form of energy production however, with energy derived from wind power costing as little as one-sixth as much.

The Greener Homes Scheme provided grants for owners of existing homes who wished to retrofit a variety of technologies, including heat pumps and solar panels. Over half of the 26,500 applications were for grant assistance for solar thermal panels.

## Reports of the Irish Academy of Engineering

The Irish Academy of Engineering (IAE) report *Ireland's Energy Policy in the Context of the Changing Economy* expressed views in stark contrast to much of the analysis that prevails in relation to energy policy in Ireland.[489] Taking cognisance of the changed economic circumstances in which any future policies will be made or implemented, the IAE report recommended that all current capital expenditure should be halted, pending a robust techno-economic analysis that would incorporate changed patterns of energy demand, the requirement for greater energy security, and current pricing trends.

The report confirms that, as a general principle, investment in reducing energy usage (which can be expressed as improved energy efficiency or energy conservation) shows a better return than investment in new energy supply. In this one statement, the report casts doubt over the necessity for investment in renewable energy sources of electricity when an alternative exists to act in a more energy-efficient manner. Energy-efficiency goals are supported by the IAE report, which recommends a diversion of capital from energy production/distribution projects towards conservation/efficiency programmes. One method of improving efficiency is smart metering,[490] but the IAE report recommends postponing any major commitment to smart metering invest-ment pending the result of national and international pilot schemes.[491]

The REFIT scheme to support renewable energy production through Government subsidies is supported only in so far as it is required to meet Ireland's EU RES obligations. Even within this commitment, the report recommends that capital invest-ment should be focussed on those projects that provide the greatest value for money, preferably using a system similar to the American 'rate impact analyses'.[492]

The IAE is also supportive of overturning the legislative ban on nuclear power generation in this jurisdiction, support-ing what it terms 'technology neutrality'.[493] The report avoided pointing out what Noel Dempsey (the then Minister for Com-munications, Marine and Natural Resources) said in 2006: 'as far as the existing interconnector goes, we are already using nuclear power generated in Britain'.

Although the report states that purchase of emission allow-ances is a valid low-risk policy option, it provides the caveat that domestic efforts to reduce carbon, or produce carbon sinks (sequestration), can be almost revenue-neutral when one con-siders that it could create employment and other externalities.

The report is keen to point out the inefficiencies inherent in Eirgrid's current network, as well as those in the network operator's plans for infrastructural development. What the IAE terms 'optimum transmission locations' are places that should be prioritised for infrastructural development so as to reduce the requirement to expand the network unduly. Included in this critique of Eirgrid is an analysis of the interconnector plans to connect the Irish distribution network directly with that of mainland Britain (the east–west interconnector (EWIC)). By comparing this project with a similar connection between Britain and the Netherlands, the report asks 'whether the EWIC has been optimised for size', and criticises the assumption that the EWIC would be used at 100 per cent capacity all of the time, which is unlikely to be the case.

The IAE's latest report continues much of this analysis.[494] Given the current economic situation, the priority should be a significant reduction in energy costs in a scenario where energy demand has dropped substantially since 2007 and is forecast to remain low for the next decade. The IAE argues that the Irish power industry is now over-invested and as a consequence there is no need for additional generating capacity (or in gas and electricity networks) for at least ten years. As wind power receives priority dispatch it has the effect of dramatically reducing the load factors of existing generating plant thus partially 'stranding' these assets: upward price pressure will result as investors (including state-owned generators) seek compensation.

The IAE points to recent technical developments in the international gas industry that have led to a major upward re-evaluation of global gas reserves and credible predictions of cheap and reliable supplies beyond 2020. According to the IAE as Ireland has a significant number of efficient gas-generating plants these assets should not be stranded by the building of thousands of MW of unnecessary wind power. There is therefore a compelling economic and environmental case for launching a significantly scaled-up conservation programme to reduce national energy consumption by 20 per cent by 2020. With a potential investment of €1 billion a year, the IAE acknowledges that the funding mechanisms put in place must minimise Exchequer exposure.

Its most trenchant criticism is directed at the NREAP's aim to produce 40 per cent of Ireland's electricity from wind by 2020. The IAE believes this is not appropriate as it would involve some €10 billion in capital expenditure when no new generating capacity is required. In addition to the asset stranding argument, wind is an 'extremely expensive way of reducing GHG emissions when compared to other alternatives'. The IAE notes the notion that large-scale wind energy production could be exported in a commercially profitable way is without any sound economic basis.

As for the REFIT system, the IAE says its terms should be reviewed because as constituted it is price inflating and lacks incentive to produce wind power more economically.

Finally, the IAE says Ireland should meet its binding EU GHG emission-reduction targets by buying permits on the market.

## Conclusions

The International Energy Agency is conducting a periodic in-depth review of Irish energy policy. Informed by this assessment, the DCENR and the CER will prepare an energy policy framework for the period 2012–2030 reflecting national, EU and international developments in the energy sphere.[495]

Investors in renewable energy need a clear strategy and a consistent regulatory framework. Hence there are high expectations that the energy policy framework will prioritise the expansion of the renewables sector in a sustainable manner.

With the publication (May 2012) of the Government's *Strategy for Renewable Energy*, the focus now turns to implementation of the key actions identified. In particular, the sector will welcome the Government's belief 'that there is great potential for Ireland to become a renewable energy exporter within the next few years.'

The Renewable Energy Development Group (comprising public and private sector representatives) will have a full work programme over the coming years.

## Chapter 14

# Energy efficiency

Two roads diverged in a wood, and I took the one less travelled by, and that has made all the difference.

Amory B. Lovins

## Introduction

Energy efficiency is essentially about achieving the same result with less energy, be it space heating, hot water, lighting, driving or powering the workplace. Efficient use of energy directly contributes to security of energy supply, sustainable transport, affordable energy, competitiveness as well as environmental sustainability. By saving 20 per cent of energy consumption, the EU hopes to cut GHG emissions by some 800 Mt by 2020.

Ireland's first National Energy Efficiency Action Plan (NEEAP) *Maximising Ireland's Energy Efficiency, National Energy Efficiency Action Plan 2009–2020* was published in May 2009 and sets out 90 actions that are being taken or will be taken in the period to 2020 to achieve 20 per cent energy-efficiency savings across the public, business, residential, transport, and energy supply sectors. The savings identified in the NEEAP represent approximately a reduction of €1.6 billion in annual energy costs in 2020 and will reduce Ireland's $CO_2$ emissions by approximately 5.7 Mt per annum if the NEEAP is fully implemented.

Improving Ireland's energy efficiency is an essential part of Ireland's sustainable energy policy, and will play a vital role in reducing our dependence on fossil fuels. The Government's energy policy is designed to steer Ireland to a new and sustainable energy future, one that helps us reduce GHG emissions and energy costs. Efficient energy use directly contributes to security of energy supply, sustainable transport, affordable energy, competitiveness and environmental sustainability. Recognising that government must lead by example, it set as a target a 33 per cent reduction in public sector energy use.

Since the publication of NEEAP several new policy measures have been taken or will soon be launched to strengthen and deepen Ireland's energy-savings efforts. Moreover, the EU policy context is evolving with the publication of an Energy 2020 strategy[496] and a draft Directive on energy efficiency. Ireland has submitted a second NEEAP to the European Commission.

## EU policy

A new EU energy-efficiency plan was adopted in March 2011.[497] The **Europe 2020 Energy Strategy** sets out a strategy for competitive, sustainable and secure energy over the next ten years, which will require energy investments of some €1 trillion.[498] The strategy focuses on investment, the public sector as an exemplar, buildings and transport, and the critical role of NEEAPs. The context is an acknowledgement that the EU 20 per cent energy-efficiency target by 2020 remains challenging on current projections and requires urgent action. The Energy 2020 strategy focuses on five priorities:

- Achieving an energy-efficient Europe
- Building a truly pan-European integrated energy market
- Empowering consumers
- Extending Europe's leadership in energy technology and innovation
- Strengthening the external dimension of the EU energy market.

More recently, the Commission published an **Energy Roadmap 2050**, which sets a pathway for a decarbonised energy sector within a few decades.[499]

As current estimates show the EU is not on track to achieve its energy-efficiency target with forecast savings of 9 per cent only, the Commission has proposed a new Directive on energy efficiency.500 It is significant that energy efficiency is listed as the number one priority and the Commission acknowledges that 'energy efficiency is the most cost effective way to reduce emissions, improve energy security and competitiveness, make energy consumption more affordable and create employment'. The European Parliament will have a significant influence on the final shape of the Directive.

Nevertheless, the Commission expresses disappointment on the efforts to date to achieve 20 per cent energy savings by 2020. Its Communication states:

> [T]he quality of National Energy Efficiency Action Plans developed by Member States since 2008 is disappointing, leaving vast potential untapped. The move towards renewable energy use and greater energy efficiency in transport is happening too slowly. While we are broadly on track for the 20 per cent target for renewable energy, we are a long way from achieving the objective set for energy efficiency.

The European Council, while acknowledging that the EU is not on track to meets its 20 per cent energy-efficiency goals, has called for further measures to be taken but stopped short of calling for a binding target. The Council did agree that from 2012 all Member States should apply efficiency standards when purchasing goods for public buildings and services. Finally, a review of progress towards meeting the 20 per cent goal will take place in 2013. And it is in that context that Ireland's efforts to promote and facilitate energy efficiency must be judged.

The **Energy Services Directive** (ESD) is the main legislative mechanism through which energy-efficiency policy at EU level is delivered.[501] The Directive seeks to promote end-use energy efficiency in Member States through support measures and the removal of institutional, financial and legal barriers. It applies to government, energy suppliers and final energy users. It is intended to increase the focus on cost-effective energy-efficiency measures and the development of new activities in the energy services area. Ireland has transposed the ESD and in so doing set national energy-efficiency saving targets; energy services including the availability of energy audits to final customers; the exemplary role of the public sector; and the promotion of energy efficiency by energy suppliers.[502]

A primary focus of the ESD is on domestic and commercial buildings as these sectors account for 40 per cent of total energy consumption and 36 per cent of $CO_2$ emissions in the EU. The (2002) Directive on **Energy Performance in Buildings** (EPBD) is the main legislative instrument affecting energy use and efficiency in the building sector in the EU. In transposing the EPBD, Ireland provided for the building energy rating (BER) system to be administered and enforced by SEAI.[503] The revised EPBD adopted in May 2010 clearly states that a reduction of energy consumption and the use of energy from renewable sources in the building sector constitute important measures needed to reduce the EU's energy dependency and GHG emissions.[504] The Directive proposes to calculate the energy performance of buildings on the basis of a methodology that may be differentiated at national and regional level. Member States may set minimum requirements for the energy performance of buildings. Ireland is required to implement the Directive by 9 July 2012. Some of the new features introduced include:

- As of 31 December 2020, new buildings in the EU must consume 'nearly zero' energy, which will be to a very large extent from renewable sources.

- The 1000 m² threshold for the application of national minimum energy-efficiency requirements to existing buildings undergoing major renovation has been removed. So, with buildings under 1000 m² included as well, now almost all buildings are covered under the EPBD.

- The Directive requires all Member States to push up the national minimum energy performance requirements for new building and existing buildings undergoing renovation to a proven cost-optimal level.

**Key challenges for Ireland in transposing the revised EPBD**

- Adjusting the Building Regulations (Part L) to confirm minimum energy performance requirements for new and existing buildings are continually pitched at cost-optimal levels and that full effect is given to the EPBD provisions in relation to major renovations

- Developing and implementing a cohesive national plan for increased numbers of low- or zero-energy and carbon buildings in new and existing building stock

- Further developing the exemplary role required of public sector buildings

- Providing for BER certificates to be included in all promotional material when properties are being advertised for sale or rent.

## NEEAP 2

In accordance with the ESD, Ireland has submitted a second Energy Efficiency Action Plan (NEEAP 2) to the European Commission.[505] The key focus was to unearth the strategies and measures necessary to achieve primary energy savings (supply side) and final energy savings (demand side). The Commission was keen to encourage Member States to see NEEAP 2 not only as a reporting tool, as required under the Directive, but also as a policy tool. Some of the themes to emerge from the consultation on the NEEAP included:

- There was a need to prioritise projects on the basis of cost–benefit analysis.

- It was felt that there was too small a savings contribution from the transport sector.

- The role of local authorities was seen as central to delivery and implementation.

- The crucial role for R&D was felt to be paramount on the basis that 'we should aspire to be European leaders in R&D on energy efficiency, and make sure that the benefits become business opportunities'.

The key ambition of the 34 measures that comprise NEEAP 2 is to deliver carbon savings of 7.7 Mt by 2020; 0.7 Mt by way of public sector initiatives; 1.3 Mt from the business sector (with SEAI's large industry programme achieving almost half the savings); 1.5 Mt from transport (including very modest provision for electric vehicle deployment); and 3.6 Mt from buildings (including 1.5 Mt from the Better Energy retrofit programme

– again with more modest GHG emission reductions than had previously been signalled). Indicative budgets are identified for each measure. If implemented, these GHG emission reductions will go a considerable way to bridge Ireland's 'distance to target' by 2020.

The NEEAP 2 measures will in large measure build on the following programmes.

**Accelerated Capital Allowances scheme**: The Accelerated Capital Allowances (ACA) scheme allows companies to write off the full capital cost of registered energy-efficient equipment in the year of purchase, unlike non-ACA equipment that is typically written off over eight years. By encouraging companies to purchase energy-efficient equipment, the ACA aims to improve the energy efficiency of Irish companies and assist the Government in meeting its energy-efficiency and GHG emission-reduction targets. There are now almost 8,000 products on the ACA register, covering 52 technologies and the scheme has been extended until October 2014. The scheme enables companies to claim 100 per cent of the capital cost of certain energy-efficient plant and machinery against corporation tax in the year of purchase. The purpose of the ACA scheme is to encourage businesses to purchase plant and machinery that are highly energy efficient and thus make significant savings on energy costs and reduce carbon emissions. It is estimated that up to 85 per cent of any company's equipment procurement needs can be sourced through the ACA list of high energy-efficient products.

**Large Industry Energy Network (LIEN) and Energy Agreements Programme**: SEAI's LIEN and the Energy Agreements Programme is a well-established networking and information programme for large industrial energy users. Now in operation for fifteen years, it engages 135 of the largest energy users in ongoing relationships, including site visits, workshops and annual performance reporting. LIEN members share information on energy-saving technologies and techniques to maximise savings and maintain competitiveness. Energy spend across the LIEN is approximately €900 million and accounts for approximately 70 per cent of industrial energy usage and for more than 10 per cent of national primary energy usage. The Energy Agreements Programme supports large industry to implement an energy-management system through the EN 16001 standard for energy management.

**SME Programme**: A dedicated support programme has also been established by the SEAI offering free energy management, mentoring, training, advice and other support services to any business willing to show a commitment to becoming more energy efficient. Over 1,600 businesses have already availed of this programme, with 10 per cent savings routine in the first year.

**Public Sector Programme**: The Public Sector Programme has been established to lead, inspire and support the public sector in adopting and maintaining exemplary standards of energy management and the achievement of aggressive NEEAP targets. Almost 70 demonstration projects have been supported in recent years to highlight the potential to achieve economic savings within the public sector; many of the projects supported are directly applicable to the private sector. Members of the public sector programme receive support to implement structured energy-management programmes, instilling a strategic approach to energy management across the sector.

**Affordable energy strategy**: Energy poverty represents a considerable challenge for Ireland due to an extensive legacy of poorly insulated homes. The Department's efforts to redress the effects of energy poverty have focused on improving the thermal efficiency of privately-owned homes, with the Department of Social Protection responsible for providing income supports. Since 2000, over 60,000 low-income homes have received an energy-efficiency upgrade.

**Building Regulations Part L – Conservation of Fuel and Energy – Dwellings (2008):** These Regulations upgraded the minimum energy-performance standards for dwellings (requiring a 40 per cent improvement on 2005 standards) and became fully effective from 1 July 2009. New Regulations will set a higher minimum energy-performance standard for dwellings by requiring a 60 per cent aggregate improvement in the energy performance of new dwellings relative to 2005 standards. A corresponding 60 per cent aggregate reduction in $CO_2$ emissions relative to 2005 standards will also apply. Specifically, higher energy performance standards require significant improvements in wall, roof and floor insulation levels and backstop U values; a reduction in the air permeability backstop value; clarification on the requirement for air pressure testing for single unit developments; more accurate thermal bridging heat loss calculation and specification; higher efficiency oil and gas boilers; minimum performance levels for the efficiency of biomass boilers; and the independent time control of space heating zones.

**Energy Performance of Buildings Directive – building energy rating**: Ireland's building energy rating (BER) certification scheme was introduced for new dwellings in 2007 and for existing dwellings in 2009. Under this scheme the energy certification of a dwelling is mandatory whenever a dwelling is commissioned or offered for sale or rent. The BER certificate is accompanied by an advisory report, with recommendations for cost-effective improvements to energy performance, allowing householders to plan for further improving the energy performance of the dwelling and saving money on their energy bills. Currently some 170,600 BER certificates for dwellings are in place (representing 8.5 per cent of the total housing stock of 1.9 million housing units) and BER certificates for dwellings are currently being issued at the rate of approx 6,000 per month.

## Future policy focus

NEEAP 1 set out a 2020 roadmap for energy savings across the economy and remains ambitious in scope. NEEAP 2 contains a strong focus on implementation, evaluation and monitoring in order to report progress.

The National Recovery Plan 2011–2014 sets out an overall framework for a return to sustainable growth in our economy. It identifies the areas of economic activity that will provide growth and employment in the next phase of our economic development. The energy sector has an important role to play in contributing to the Strategy for Competitiveness, Growth and Employment (NRP chapter two). In that context, the Government has reiterated its commitment to implement the NEEAP 2 targets, including additional measures to assist SMEs to lower electricity costs.

The two areas of critical importance for achieving Ireland's energy-efficiency objectives are the public sector and transport. These will have to be tackled in a holistic manner given their wider economic and energy saving impacts.

**Public sector**: During 2011, a suite of training and best practice advice services for energy management was extended, working groups were established and networking across the sector promoted. A monitoring, measuring and reporting tool for the public sector NEEAP statistical reporting is also being finalised. The green procurement action plan is designed to help the public sector meet its energy savings targets. The public sector programme also seeks to promote and facilitate ESCO (energy saving company) projects in the public sector.

**Transport sector**: The Government's smarter travel policy sets out a sustainable transport policy for the period to 2020. Such long-term policy is necessary for the transport sector, as transport demand is recognised as being relatively inelastic in the short term, and energy savings in the sector can only be achieved through long-term planning and interventions. In the context of the current economic climate, and the capital investment budget for transport set out in the National Recovery Plan, funding for sustainable transport actions will clearly be limited for the foreseeable future. However, progress is planned across a wide range of areas over next two years, which will largely focus on building on the successful interventions made to date. These areas include:

- Continued efforts to promote lower emissions vehicles in the car fleet Electric vehicle deployment
- Use of IT to improve efficiency across the broad transport sector
- Further support for the delivery of cycling infrastructure
- Continuation and expansion of mobility-management schemes
- Continued investment in public transport provision
- Continued alignment in the area of land use planning and transport provision.

## Best practice

In looking ahead to the forthcoming European EEAP, the European Council for an Energy Efficient Europe (ECEEE) set out a number of elements that merit reflection having regard to Ireland's NEEAP 2.[506] ECEEE advocates an energy-efficiency first approach, which includes measurable binding targets for energy-efficiency improvements and energy savings; greater emphasis on actual energy savings (i.e. measured reductions); better evaluation and monitoring systems for energy consumption across all sectors; and availability of adequate funding. The Council also recommend a series of sectoral initiatives dealing with energy use in the public sector, buildings and appliances, industry, transport and the energy sector.

The *Energy Technology Perspectives* paper from the IEA provides a useful overview of the long-term challenges on the pathway to a low-carbon future.[507] While acknowledging that an energy technology revolution is under way through increasing investments in renewable energy and energy efficiency, the authors nevertheless concede that, while encouraging, these efforts will prove largely ineffective when set against the trend of unrelenting growth in energy demand and $CO_2$ emissions particularly from across the major developing countries. Most striking of all, however, is the IEA's assertion that the next decade is critical. In short, if emissions do not peak by 2020 and decline rapidly in the following years, the attainment of the 50 per cent reduction by 2050 will require greater GHG emission reductions, more drastic action and higher costs over a much shorter time scale. The conclusion is that while an energy technology revolution is within reach, there are significant financing and skills shortage challenges. The IEA argues that the switch to a low-carbon energy future must be rapid and bold decisive action is required by all.

SEAI's Energy Efficient Design Methodology booklet is also helpful as it assists investors to design, commission and construct projects so that they consume the least amount of energy during their subsequent operation.

## Smart metering

Smart metering systems can empower consumers with detailed information on their energy consumption, assisting them to be more efficient in their use of energy. In 2008, the CER initiated phase 1 of the project, focussing on undertaking a number of smart metering trials (technology and customer behaviour) and producing a cost–benefit analysis for a national roll-out. The findings of these trials and the results of the cost–benefit analysis are to hand and will inform decisions regarding a national smart metering roll-out. The CER has consulted on the project and issued a document with details of the approach, design, timelines etc. for the national smart metering roll-out. Companies wishing to tender for this opportunity will find the CER's website on smart meters of interest.

## National retrofit programme: Better Energy

Better Energy is a major step forward in advancing the Government's retrofitting programme. To date over 200,000 home upgrades have been supported to the value of €210 million. This has leveraged private investment of €225 million. As part of the jobs initiative, the Minister for Communications, Energy and Natural Resources announced an additional €30 million in government funding in 2011 for domestic retrofitting; the streamlining of programmes to offer a more accessible experience for consumers; the involvement of the energy companies as partners; and the start of the process of moving to new financial models such as pay-as-you-save (PAYS). Put simply, Better Energy is a programme designed to ensure that there are more opportunities for householders and businesses to reduce their energy consumption leading to real and lasting cost savings. Better Energy builds upon what was good about the existing grant schemes and adds a role for energy suppliers, a transition to an upfront discount rather than a retrospective grant and a national PAYS scheme. Better Energy will replace the three existing programmes – the Home Energy Saving Scheme, Warmer Homes Scheme and Greener Homes Scheme – and bring them under one umbrella.

**Home Energy Savings Scheme**: The Home Energy Savings Scheme (HES), launched nationally in March 2009, is administered by the SEAI and provides grant assistance to homeowners for energy-efficiency retrofitting measures, including attic and wall insulation, high-efficiency boilers, heating controls and BER assessments. In 2010, 45,990 homeowners received HES grants resulting in 102,431 energy-saving measures. Over 62,000 households are benefitting from energy-saving measures to date, with average savings estimated at over €450 per dwelling.

**Warmer Homes Scheme**: The Warmer Homes Scheme (WHS) programme targets homes that experience energy poverty and is aimed at improving the energy efficiency and comfort conditions of affected homes. The scheme includes measures such as attic insulation, cavity wall insulation, draught proofing, lagging jackets, energy-efficient lighting, and energy advice. Over 24,000 homes were upgraded in 2010 under the WHS. Over 61,000 homes have been upgraded to date under the scheme.

**Better Energy Workplace Scheme:** A €7.5 million fund has been approved (2012) for projects that support energy performance in public, commercial, industrial and community sectors. In 2011, €34 million was spent on 85 such projects with SEAI grants of €11 million.

The extra money given to the programme will support an additional 2,000 jobs, and deliver an extra 20,000 home upgrades. The €30 million is expected to leverage at least another €30 million in private investment, and bring total energy savings worth €200 million over the lifetime of the programme. All sellers of energy (over a minimum size) will be involved: ESB, Bord Gais, Airtricity, to oil companies and solid fuel suppliers. These companies will have formal targets to deliver energy-efficiency upgrades, the size of their target being linked to their share of the market. Voluntary agreements with the nine energy suppliers and SEAI were signed in March 2012.

A typical family, spending €1,000 every year to heat the home, can choose from a range of measures, from attic or wall insulation, to upgrading the boiler and heating controls. The cost of the work will range from €2,000 for a simple upgrade to more than €15,000 for a comprehensive package. Grants of up to €5,560 are available. The family can shop around among contractors to get the best price. Their home will be noticeably more comfortable as soon as the work is complete, and they will also save as much as half of their annual heating bill.

## Enterprise opportunities

Irish firms already supply and manufacture energy-efficiency equipment and materials such as insulation and thermal-efficient glazing. There is scope to use 'intelligent' ICT-driven solutions to manage better energy usage such as heating controls, heat-recovery ventilation, energy-efficient lighting. Enterprise Ireland is actively communicating energy-efficiency opportunities to companies and start-ups in other sectors such as software. There is also the potential for Irish ESCOs to provide a suite of services such as design, engineering, installation and operation and management as procurement models move to share risk or lessen upfront investment.[508] In addition, specialist contractors who are part of Enterprise Ireland's

PEEP (power generation, energy efficiency and pharma) network have strong capabilities in the design and construction of high energy-efficiency facilities such as data centres. Another ground-breaking initiative is the setting up of the Energy Efficiency Research Centre (I2E2), which is jointly supported by IDA Ireland and Enterprise Ireland. Cylon Active Energy, a winner of SEAI's 2011 Sustainable Energy Innovation Award, is an example of an Irish company providing energy-management services to Irish and overseas corporations.

## Conclusions

If fully implemented by 2020, NEEAP 2 has the potential to reduce GHG emissions in Ireland by nearly 7.7 Mt. However, a cut of this magnitude will benefit the ETS (trading) sector as consumption of primary energy falls. A deep retrofit of one million buildings could cut emissions by 3.2 Mt per annum with a net benefit to the economy of €6 billion. Investments in home energy upgrades typically pay for themselves in five to eight years.

With the publication of NEEAP 2 project promoters and companies thinking of investing in or supplying energy-efficiency goods and services now have to hand the blueprint through to 2020.

The performance of *Better Energy* could be benchmarked against the UK's Green Deal – a more ambitious and better resourced retrofitting programme.

The Government's ambitions, to be delivered by imposing a public sector obligation on energy utilities, will not be achieved unless an ESCO model adapted to suit Ireland's requirements is put in place (by way of competitive tendering). In current circumstances, the average Irish citizen will not accept an interest-free loan so a PAYS scheme will have to be introduced. The options for a PAYS have been presented to government.[509] However, given the complexities of the scheme it is unlikely that a major domestic retrofitting programme will be fully operational before 2014.

A key challenge is for SEAI to secure full implementation of the measures contained in its Residential Energy Roadmap.

Should Ireland fall short on energy efficiency, we will have a legal obligation to do more to achieve our renewables targets.

## Chapter 15

# Forest carbon

A return to business as usual would be unwise and ultimately unsustainable, involving risks that could impose human costs and constraints on economic growth and development.

OECD, *Towards a Green Economy*, 2011

## Carbon sinks

A carbon sink is the dynamic removal of $CO_2$ through photosynthesis and is measured as the net increase in terrestrial carbon over time. In other words, to be considered a sink more carbon must be absorbed than is released so that the store of carbon is expanding.

Forests begin to sequester (absorb) carbon approximately five years after planting and this creates a time lag between forestation and the realisation of carbon benefits. Different types of trees have varying sequestration potential. As carbon is released when forests are harvested there is concern about the need to find a better balance between planting and deforestation which accounts for at least 5 Gt per annum in carbon emissions. Carbon sequestration also arises in wood vegetation and soils. The carbon value of 1 hectare of forest is in the order of magnitude of 300 tonnes of carbon.

Forest covers about 30 per cent of Earth's land and represents the largest global terrestrial store of carbon, or some 20 per cent of global GHG emissions. The oceans account for 48 per cent of the carbon we produce.

**Figure 36: Breakdown of carbon emitters and sinks**

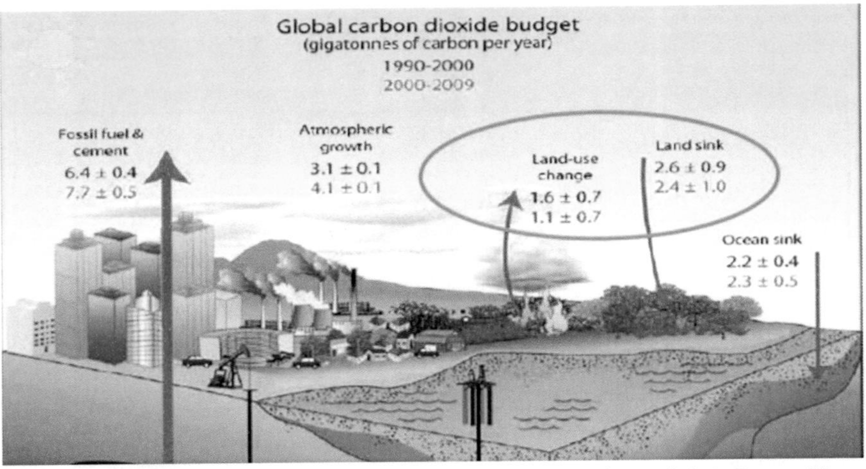

Global carbon dioxide budget
(gigatonnes of carbon per year)
1990-2000
2000-2009

Fossil fuel &
cement
6.4 ± 0.4
7.7 ± 0.5

Atmospheric
growth
3.1 ± 0.1
4.1 ± 0.1

Land-use
change
1.6 ± 0.7
1.1 ± 0.7

Land sink
2.6 ± 0.9
2.4 ± 1.0

Ocean sink
2.2 ± 0.4
2.3 ± 0.5

*Source:* Coillte (2010), Presentation to the Oireachtas Joint Committee on Climate Change and Energy Security, November.

## Kyoto rules

Under the terms of the Marrakech Accords (agreed in November 2001), there is no limit to the amount of a credit a country such as Ireland may claim under Article 3.3 of the Kyoto Protocol. But in terms of Article 3.4 which covers additional activities, the amount of credit Ireland may claim has been set at only 50,000 tonnes of carbon/year during the 2008–2012 commitment period. On foot of the EU's 20–20–20 agreement, it is to be anticipated that post-2012 there will be a change in the rules allowing for a wider and more inclusive treatment of agriculture and forestry land use (AFOLU). Agreement has been reached at the UN climate negotiations on how emissions and removals from activities related to LULUCF may be included towards meeting the EU's (and Ireland's) 20 per cent reduction target. This is critical for Ireland as the inclusion of carbon sequestration offers the prospect of the Government not having to buy carbon credits equivalent to the amount of carbon sequestered and/or using the carbon sequestered as an offset against other land use emissions such as farming.

## Ireland's forestry programme

As the Irish forestation programme will play an important role in carbon sequestration, it is important to take stock of achievements to date.

Ireland has the lowest forest cover by percentage of land area in the EU, at just 10.5 per cent (some 730,000 hectares), compared to an EU average of 35 per cent. Some 63 per cent of this amount is owned and/or managed by Coillte.

The 1996 National Forestry Strategy *Growing for the Future* provided for 20,000 hectares of new forestation per annum up to 2030. If achieved, these proposals would have increased forest area to 860,000 hectares by 2010 and to over 1.2 million hectares by 2030, almost doubling the area under forest in the state to 17 per cent. However, forestation rates in the period 1996–2006 averaged just 12,800 hectares per annum; over the period 2003–2006 this fell to an annual average of 9,200 hectares. These trends indicate that the rate of forestation coming into the 2008–2012 period will be approximately 35 per cent below the NCCS assumption of 14,000 hectares per annum and some 55 per cent below the National Forestry Strategy target. The reasons for this performance are complex and include the cost of land; the attractiveness to farmers of competing schemes; and the decline in public planting.

The indicative cost of forestation under the Rural Development Plan (2007–2013) is in the region of €900 million. The Forest Environment Protection Scheme is cofunded by the plan.

Unless there is a radical and immediate increase in planting levels the target of 17 per cent overall forestry cover by 2030 will not be met.

The forest sector is an important contributor to achieving Ireland's climate change targets. For example, the annual removal of $CO_2$ from the atmosphere by Ireland's forests exceeds 6 million tonnes (Mt) per annum, or some 2.4 Mt net when harvesting is taken into account. This is at a time when afforestation has fallen to just 7,800 hectares in 2010.[510] The NCCS values carbon sequestration from Irish forests at between 1.56 to 2.39 $MtCO_2e$ (2012); potentially rising to 4.59 Mt by 2020. At a carbon price of €15 a tonne the offset value of carbon sequestration could be €69 million in 2020. However, on the basis of more recent COFORD estimates of an average forestation of 8,000 hectares per annum up to 2020, it is forecast that carbon sinks (including forestry) will sequester some 4 Mt by 2020.

## Oireachtas Report on Forest Carbon

The Joint Committees on Climate Change and Energy Security and on Agriculture, Fisheries and Food report on the European Commission's Green Paper on Protecting Europe's Forests Against Climate Change concluded for Ireland to meet its climate change obligations it is essential that its forestry sector is part of any solution.[511, 512] This will ultimately allow Ireland to develop a forestry sector that will put it on par with its European counterparts, both in terms of the percentage of land cover and the need to build up an indigenous industry with a plentiful supply of raw material. A more detailed assessment of Ireland's forest carbon potential was approved on a cross-party basis the following year.[513]

## LULUCF

Ireland has much higher than (EU) average GHG emissions from the agricultural sector at 28 per cent; this is primarily due to the structure of Ireland's agricultural sector, which is a grass-based livestock system using cereals as supplementary feed. Ireland is without doubt one of the most efficient producers of food in terms of carbon output per unit of food produced. This fact is supported by research that shows that Ireland's temperate grass-based dairy system has one of the smallest carbon footprints in the world. The Joint Committee pointed out that these unique features need to be better reflected in EU forestry policy and the Commission's approach to LULUCF.

The accounting rules about carbon sequestration from forest sinks and other land uses in the period post-2012 were decided as part of the Durban COP. There is now a much better appreciation that forest and indeed agriculture sinks should make a greater contribution as regards national efforts to reduce GHG emissions. The Commission's official position is that no formal proposals will be made until the EU decides to introduce targets (by 2020) in excess of the 20 per cent emission-reduction figure already agreed. This will only happen if the EU is convinced (which it is not for the present) that developed and emerging economies are prepared to share the burden by agreeing to a more ambitious GHG emission-reduction programmes in a more equitable manner. However, the latest assessment by the European Commission of the LULUCF sector does not recommend that LULUCF activities contribute to compliance under the EU's 2020 climate change and renewable energy package. While this may well suit the majority of Member States, the situation in Ireland is different and requires a more flexible approach as a consequence.[514]

If EU policy on LULUCF were to change there could be a significant uplift in current afforestation levels (what could be termed a 'carbon afforestation scheme'). In particular, forest carbon offset schemes should be provided for in the context of the EU's evolving climate change strategy. The absence of any assessment in the Green Paper on Protecting Europe's Forests Against Climate Change of the potential for increased afforestation in the context of climate change is a disappointment. The Commission has not adopted proposals on foot of the submissions it received following public consultation on the green paper.

An encouraging first sign is the publication by the European Commission of proposals for new accounting rules for forestry and agriculture (cropland management and grazing land management). A separate proposal would need to be adopted to allow Member States to count LULUCF towards their individual reduction commitments. The Commission is conscious of the value of this 'trapped' carbon; increasing this by just 0.1 per cent through improved forest or grassland management would remove annual GHG emissions from 100 million cars.

The EU has policy competence in relation to the inclusion or otherwise of forest carbon sinks. In addition, under the CAP, the EU can determine whether planting forests as a carbon sink is an eligible activity and – assuming it is – what the maximum EU cofinancing rate ought to be as part of a much reformed post-2013 CAP.

## Coillte's proposition

Coillte, the state's forestry company, which has been working on a carbon afforestation scheme, presented the emerging findings and issues to the Joint Committee at its meeting on 10 November 2010.

### Coillte's proposal

- Coillte owns 445,000 hectares of forest
- Employs some 800;

- Business is very reliant on prospects of construction sector (with an average house consuming some 24 m3 of wood products)
- Sharp fall (77 per cent) in profits in 2008 on group turnover of €249 million which was down 22 per cent
- Significant investments in Medite and SmartPly
- Value of forests and lands estimated at €1.3 billion (end December 2007)
- Coillte's forests will sequester about 500,000 tonnes of carbon a year between 2008 and 2012 (a saving of some €40 million in the reduced amount of carbon credits requiring purchase).

There is a significant emphasis on the production of biomass products, with a potential supply of 450,000 tonnes per annum for co-firing at peat power stations and in a CHP plant (by 2020).

A significant number of Coillte projects were successfully included in the list of CER-approved Gate 3 renewable projects. Through co-developments, Coillte has some 400 MW of potential wind capacity in its portfolio.

The scheme will, if implemented, be available to all; the people who own the land will benefit.

The proposed scheme is consistent with (then) Programme for Government which stated: 'there will be an overhaul and significant enhancement of the current range of programmes and supports to facilitate the attainment of 17 per cent forestry cover by 2030 and contribute to meeting our climate change commitments'.

In essence, Coillte made the case that a doubling of current afforestation rates (to 15,000 hectares/year) could generate – in addition to timber revenues – significant value from the carbon sequestered. Irish forests will sequester about 4.8 $MtCO_2$ in 2020, or between 40 and 60 per cent of Ireland's distance to target. Over the period 2013–2020 upwards of 35 $MtCO_2$ could be sequestered. However, if current levels of planting are not increased there may be a gap of 45 $MtCO_2$ between 2035 and 2055 and in such a scenario the Exchequer would have to purchase replacement carbon credits on the open market.

Coillte see the scheme running alongside current afforestation schemes with the level of forest incentives being directly related to the carbon benefits. Thus access to the revenue stream would be available to a much broader range of investors, including pension funds.

The following chart prepared by Coillte sets out the outline of the proposed scheme, which envisages the monetisation of forest carbon credits.

**Figure 37: The Coillte Forest Carbon Business Model**

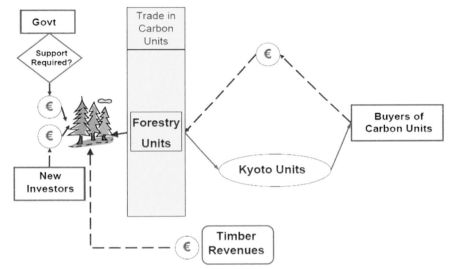

*Source:* Coillte (2010), Presentation to the Oireachtas Joint Committee on Climate Change and Energy Security, November.

In addition to explaining to the Oireachtas how the proposed scheme might work, Coillte has also demonstrated the potential benefits to a range of stakeholders e.g. the Exchequer, growers, farmers, investors and foresters. The scheme is capable of creating jobs and profits in Ireland's forest sector (through increased nursery, planting and forest management services); in Ireland's renewable energy service (through increased deployment of biomass solutions); and, in the wood-processing sector (through an increase in output and range of timber-based products).

Coillte argued if Government supported the proposed scheme it could represent the largest single mitigation project to deliver Ireland's post-2013 NCCS.

The current situation is that the Exchequer has assumed ownership of the 2.32 Mt of forest sinks (2009 figure) which is used to balance Ireland's climate change account. The Coillte proposition will only work if legal rights to the carbon value of forests are guaranteed to investors; this will require the introduction of primary legislation.

The most prominent risks include the absence of enabling legislation on forest carbon rights; absence of a proposal from the European Commission; and only one country (New Zealand) has endeavoured to implement such a scheme.

The commercial success of the scheme is critically dependent on the projected price of carbon (which was €7/tonne, January 2012). Coillte does not have a 'price point' above which the company believes the project should become a commercial success.

The wider costs and benefits of the scheme are an important issue for the Departments of Finance and Agriculture, Food and Marine given current levels of premium support.[515]

## Views of stakeholders

**Irish Timber Growers' Association** (who represent members that account for 46 per cent of Ireland's forests):

- They share Coillte's broad objectives and forest carbon strategy.
- Future supply will come from private forests as Coillte owns more mature forests.
- There is, in addition, huge potential in wood biomass (in terms of RES-Heat).
- Instead of purchasing carbon credits abroad these same funds should be invested in afforestation.
- Some 490 jobs will be created for every 15,000 hectares planted.
- Continuity of policy is key to maintaining confidence of land owners and investors.
- There should be a five-year multi-annual commitment to additional afforestation in the carbon budget.

## IFA Farm Forestry

- They also support Coillte's broad proposition as farmers see forest carbon sequestration as a safe, environmentally acceptable and cost-effective way to capture and store substantial amounts of carbon.

- EU standards are needed for issues such as measuring the permanence, verification, leakage and additionality.
- Developing a carbon accounting scheme at EU level will be a significant challenge.
- The commercial success of the scheme is heavily dependent on the price of carbon;
- Fragmentation of ownership and lack of knowledge are considered to be the main obstacles to sustainable forest management.
- Maintaining forest premiums and support for the forestry programme is vital to the success of Ireland's climate change strategy. Farmers are unhappy with cuts in premiums.
- More effective policies are needed to support and encourage the development of well-functioning forest owner organisations with strong technical and marketing services.

## Private forestry sector

- Sustainable forestry has a major role in carbon sequestration and wood energy.
- The private sector is best positioned to deliver a competitive sustainable forestry programme as the majority of carbon sequestered will be in private forests.
- Farmers have surpassed the 20 per cent broadleaf target as native species now amount to 40 per cent of total planting.
- There are potentially huge biomass opportunities as yields in Ireland are among the highest in Europe.
- Contribution of carbon benefits need to be realised, valued and credited to the sector.
- Wood energy sector needs development through market access (for example all public bodies should be required to procure renewable heat).
- Planting 15,000 hectares per annum is the minimum target.

## Realising the value of carbon

From a financial perspective the following points could be noted:[516]

- The key issue is to ensure that afforestation is a viable and an attractive investment proposition.

- A potential key barrier is liquidity as forests planted now will not generate cash from the sale of carbon allowances for very many years.

- Various risks (including default) would have to be factored into the pricing and the product.

- The appetite for forest offsets is growing (for example, China has launched a Centre For Forests for their domestic market; some 18 per cent of offsets generated in the voluntary sector in 2008 were from forestry; and the New Zealand ETS has generated its first Kyoto AAUs-backed forestry credits).

- Further investment by the National Pension Fund Reserve could be anticipated.

- A variety of SPVs could be set up to hold forest portfolios with forward sales agreements.

- Investments (with a typical ROR of 7.5 per cent over 20 years) could be made through several routes, including bonds, pension funds and equities.

In so far as transactions are concerned:

- The New Zealand ETS has NZ units that are derived from forestry and are convertible into AAUs.

- Similar arrangements could apply if forest carbon offsets were allowed at EU level.

- Transactions of carbon units are organised through national registries (the EPA in Ireland's case) for compliance purposes.

- There are a variety of voluntary cap and trade schemes that also use platforms such as Markit, APX and CCAR to trade forest carbon units.

- The price of voluntary credits is well below those of CERs – €4–8 against €11–13.

- Cosain is pioneering a voluntary cap and trade scheme for non-ETS participants.

Reflecting a wide variety of trades, the average price for offsets across the primary forest carbon market was $5.5/tonne in 2010. Over 90 per cent of volumes (some 30 Mt) occurred in the voluntary OTC market.[517]

In addition, the technology now exists to enable forests to be harvested in the most efficient manner using Treemetric's Real-Time Foreign Intelligence service.

In summary, there is growing interest from potential investors in forest carbon offset credits and the mechanics of trading such units are already in place.

## Government policy

The forestry sector is recognised as a key element of the Irish economy and has the potential to contribute significantly to Ireland's economic development. In October 2009, the Government published a Renewed Programme for Government, which contained many positive aspects in relation to forestry including a commitment to increase annual planting to 10,000 hectares. Specifically the Government committed to:

> ...review state forestry policy to take account of its critical role in relation to climate change and its importance to construction, bio-energy, bio-diversity and its potential to deliver long-term employment in other downstream industries e.g. eco-tourism, furniture, crafts etc. The review will include the role of Coillte and its functions and operations. It will also assess the effectiveness of current forestry grant schemes and make recommendations on how best to deliver supports in the future.

The Department also engaged in a '2020 Strategy' consultation process for the agriculture, food, fisheries and forestry sectors. The key recommendations about forestry and climate change in *Food Harvest 2020* are, in summary, as follows:

- Setting target planting rates is urgent given the need to increase significantly afforestation levels through to 2020.
- Industry should promote producer groups.[518]

- The Department should continue to support the growing bio-energy sector through the Bio-Energy Scheme, cofunded by the EU under the Rural Development Programme.

- The Department and relevant state agencies should continue to research the ability of forests to sequester carbon and the extent to which it can help to reduce Ireland's GHG emissions from agriculture and the non-emissions trading sector in general.

## In summary

- Ireland's forestry sector (employing 16,000) is playing an important role in Ireland's economic recovery, especially in the export market, and is contributing to the ongoing development of an indigenous renewable energy source.

- The Government allocated some €114.5 million to fund the forestry programme in 2011. It is expected that the afforestation level in 2011 will be around 8,400 hectares. An additional €3.2 million has been allocated to support ongoing research and development activities, with a particular focus on the interaction between forestry and climate change.

- In 2008, the net contribution of these forests to Ireland's carbon emission-reduction target was 2.8 Mt; a saving of some €45 million to the Exchequer in avoided carbon credit purchases.

- In addition, the substitution of fossil fuels and carbon-intensive products with wood fuels and timber products also makes a significant contribution to climate change mitigation and there is a significant potential to increase this contribution.

- There is a considerable volume of wood potentially available to the energy sector from privately owned forests.

- The current legal position is that the state owns forest carbon rights.

- A comprehensive review of the grant and aid schemes to support forestry in other countries has been completed.

- The option of securing EU co-financing under the CAP's Rural Development Programme post-2012 is been assessed.

## Conclusions

The Coillte proposition has clear commercial potential and appears to have wide support.

Some key bottlenecks, as follows, need to be addressed before a carbon afforestation scheme could become operational:

- The scheme cannot operate unless domestic forest offsets are allowed at EU level.
- Primary legislation is needed to address the issue of 'carbon rights'.
- Further details need to be worked out as to how the scheme will be financed.
- The commercial potential for biomass from forest thinnings is also significant.

If such a scheme were adopted it would enhance the value of Coillte's inherent assets; a point that Government should take into account as it prepares to sell this commercial semi-state company.

## Chapter 16

# Waste

> The nature of waste management continues to change at a rapid pace and it is clear that the recent and changing policy environment will drive further changes in how waste is managed.
>
> Environmental Protection Agency, *National Waste Report*, 2006

## Introduction

The approach to waste management on the island is based on the internationally adopted hierarchy of options that has been embraced by the EU since 1989 as the cornerstone of its waste management policy. The most preferred option is prevention and minimisation, followed by reuse and recycling, energy recovery and, least favoured of all, disposal. Waste management policy is set at EU level and a significant body of legislation has been developed since the adoption of the first Waste Framework Directive in 1977.[519]

Ireland has adopted the proximity principle, which says that waste should be treated as close as possible to the source of generation.[520] Within Ireland, inter-regional movement of waste has been allowed to avoid the implementation of the regional waste management plans, excessively restricting the establishment of economies of scale for infrastructure and markets. However, large quantities of waste continue to be exported primarily because of infrastructure deficits in relation to facilities and indigenous market size.

## The waste management sector

It is estimated that there are some 250 companies involved in the waste management sector in Ireland and approximately 75 in Northern Ireland.[521, 522] In addition, local authorities are active players in this sector. The recycling sector comprises some 40 companies, employing 530 with a turnover of €139 million, demonstrating their SME nature with an average employment of 13 persons and turnover of €3.4 million. Some 560 IPPC and waste licences have been issued by the EPA. On the basis of feedback from the sector, it is estimated that the value of the waste management market in Ireland is in the range €1.2–1.6 billion, and the corresponding figure for Northern Ireland is estimated at £250–300 million.

The market in Ireland is fragmented with the top five companies accounting for just 25 per cent of the total market. Quite a number of companies are of a sufficient scale to use their skills and know-how to take advantage of the growth in this sector in the medium term and to expand their businesses in export markets. Levels of profitability vary widely in the sector. While the local authorities operate the majority of Ireland's municipal landfills, the private sector is the predominant service provider for commercial, industrial and hazardous waste management; with 67 per cent of the municipal waste collection capacity and nearly 50 per cent of the direct kerbside household waste collection.[523]

A plethora of companies were established once deregulation commenced with domestic and commercial waste and the requirement for additional separation of waste streams. There has been a steady move towards consolidation as the ability of the small regional operators to compete with the scale of the large waste management companies becomes less commercial to sustain. It is widely expected that there will be further consolidation within the sector and this should be welcomed as it will help create waste companies capable of competing internationally in the provision of services. The key players in the sector believe it is critical to reach scale and many expect that two or three dominant companies will emerge. The number of mergers and acquisitions reflects the continuation of a process commenced over the past few years where the larger, well-funded waste management companies have acquired smaller regional operators or specialist waste contractors.

While all operators feel frustrated at the absence of a clear regulatory framework, feedback from the sector is generally positive about growth prospects and new business opportunities. Greenstar for example has been especially proactive in seeking to stimulate debate and to inform waste policy decisions on a variety of issues confronting Ireland.[524]

## The regulatory framework – Ireland

**Legislation**: Ireland has transposed the waste management provisions of the relevant EU Directives by means of primary legislation.[525]

**Policy initiatives**: Policy has been guided by key statements, e.g. *Changing Our Ways* (1998), *Delivering Change* (2002), *Taking Stock and Moving Forward* (2006), regional waste management plans, and plans for specific streams e.g. hazardous waste, biodegradable waste, etc. Producer responsibility initiatives have been introduced, e.g. packaging, WEEE, end-of-life vehicles and a major public awareness campaign i.e. Race Against Waste has been implemented. The primary aim of the National Waste Prevention Programme (2004–2008) was to reverse trends in waste production, decouple waste generation from economic growth and minimise the environmental impact of waste. In August 2006, the Minister for the Environment, Heritage and Local Government published a consultation paper on options for future regulation of the waste sector. Submissions were invited on whether there is a need for a regulator for the sector, if so on what model of regulator might be most appropriate and on what powers any such regulator should be given, the role of local authorities as regulators and/or direct service providers, waivers, universal service obligation, recycling and other obligations on private collectors, etc.

**Hazardous waste**: The EPA's National Hazardous Waste Management Plan sets out a framework for a revitalised approach to hazardous waste prevention, collection and management. Aspects of this plan are being reviewed.

**Biodegradable waste**: The National Strategy on Biodegradable Waste (2006) set stricter recycling priorities. More recently, the European Commission has identified a number of priority actions including rigorous enforcement of the targets for diverting bio-waste from landfills, proper application of the waste hierarchy and the introduction of separate collection systems for bio-waste.[526]

**Public capital expenditure**: Some €753 million in public funding was approved under the NDP with investment in the 'legacy' issues of old landfill sites the priority. In the context of the comprehensive spending review the capital budget for (environment) and waste management in 2012 has been cut to €4.6 million from €16.6 million in 2011.[527]

**International review**: A consultancy study to carry out an international review of waste management policy has been published.[528] The review identified possible policy changes and, in addition, examined institutional and organisational arrangements that could assist in achieving Ireland's policy goals. Of critical importance, given divergent views within the industry, the study evaluated the scope for the extension of the use of proven technologies for the mechanical, biological, chemical or thermal processing of waste (or combinations thereof).[529]

## Future policy

In the longer term, the proposed revision of the EU's Waste Framework Directive and the introduction of a sustainable consumption and production policy may shift the emphasis to the prevention of waste and may generate new opportunities, either in providing consultancy services or in cleaner technologies that produce less waste. The proposed Directive would merge legislation on waste and hazardous waste and simplify it, reflecting technological progress and also bring its provisions up to date. It would introduce the life-cycle approach into waste policy to focus on key environmental impacts and on improving the way we use resources. A revised definition of recovery confirms that the basis for this definition is the substitution of resources. The definition of waste is unchanged in the proposal, but it does allow for future clarification of when certain wastes cease being wastes by specifying criteria for those waste streams that meet certain specified tests. The Directive, once implemented, would introduce minimum standards or a procedure to establish minimum standards for a number of waste management operations and would improve the recycling market by setting environmental standards that specify the conditions under which certain recycled wastes are no longer considered waste but high-quality secondary materials instead. There is also an aim that a product eco-design policy would be formulated to address both the generation of waste and the presence of hazardous substances in waste, with a view to promoting technologies focusing on durable, reusable and recyclable products.

In 2009, the Minister for the Environment, Heritage and Local Government conducted a public consultation on an environmental report, prepared by environmental consultants according to strategic environmental assessment requirements, to inform the policy-making process for waste management in respect of a proposed section 60 policy direction to achieve the following objectives:

- To ensure that incineration capacity does not reach a level such that waste is drawn to incineration that could have been dealt with by prevention, reuse, recycling, composting/anaerobic digestion of source segregated bio-waste, Mechanical Biological Treatment (MBT) or other methods higher up the waste hierarchy.

- To ensure that the waste hierarchy is complied with in that local authorities, as waste management authorities, do not direct holders of waste to deliver it to lower elements in the waste hierarchy, thereby preventing them acting in support of waste-management options at the bottom of the hierarchy.

- To ensure that the waste hierarchy is complied with in that local authorities, as waste management authorities, could direct holders of waste to deliver it to higher elements in the waste hierarchy, thereby encouraging them to act in support of waste management options at the top of the hierarchy.

- To minimise the air pollution arising from trucks accessing waste facilities in built-up areas.

- To ensure appropriate monitoring of air pollution in the vicinity of major waste facilities.

- To reduce air, soil and water pollution from incineration and comply with the Stockholm Convention.

The Minister for the Environment, Community and Local Government has prepared a new statement of waste policy arising from recommendation identified in the Eunomia report, and is currently seeking comments before final decisions are taken on such important issues as:[530]

- The implementation of a national waste prevention programme

- Measures to promote the reuse of products (such as WEEE)
- Extending producer-responsibility schemes
- A new policy framework for waste recovery
- Exemptions from the landfill levy
- Setting up of a waste regulator (independent of the EPA).

This consultation is closed and the Minister's decision is awaited.

As part of the policy-development process, the Minister is prioritising the management of biodegradable waste. Therefore, draft regulations, which would have the effect of requiring authorised waste collectors to provide a food waste collection to households on a phased basis, have been published for public consultation.

The Department of the Environment, Community and Local Government has consulted with industry, other stakeholders and the public on a possible levy on packaging. The Programme for Government contains a commitment to drive a waste-reduction programme as part of the overall policy in the area of sustainable waste. One of the possible elements of this waste-reduction strategy is a levy on packaging. The main issues on which a decision is awaited are as follows:

- The overall views by stakeholders on a packaging levy
- How a packaging levy might be operated
- International experiences of similar levies
- How a possible packaging levy might be structured in order to contribute to a reduction in packaging waste.

## Trends

The nature of waste management continues to change at a rapid pace. For example, there is an increased emphasis on promoting the idea of waste as a potential resource. While good progress is being made in relation to recycling, significant problems remain on the waste-disposal front with the top priority to divert waste from landfill.

**Trends in waste generation and management[531]**

* **Hazardous waste** is down 9 per cent.

* **Construction waste** has dropped 62 per cent.

* Household **WEEE** collection (at 9 kg) is over twice the requirement set out in the WEEE Directive.

* **Municipal waste:** In 2009, a total of 2.9 million tonnes of municipal waste was generated in Ireland; a decrease of 8.4 per cent on 2008. The national target of 35 per cent recycling of this waste stream is close to the EU norm of 40 per cent.

* **Household waste:** There has been a drop of waste to 1.6 million tonnes representing 237 kg per household. Private collectors account for 60 per cent of the market. Disposals to landfill decreased by 8.6 per cent to 1 million tonnes.

* **Biodegradable waste:** The quantity of biodegradable municipal waste disposed at landfill decreased by 11 per cent from 2008.

* **Commercial waste:** This waste-generation stream has also dropped (by 12 per cent on 2008 figures).

* **Packaging:** A 70 per cent recovery rate has been recorded for packaging waste (up 5 per cent on 2008).

* A total of 29 active **landfills** accept municipal waste. At current rates, some 16 landfills will be at capacity by 2012. As a consequence waste will have to be moved between regions.

Apart from end-of-life vehicle and diversion from landfill targets, Ireland is well advanced in meeting most of its EU obligations.

## Drivers

Government waste policy and compliance with EU Directives have been the key drivers to date – specifically, the Landfill, WEEE and Packaging and Packaging Waste Directives. Initially, restrictions on landfill capacity, the requirement to upgrade landfills and obligations to recycle packaging prompted a major rise in the cost of waste disposal and the formation of private service providers. Investment in landfill capacity has reduced this driver somewhat, though cost remains a concern and is now the critical driver, after legislation. There is a view among some of the waste management providers that the full cost of waste has still not been identified by waste producers and that this inhibits the adoption of less traditional waste-management practices and technologies.

The full application of the EU Landfill Directive will require the diversion of biodegradable municipal waste from landfill. In 2009, some 1 million tonnes of biodegradable waste went to landfill; the EU target for 2013 is 610,000 tonnes and only 427,000 by 2016. Achieving these targets will require significant investment.

A future driver will be the need to reduce the level of GHG emissions from landfills, which is currently 3 per cent of the national total. This will provide a further incentive to segregate collected waste, whether at source or subsequent to collection, prompting demands for additional outlets. While the existing practices in response to current requirements may be relatively 'mature', management of biodegradable waste will represent a step change in demands and one that will not be easily accommodated by export.

As from 31 December 2011, Ireland has been fully compliant with the EU's Packaging and Packaging Waste Directive, and this will increase the pressure on packaging collection and recycling. In addition to better recycling, the EPA has suggested that a targeted approach be undertaken to reduce the quantity placed on the market in an attempt to take an alternative approach to increasing the percentage achieved.

The desire to segregate waste and to apply the 'pay by use/weight' approach has led to the development of improved waste handling and accounting systems. This expertise may be provided as a potential service to other markets, e.g. eastern Europe.

Finally, increasing waste costs that impact on company competitiveness is a concern that has been articulated on many occasions by the National Competiveness Council.[532]

## Weaknesses

The main concerns expressed by companies are uncertainty in policy and the time required to bring projects to fruition. Thermal treatment with energy recovery is the expressed preferred option for dealing with residual waste after achieving ambitious targets in respect of waste prevention, recycling and recovery and is reflected in the regional waste-management plans, for which the local authorities have statutory responsibility. These waste-to-energy plants will be provided as entirely private sector developments or by way of public–private partnerships. At present, there are a number of proposals for thermal treatment. MBT has been introduced in a number of localities and has received some positive comment. The review of national waste policy with reference to international best practice will inform future policy and the choice of technology.

Private operators have also expressed concern about the apparent ability of local authorities to control the waste market through their adjustment of the prices charged by their own landfills and the potential to direct the fate of the waste.

Waste is largely exported for recycling, due in large part to the absence of an indigenous reprocessing infrastructure. Economies of scale are most often suggested as the reason for this deficiency, since there is free movement of waste for recovery and the Irish market is small in European terms.

A risk-averse procurement process and a sense of needing to take rapid and certain steps to prepare for the Landfill Directive favours maintaining the status quo of technology.

## Barriers

A key concern expressed by companies in the waste management sector is the issue of unfair competition due to the dominant position held by local authorities: they are waste-management service and facility providers, regulators and planners. The Irish Waste Management Association (IWMA) has stated that this situation has created inefficient and uneconomic waste-management services and delays in the delivery of necessary waste-management infrastructure. The IWMA also pointed out that the sector is controlled by fifteen regulators: the EPA, An Board Pleanala, the Competition Authority, the National TFS Office, the Health and Safety Authority and ten regional waste authorities, which collectively impose a significant regulatory burden on business. The Dublin local authorities challenged these assumptions by commissioning a report that argues that from a competition policy perspective household waste collection constitutes a separate product market.[533] In addition, this report argues that the household waste-collection market is a natural (local) monopoly. Both of these conclusions are consistent with the national (e.g. Competition Authority) and international (e.g. UK Office of Fair Trading and OECD) literatures, though the IWMA does not accept this.

It is argued that the actual identity of this single provider (i.e. public or private) is of secondary importance compared to the institutional environment within which the actual provider subsequently operates. However, this issue remains a major concern of the private waste-management sector in Ireland who feels the lack of clarity and resolution of the dual role of local authorities. The local authorities have additional competitive advantages in that unlike private operators they do not charge VAT and are in receipt of funding from the Environment Fund and public capital and current expenditure.

The IWMA has also stated that the 'waste sector is characterized by a raft of unconnected national regional waste plans dreamt up in isolation by various regulatory bodies and state agencies'.[534]

To date, despite calls from the IWMA, there has been no serious attempt to explore and develop opportunities for an all-island waste management market.

The planning process, notwithstanding the enactment of the Strategic Infrastructure Act 2006, continues to delay the implementation of critical infrastructure projects.

The motor industry has argued that the way the End of Life Vehicle Directive has been implemented – by requiring registration in each local authority area – is cost-ineffective and will not encourage any significant investment in end-of-life vehicle technologies and processes.

## Opportunities

Ireland has the highest level of municipal waste generation per capita in the benchmark countries assessed in a Forfás Report.[535] While this could be viewed as a problem, in reality it is a business opportunity. To date, policy-makers have not looked at the crisis in waste management in Ireland as a business opportunity.

The vast majority of Ireland's recyclable materials are exported for further treatment; some 1.6 million tonnes were exported in 2006.[536] The cost of transporting these materials abroad adds to the above-average cost of waste in Ireland.

This suggests that feasibility studies should be completed on the setting up of all-island recycling, materials recovery and treatment facilities for all waste streams. One such study (on paper) has been completed but not yet implemented. In April 2007, the Government launched the Market Development Programme for Waste Resources 2007–2011. This aims to promote more recycling in Ireland of recovered waste resources, focusing on organics, paper and plastics in particular. The €13 million programme (now called rx3) is sourced from the Environment Fund (€11 million) and the private sector (€2 million). Reprocessing of selected streams on the island is a potential opportunity. Where recycled materials continue to be exported, analysis of segregated streams to confirm that the recyclate is of higher quality and therefore higher value may provide an opening for laboratory services.

The implementation of improved segregation of biodegradable waste will create a new resource stream, one that will require local processing. Equipment that will effectively achieve this segregation or will subsequently process the waste will be required. Decentralised solutions will include contained composting processes ('in-vessel composters') that would be applicable to large individual waste producers e.g. food processers, or closely located groups of smaller producers. Anaerobic digestion of the waste to produce combustible gas will have the dual economic benefit of avoiding methane emissions and producing energy from, in some instances, a source that may be classified as renewable. Alternative technologies that generate energy from waste via pyrolysis or produce a secondary energy carrier, e.g. gasification, are also emerging.

As the key driver in the waste-management business is EU legislation, all Member States and not just Ireland are facing the same challenges in seeking to comply with waste treatment, disposal and recycling targets. Many of the new Member States are addressing a significant infrastructure requirement with the assistance of EU cohesion and structural fund cofinancing. The spending plans of these countries in relation to waste management should be assessed with a view to identifying specific new business opportunities and this market intelligence should be made available to the entire waste sector on the island. Waste management expertise has been locally developed and is exportable, though in competition with other Member States with more advanced waste management systems.

**Areas with future growth potential**

- MBT development and operation

- Engineered in-vessel composters

- Analysis of segregated fractions from MRF or MBT, and compost quality assurance (though overall a small market)

- Niche reprocessing of recyclable materials

- Outputs from producer responsibility initiatives: for example waste tyres; there is some scope for vehicle dismantling before compaction and export; but battery processing is unlikely

- Small- or large-scale anaerobic digestion of biodegradable materials (in conjunction with water sector study)

- Export of waste management expertise: planning, development of infrastructure, tracking software (pay-by-use, hazardous waste streams)

- Development of packaging-design expertise that reduces the packaging quantity or facilitates reuse or material recycling.

*Source*: EPS Consulting, 2008

The UK's market for waste management is forecast to grow to £15.9 billion by 2015. WRAP (the Waste and Resources Action Programme) put the figure higher at up to £30 billion by 2020.

## Conclusions

The waste sector has great potential in terms of exporting services to other Member States who, like Ireland, are struggling to comply with ever-stricter EU regulations and targets. Industry sources forecast that the Irish waste management market could double in size within five years.

**Key messages**

- The problems inhibiting the growth of the waste management sector in Ireland are well documented.

- Lack of a clear government policy and robust implementation of waste regulations are barriers. In particular, the dual

- role of local authorities in the area of waste management needs to be settled.

- The waste industry has expanded rapidly with little recourse to state financial supports.

- The waste management sector is well organised as a network in Ireland.

- Infrastructure requirements identified in the National Hazardous Waste Management Plan, the National Strategy on Biodegradable Waste, and regional waste management plans have not been implemented.

- An all-island waste-management strategy has the potential to provide economies of scale in relation to some waste streams.

- Life-cycle thinking and assessment is driving EU and national policy.

- The REFIT for biomass will have a significant bearing on the level of the landfill levy at waste-to-energy plants and vice versa.

The waste management sector has been the subject of many studies and assessments. Despite the depth of analysis, key policy recommendations that could generate new business opportunities have yet to be adopted. There is a large consensus among the companies operating in the sector – a view that has persisted for many years – that there is an urgent need for a national waste regulator with a remit to centralise decision-making in relation to waste management policy and waste infrastructure investments. The view of the sector is that at the very least a coordination of existing separate structures/ institutions to encourage regulatory and market certainty and ensure implementation that meets national policy objectives would be welcome.

As scale is critical in the waste management business, the state agencies should actively partner and support companies who acquire capacity by way of mergers and acquisitions.

WRAP advises waste companies in the UK and Northern Ireland and does so very successfully. There is a need for a similar advisory service in Ireland. The sector does not appear to need direct financial assistance from state agencies for the operation of the waste management system but financial support for R&D, market development and commercialisation, along the lines of that provided by WRAP, is desirable.

If key investment decisions were implemented – and the Strategic Infrastructure Act 2006 will certainly assist in this regard – this would unlock private sector investment and expertise.

Once the problems of the island's waste market are resolved, problems that occupy much of the attention of companies in this sector, then the significant know-how of these companies can be deployed to search for export opportunities.

If some local authorities were not so dependent on the revenues they receive from waste charges it is probable that the entire waste collection business would be outsourced.

The findings of the international review on waste policy and the decisions taken on foot of the current review are likely to have a significant influence on the choice of technology and on the optimum organisational structures required. Assuming that the findings are acted on promptly, then Ireland should have a clear waste management strategy from 2012. A robust regulatory framework will unlock significant potential investment if the market believes the right strategic choices are made.

If an all-island approach to growing this sector is to be taken, it will be essential that waste management is seen more as a business opportunity than a sector that should be strictly regulated.

## Chapter 17

# Water

> We were faced with the consideration that unless steps were immediately taken to reconstruct our broken industries, the rest of the world would have passed us by ... we have not yet struck oil, consequently we resorted to water, of which we have plenty.
>
> Speech by William T. Cosgrave at the Drake Hotel Chicago, January 1928 (referring to Ardnacrusha)

## Introduction

We think of water as free, falling from the sky in abundance. We all enjoy clean water at the turn of a tap and watch it drain away without a thought.

A barrel of oil (Brent crude) is €88. We are all conscious of the price of oil and energy and significant investment is spent producing oil and indeed in energy efficiency measures. But what is the price of a barrel of potable water (a litre of branded drinking water purchased in your local supermarket)? The answer is €88![537] Yet consumers' and indeed investors' attitude to both products is diametrically opposite.

Global demand for water is expected to be 40 per cent higher in 2030 than it is today and by more than 50 per cent in some rapidly developing economies.[538] In Europe, at least 11 per cent of the population and 17 per cent of its territory has been affected by water scarcity with droughts costing the European economy over €100 billion in the past 30 years. Some $6 trillion in water sector investment is forecast over the next 20 years.[539]

Predictions for Ireland indicate that we will be subjected to much more unpredictable and volatile weather patterns in the future (as explained in chapter 1) and there will inevitably be impacts on water supply.[540] The IAE has also highlighted the significant impacts resulting from climate change.[541] Dublin City is already suffering supply shortages and as a consequence is looking at diverting water from the Shannon as a possible option.

While approaches to water service provision and regulation differ across the world, all customers want an efficiently-run service that seeks to minimise price increases and provide good levels of customer service.[542] The scale of the sector and its ownership is also an issue. For example, the water industry in England and Wales consists of 23 fully privatised companies, with ten providing both water and sewerage services and 13 providing water only. In contrast, the water industry in Northern Ireland is not privatised but is managed by one agency, NI Water. Outside the UK, ownership and operation is normally organised in the form of a public utility, either as part of a municipal organisation or a publicly owned company. On average across the developed world, water companies supply between 142,000 and 420,000 properties. However, in England and Wales the figure is much higher with medium-sized companies servicing up to 1.7 million properties. In Ireland by contrast, 34 local authorities are responsible for water and wastewater treatment.

Following the completion of an independent assessment, the Government has announced the setting up of a new national entity 'Irish Water' as an independent state-owned company within the Bord Gais Group.[543]

Are Irish companies equipped to take advantage of the global market in water products and services?

## Ireland

Water supply and wastewater treatment are two vital components of Ireland's national infrastructure, essential for human health and well-being. Water is required for many industrial and service activities and is a prerequisite to the efficient functioning of the economy while wastewater treatment is essential for environmental sustainability and to protect public health.[544] The water supply sector is predominantly divided into the potable water supply required by one-off housing throughout Ireland or RWSS (regional water supply schemes) approved at a central level via the DECLG. A similar situation pertains for the collection and treatment of wastewater locally (onsite treatment or in-group schemes) or collectively (in municipal wastewater treatment plants).

Ireland has a very diverse water supply system, with over 950 public water supplies producing over 1,600 million litres of water daily through a network of 25,000 kms of pipes. Some 85 per cent of the population is connected to public water supplies and a further 8 per cent are served by group water schemes. There are approximately 2,700 industrial wastewater treatment plants in Ireland (700 IPPC licensed activities by the EPA and 2,000 licensed by local authorities under the Water Pollution Acts). The local authorities may provide this service themselves or procure this from the private sector.

Over €5 billion was invested in new and upgraded water ser-vices infrastructure in the decade to 2010. Some €4.7 billion has been provided under the current NDP (2007–2013). The capital allocation for water was €435 million in 2011, is €371 million in 2012 and falls to €296 million by 2014. Operational costs have risen sharply and were €780 million in 2010. A value for money review of the Water Services Investment Programme has concluded that investment has been well spent. That said, the average leakage rate nationally is 41 per cent. A 'steady state' minimum investment requirement has been estimated by PwC at some €600 million annually.[545]

Wastewater treatment capacity has been put in place since 2000 to treat a population equivalent of 3.1 million. This has resulted in a reduction in the pollutant load discharged into rivers, lakes and seas from our cities and towns by 45,000 tonnes per annum. During the same period, water treatment capacity has also been increased (by an amount sufficient to meet the needs of a population equivalent of 666,000 people) and has become the main focus for the current NDP.[546]

Statutory responsibility for water management and protec-tion rests primarily with local authorities. The Water Pollution Acts, 1977 and 1990, and regulations made thereunder, includ-ing regulations giving effect to EU Directives, in particular the EU Water Framework Directive (WFD), constitute the main national legislation in this regard.[547]

> ## The Water Pollution Acts enable local authorities to:
>
> - Prosecute for water pollution offences
>
> - Attach appropriate pollution control conditions in the licensing of effluent discharges from industry, etc., made to waters or to sewers
>
> - Issue notices ('section 12 notices') to farmers, etc., specifying measures to be taken within a prescribed period to prevent water pollution
>
> - Issue notices requiring a person to cease the pollution of waters and requiring the mitigation or remedying of any effects of the pollution in the manner and within the period specified in such notices
>
> - Seek court orders, including High Court injunctions, to prevent, terminate, mitigate or remedy pollution and its effects
>
> - Prepare water quality management plans for any waters in or adjoining their functional areas
>
> - Make bye-laws regulating certain agricultural activities where the local authority considers this to be necessary so as to prevent or eliminate pollution of waters, issue notices requiring farmers to prepare nutrient management plans with the aim of ensuring that nutrients applied to land from chemical fertilisers and organic farm wastes, e.g. slurries, take account of nutrients already available in the soil and are consistent with recommended application rates, crop requirement and the need to avoid water pollution.

In comparison with other EU Member States, Ireland has better than average water quality.[548] However, the WFD requires Ireland to achieve even higher standards by 2021.

## UK and Northern Ireland

The privatisation of the UK water industry (in 1989) has been a success story with over £90 billion invested in the past two decades. Despite this the UK Government has published a white paper on water because only a quarter of the UK's water bodies are fully functioning eco-systems and due to rising population and climate change there will be increasing pressure on water quality and water supplies.[549] The white paper describes a vision for future water management in which the sector is resilient and where water is valued by consumers as the precious resource it is. The white paper is a call to action. Several of the UK's water companies have been taking a close interest in the Irish Government's plans to set up Irish Water.

NI Water is a government agency that manages Northern Ireland's water resources, including 38 major water treatment works, 26,625 kms of water mains and 14,465 kms of sewers. Its assets have been valued at £6.5 billion. It is subject to price control, determined outputs and efficiencies. The NI Assembly has deferred domestic water charges.[550]

## Global trends

The amount of fresh water on Earth is finite. Its distribution varies considerably. Apart from natural cycles the growing requirement for water for industry and domestic use is putting severe strains on the water and wastewater treatment systems in practically every country in the world. Many see water linked to sustainable development, but do not necessarily take investment decisions based on sustainability principles. The most immediate issue is a growing acceptance that climate change may already be affecting the global hydrological cycle. The recent floods in Thailand for example cost the equivalent of 1.5 per cent of the country's GDP. The UN's *World Water Development Report* (issued every three years with the next edition due in 2012) is the global flagship report on water.[551] It has been estimated that the demand for water will outstrip supply by 40 per cent by 2030 and that closing this gap could cost as much as $60 billion a year for twenty years.[552]

Given the huge reliance on guaranteed water supply, global businesses are taking a keen interest. Flood damage causes disruption to global supplies (as the Thai floods did in relation to computer and automotive components). The Texas drought cost some $5 billion in lost output and a reduction in exports. Thus assessing water risk has become a factor in investment decisions. The global business community is acutely aware of water-related business impacts with some 60 per cent exposed to water-related risk. A similar number of companies see opportunities associated with increased water efficiencies or new revenue opportunities.[553]

## The water and wastewater treatment sector

The sector falls into three categories:

- Mechanical/electrical/civil contractors
- Consultants/engineers/architects
- Local authorities/private industry.

There are approximately 270 companies involved in the water and wastewater sector in Ireland.[554,555] In addition, local authorities are active players. The market in Ireland has been estimated at €622 million (€445 million for wastewater treatment and €177 million for water supply).[556]

The single house and cluster market for wastewater treatment plants is worth some €80 million per annum, with un-sewered onsite wastewater treatment systems accounting for €52 million of the total. Bord na Mona Environmental, EPS Bison, Envirocare, and Klargester are the main players having a 50 per cent market share. The remaining 50 per cent of the market is shared by some 30 companies. Increasing concerns about the performance of existing treatment systems indicate there will be a market for retrofitting of superior technology. There has been increased business in the commercial sector due to increased regulation of leisure centres, nursing homes, hotels and schools.

The water treatment market includes clarification, filtration and disinfection equipment. The wastewater treatment market includes pre-treatment, primary, secondary, tertiary (advanced) and sludge treatment equipment. Double-digit growth is forecast over five years to 2013, reaching a size of some €307 million.[557]

Investment is focused on delivering traditional solutions, particularly in the wastewater sector. Current issues of micro-biological contamination (chryptosporidium and e.coli) in some water supplies is encouraging the water sector to look at new technologies, such as membrane filtration and UV treatment, where conventional solutions have not worked. There are currently only two membrane filtration plants on a large scale in Ireland: a plant in Ennis where there are continuing water quality issues and an ultra-filtration plant in Lough Nagharaman, Co. Monaghan where the Donaghmoyne Group Water Scheme supplies the needs of 1,700 domestic, commercial, industrial and agricultural customers.

**Recent trends**

- Decreasing price for water and wastewater equipment
- Consolidation of water and wastewater equipment companies with multi-nationals acquiring Irish companies
- Few green field projects, with expansion and improvement of current facilities the main priority
- Tangible shift towards small and medium agglomerations as well as rural communities
- Increasing population and the service land initiative providing new opportunities.

## Drivers

The EU's WFD is a key instrument aimed at improving water quality throughout the EU. It applies to rivers, lakes, groundwater, and coastal waters. The Directive requires an integrated approach to managing water quality on a river-basin basis (with the aim of maintaining and improving water quality) and that management plans be prepared on a river-basin basis. It requires that a programme of measures for improving water quality be brought into effect by 2012 at the latest. River basin management plans (RBMP) are to be prepared and renewed in six-year cycles and the first plans cover the period to 2015. Eight plans have been identified on the island of Ireland for the purpose of implementing the Directive. Three of these are shared with Northern Ireland (Shannon, Neagh-Bann, and North Western), four river basin districts are wholly within the state (Eastern, South Eastern, South Western and Western) and one is wholly within Northern Ireland (North Eastern).

RBMPs were finalised for each of the seven river basin districts in July 2010. They cover approximately 800 groundwater bodies and 5,000 surface water bodies (canals, rivers, lakes, transitional and coastal waters). The plans set out the current status of our waters, the objectives to be achieved by 2015, and the programme of measures to be implemented in order to achieve those objectives. The plans are ambitious yet realistic. They aim for significant improvements in water quality but they also recognise that in some cases soils and waters will take time to recover even where measures to address pollution have been put in place.

The plans aim to improve the proportion of rivers and canals at good or high status from 54 per cent currently to 68 per cent by 2015, and the proportion of lakes at good or high status from 65 per cent currently to 84 per cent by 2015. The RBMPs are supplemented by water management unit action plans, which provide more detail on measures at a sub-river basin level.

More stringent requirements in relation to discharges to waters under the EU Dangerous Substances Directives will also impact on all sectors whose actions influence water quality. Ireland's compliance with the EU Urban Wastewater Treatment Directive improved from 25 per cent to 90 per cent during the NDP 2000–2006 implementation period. Ireland is fortunate in that we are on a small island with our major conurbations on the coast. As a consequence there has not been a requirement to go beyond secondary treatment save for those plants discharging to sensitive areas and inland waterways. The EU Directive on Priority Substances, a daughter Directive to the WFD, will increase the compliance burden and by definition generate new business opportunities. Listed heavy metals and organic chemicals must be monitored and removed, where necessary, to comply with limit values.

Drinking water regulations continue to influence water-treatment options. There are currently no limits for the chryptosporidium parameter in Ireland while limits have applied in Northern Ireland for a number of years.

Infrastructure and technology procurement is another key driver. The Water Services Investment Programme presents a unique opportunity to drive sustainable procurement and maximise the options for local technology suppliers (technology forcing) to provide these systems. In the absence of such a decision, traditional systems, lacking innovation, delivering conventional standards are likely to be installed with Irish companies acting as agents for overseas technologies. This is a window of opportunity to provide demonstration sites and develop a knowledge economy – a window that is narrow in time.

There is near-universal metering across Europe, the US and Australia. High meter penetration influences the approach that companies may take to certain activities. Water metering and unit charges have created an opportunity for greywater recovery for use in non-potable applications such as toilet flushing in schools. Harvesting, treatment and distribution/storage of greywater are the main markets. Such systems benefit consumers by avoiding charges for local authority supplied water and benefit local authorities by reducing supply demands, which in turn avoid collateral leakage losses, treatment chemicals and energy requirements for purification and distribution.

## Weaknesses

**Problems with design, build and operate process**: There is concern that specialist water companies are not maintaining or growing technical competence due to pricing pressures from the tendering process in design build and operate (DBO) plants, which is turning what was a service-led business into a commodities one. Feedback from bidders is that they cannot compete with non-specialist suppliers for municipal contracts in the supply of treatment chemicals. The poor quality of work provided by these new entrants has often been reflected by way of low prices. Unfortunately, the low quality of work has often been accepted by public sector clients, as the overriding consideration is the price rather the quality of the service. Engineering consultants have also identified the 'commodification' of engineering services. DBO is being promoted by political considerations rather than the needs of the industry. Design has moved to the DBO contractors, stifling innovation in design and the implementation of new technologies. The DBO providers offer a completely different viewpoint, however, claiming that DBO has raised the bar in providing unique solutions for each site with innovative designs that operate as efficiently as possible with minimum power, chemicals and labour requirements.

**Monitoring and enforcement**: Failure by water suppliers continuously to monitor basic parameters such as chlorine (indicator of the effectiveness of disinfection and removal of e.coli) and turbidity (indicator of effectiveness of the treatment barrier to cryptosporidium) puts populations served by those water supplies at risk. Water suppliers can avail of the contingency fund provided by the DECLG (Circular L7/07) for the installation of such equipment where funding has not already been provided for this purpose. Local authorities need the powers and resources to regulate the installation and ongoing performance of water supply and wastewater treatment systems. In the absence of such enforcement, health risks will continue and there is little incentive to adopt better quality systems and management practices.

**Non-domestic water metering**: Charges for water services differ between local authorities, depending on the cost of their water and wastewater infrastructure programmes, the cost of operating their treatment plants and the cost of administering the metering/billing elements of their programmes. Water-services metering for non-domestic users was to be introduced by all local authorities by the end of 2006. Fingal County Council (as the lead authority on behalf of the four Dublin local authorities) awarded the €40 million contract to Gerry McCloskey Engineering Ltd, to supply and install an estimated 42,000 automatic reading water meters on non-domestic connections across the Dublin region.

**Research & development**: There has been relatively little investment in water-related applied research with the notable exception of limited EPA funding. One of the seven principal thematic areas under the EPA Programme for Science, Technology, Research and Innovation for the Environment (STRIVE) is 'Water Quality and the Aquatic Environment'.

## Barriers

The Irish market is small and results in Irish companies acting as agents for technologies developed elsewhere. In water treatment the much larger markets in Germany, UK and the US are ahead of the Irish market in terms of available technology.

Companies involved in supply of consumables to municipal water and wastewater treatment plants see the tendering approach to procurement as a bureaucratic one and prefer to concentrate on the commercial/industrial market where the decision-making process is quicker and less price-sensitive.

Investing in traditional technology is a conservative approach that will not develop indigenous expertise or anticipate future quality standards. A very high proportion of planned investment will go into construction costs rather than into knowledge services.

High standards must be specified, monitored and enforced. Such an ongoing requirement will favour more reliable systems with a valuable service element. Because of the dispersed occurrence of effluent treatment in Ireland, it falls to the local authorities to regulate many small installations. The local authorities lack the capabilities to do this, resulting in the health threats already experienced and not providing the incentive for users to invest in higher quality systems and services. Stricter regulation and enforcement to include performance monitoring and maintenance review is needed.

Small-scale goods and consultancy service providers are being squeezed out of the market by the tendering process for major contracts. Arguably this is delivering better value for money in the short term. But the demise of small businesses will reduce the overall national technological competency, increasing reliance on external providers and restricting the potential for the emergence of new business. Irish companies may be confined to agents for overseas technologies lacking the expertise to enhance a knowledge-based economy.

## Opportunities

The challenges – therefore the business opportunities – facing Ireland in water and wastewater treatment include:

- Completing outstanding infrastructure projects under the Urban Wastewater Directive
- Inadequate water supply (Dublin region) and impact of global warming
- Meeting water-quality regulations
- Protecting human health (chryptosporidium and e.coli outbreaks in water supplies)
- Infrastructure deficit in water supply and wastewater treatment
- Meeting increased demand from users
- Water leakage
- Water pricing and metering
- Diffuse pollution from agricultural sources, municipal wastewater treatment plant discharges and septic tanks
- Implementing the WFD's water-quality objectives.

The market opportunities created by the implementation of the Urban Wastewater Directive are nearing maturity with some niches – such as sludge treatment and disposal – remaining to be filled. Wastewater treatment plants effect a reduction in oxidation demand by biological processes. The ensuing micro-organisms must be periodically removed, in combination with inorganic materials and other non-degraded substances. The traditional approach to dealing with this 'sludge' has been land filling or land spreading. Some 122,000 tonnes of dried sludge is produced nationally by wastewater treatment plants and around 76 per cent of this went to agriculture and 17 per cent went to landfill. Implementation of the Landfill Directive will prohibit the latter and there are concerns about the former.

Intensive agriculture and a spreading of dwellings with an increasing population unmatched by development in services have threatened Ireland's water quality. Water supplies have been contaminated and eutrophication is a concern is some areas. Privately operated (single dwelling, group schemes) as well as public systems have been found to be inadequate on occasions. Major public investment in the supply of water and wastewater treatment is underway, leading to very large new plant as well smaller, local systems.

The market for water supply and wastewater treatment systems covers a wide scale, from one-off housing to cities. There are opportunities to provide integrated packaged systems across this scale. Such systems can be constructed from supplied components and integrated in a DBO service, remotely monitored and serviced as required. They can be engineered to provide high quality potable water or effluent as relevant, with a small footprint that will address likely future requirements.

The European Commission estimates 40 per cent of water is wasted across the EU. Opportunities lie in leak detection and repair and water-use reduction through metering and monitoring. Demand-side management services will become more attractive as metering and associated charging is introduced. This will present opportunities for consultancy services, with follow-on sale of more efficient water-using devices.

Many of the existing group water schemes have been operated on a voluntary basis. Clearly, the provision of operating and maintenance services is a future demand. Remote sensing and control of small water and wastewater treatment plants is consistent with the previous point. In situ sensing, telemetry and automation of validated systems will grow.

Ongoing contamination of water supplies by cryptosporidium and e.coli will present opportunities to provide retrofit final purification equipment.

Provision of individual household water purification treatment units is another growth market created by contaminated water supplies. In principle, wastewater can be purified to a quality that allows it to be reused. In the extreme, it can be recovered to potable quality and better. The availability of water in Ireland is such that this is an unlikely approach for human potable supply, but the industrial application of such closed water cycles is reasonable where there is a requirement for a substantial quantity of water at less than potable quality. Application of water unit charges and increases in these charges has induced some companies to examine such an integrated approach. The feasibility of this will be driven by an economic balance of the capital and running cost of water recovery versus the purchase and disposal cost of local authority supplied water.

New approaches to monitoring are being developed at a number of research institutes across the country. These include advanced remote sensor and monitoring technology that can be applied to the EU WFD. Analytical services to confirm ongoing quality is another growth area. Since these technologies can be applied not only in Ireland, but also across the world, this offers an opportunity for Irish researchers and businesses to play a significant role in what could be a highly lucrative market, estimated to be worth some €550 million in Europe alone.

Energy efficiency in the operation of systems will require more efficient equipment e.g. pumps, blowers, diffusers; more efficient use of equipment e.g. variable speed drives, management systems, instrumentation and automation; and local energy generation e.g. biogas-fuelled systems, solar or wind powered – even if only for instrumentation.

### Areas with future growth potential

- Integrated, packaged, compact plants for water supply, wastewater treatment. Such plants should achieve high quality outputs, requiring the use of 'non-conventional' (in Irish terms) technologies: membrane filtration, membrane bioreactors, sequencing batch reactors, UV disinfection, ozonation exceeding existing Irish standards, anticipating future concerns about micro-biological and micro-pollutant contamination

- Technologies and processes that reduce the GHG emissions or carbon footprint associated with water or wastewater treatment
- Instrumentation and automation of such plant to support remote monitoring, operation and management
- *In situ* sensing of relevant parameters and laboratory-quality assurance services
- Energy-efficient equipment, e.g. diffusers and local energy generation e.g. solar-powered systems for instrumentation
- Waste-to-energy plants e.g. anaerobic digestion, supercritical water oxidation.

Due to the nature of our island status tertiary treatment technology has had limited implementation in Ireland. However, there is opportunity in European and other markets where nutrient and microbial removal are more pressing.

As many Member States continue to have poor water quality, companies could target those countries that clearly needed additional investment where Irish companies have the requisite technologies or expert services. Water and wastewater projects are generously co-financed by the EU Cohesion and European Regional Development Funds.

## Reform of the water sector

The EU–IMF agreement required the Government to undertake an independent assessment of the setting up of a water utility; to examine existing organisational arrangements; and to consider the best assignment of water functions for the future. The study undertaken by PwC took account of lessons learnt from international models as well as benchmarking Irish performance data with experience in other jurisdictions.[558] PwC also considered potential forms of company structures, including the assignment of responsibility for water services provision, or part thereof, to an existing state agency. The majority of models identified were public utility structured.

The weaknesses of the current arrangement identified by PwC include over-staffing; inability to realise economies of scale; the disconnection between river basin and local authority boundaries; and long-term under-investment.

The present funding model includes direct Exchequer support, local authorities' own resources and income from the non-domestic sector. Given the current budgetary constraints, rising operational costs and significant capital investment requirements, water charges are an inevitable consequence as providing households with unlimited quantities of water free of charge is not sustainable.[559] Ireland is the only European country that does not charge for water services. Thus it is not at all surprising that the OECD among others has recommended the introduction of domestic water pricing.[560] It is also critical that Irish Water, in common with other Irish utilities, has access to the international bond markets.

The Government decided on 17 April 2012 to set up Irish Water as an independent state entity within the Bord Gais Group and that the utility will remain in public ownership. The rationale for the reform was explained as follows. There is a need to:

- Develop a sustainable funding model to meet ongoing operational and capital costs (which amount to some €1.2 billion);

- Reduce levels of leakage; Ireland's leakage levels at nearly 40 per cent are higher than international norms;

- Support the development of strategically important national water services projects that would otherwise be delayed due to a lack of funding;

- Ensure ongoing compliance with public health and environmental standards;

- Address fragmentation in the existing structures and achieve real economies of scale;

- Exploit the full potential for industry standard IT systems for water management;

- Introduce an independent regulator for the sector;

- As the value of water increases due to global shortages, ensure that Ireland can use its rich water resources as a strategic asset.

**Irish Water will be responsible for:**

- Attracting investment from private sources
- Abstraction, treatment and distribution of drinking water

- Strategic planning for the sector including water-resource management
- The roll-out of the water meter programme: meters reduce consumption by at least 10 per cent
- Collection and treatment of wastewater and disposal of sludge
- Customer billing and relationship management
- Conservation of water supplies

Nobody could argue with the proposed remit. It is encouraging that the City and County Managers' Association supports the setting up of Irish Water. The Government's decision also sets down a realistic timescale (2015) for the full transfer of operations.

The core aim should be the delivery of secure, high quality and competitively priced water services on a sustainable basis to both domestic and commercial customers. Irish Water must have a mandate and resources to drive continuous improvement in the quality of such services.

The price charged for water supply and wastewater treatment is a key factor that will influence the ability of the new entity to fund the required investment.

The setting up of Irish Water makes economic (and political) sense as the current system of 34 water authorities services are fragmented and economies of scale not achieved. Some of the 3,400 staff currently employed by local authorities will be deployed under the terms of the Croke Park Agreement.

The sector will need to be regulated as part of a consolidated single entity covering energy, transport, waste and broadcasting. The UK's OFWAT is a good exemplar as to how a modern regulatory regime is managed. However, it is currently envisaged that Irish Water will be regulated by both the EPA and the CER (from an economic perspective).

While the water network itself may constitute a natural monopoly, many other aspects of water-services delivery, including supply, wastewater treatment, operations and maintenance, do not. Irish Water will have to encourage better competition in these areas and could do so using green procurement techniques.

While it is envisaged that Irish Water will begin meter infrastructure installation by the end of the year and the project will be rolled out 'on an accelerated basis', it remains to be demonstrated whether a nationwide domestic metering programme for the 1,093,189 households connected to the public mains supply is a cost-effective solution. The capital cost of such a programme has been estimated at between €500–650 million; an estimation on the high side as tender bids will no doubt confirm. While citing the benefits of meters, the DECLG has published neither a cost–benefit assessment nor details of the business case for such a programme, nor has it been clarified how the water meter programme will be coordinated with the roll-out of smart meters.

The Department notes even with a projected annual income of €200 million the funding deficit will be around €1 billion. This implies that the gap will be met by high water charges over time. There has been some speculation about the actual level of charges with one commentator suggesting the figure could be as high as €560 per annum.[561] The CER will determine the funding model, including a dividend policy to Government.

## Conclusions

The market is very competitive at present. The majority of the opportunities over the next years will relate to the supply, installation, reading and maintenance of water meters. The 150 to 200 local installers who will benefit as sub-contractors from the tender contract will be the first beneficiaries. Opportunities in the water segment are limited in number with signs of an acceptance and demand for advanced solutions such as membranes.[562]

New water sources/supplies are required for Dublin; with the Bord Na Móna Garryhinch Bog project (a 700-acre storage lake) a key element of the Greater Dublin Water Supply Project. Upgrades may be required to existing infrastructure including treatment and supply systems.

The NDP and the Investment Strategy for Northern Ireland provide an opportunity to introduce improved technologies by the creation of a market for goods and services using green procurement.

Setting high standards for water quality and enforcing these standards will stretch providers to innovate. Existing and new infrastructure may be considered as pilot and demonstration sites for better technologies. Since the local authorities are the operators of this infrastructure (at least until Irish Water is set up) they should be engaged to support this development.

In common with other green economy sub-sectors, the water and wastewater treatment sector is not networked to take advantage of market intelligence, legislative change, emerging technologies and current and planned R&D effort. Building the capability of the sector to take advantage of significant future investment in infrastructure on the island and in some export markets in Europe should be a priority.

The Government should publish the business case justifying the capital cost of €600 million for the installation of water meters. Given the scale and complexity of the tender, it should also engage in market soundings with potential bidders before the formal launch of a tender competition. For example, the technical specifications will need to encourage innovation; the scope of the service will have to be clarified, for example will the contract be for supply and installation only or will it be expanded to include meter reading and maintenance; and the plans for regional delivery by river basin district will need to be carefully explained. One approach would be to announce that €450 million only is available and ask contractors to set out what they could do within this fixed-fee budget.

The imminent large-scale Irish investment in the water sector should be seen as a proving ground for Irish companies and a stepping stone to export markets.

Once Ireland has a single water and wastewater utility, it is likely that this will generate significant economies of scale, for example in terms of bundling projects to attract global investors who have a track record in providing private finance for water.[563]

Now that the political decision to set up Irish Water has been taken, the Government would be well-advised to prepare a white paper on the future of water and wastewater in Ireland.

# Chapter 18

# Conclusions

> The recession has presented us with a once in a life-
> time opportunity. Let's not waste it.
>
> *Green Business Quarterly*, June 2009

The combined pressures of population growth (an additional 1.7 billion people will be born between 2010 and 2035), energy demand, failing supply of fossil fuels (and rising fuel prices) and carbon constraints represent an unprecedented challenge for Ireland, even if we did not have to deal with the consequences of the EU–IMF Programme.

Critics of the Government's apparent u-turn on Ireland's climate change policy would be well advised to read the well-written *Review of National Climate Policy*.[564] The Government has got the message: the debate has moved on from one of strict compliance with a view to reducing GHG emissions and to increase the share of renewable energy to a much more strategic discourse about how Ireland must prepare to become a low-carbon economy.

Yes, legislation will be needed, but as correctly stated by the Minister for the Environment, Community and Local Government its content must be informed by evidence-based policy research. Hence the NESC has been tasked with this job. The big unknowns are: how the effort to meet the current (-20 per cent by 2020) GHG emission-reduction target will fall in an equitable manner on households, farmers and businesses; the impacts of the higher targets that will be introduced if international negotiations on climate change are concluded; and how to deliver the EU's and Ireland's political commitment to reduce GHG emissions by 80 per cent by 2050.

Ireland needs a *National Low Carbon Plan 2050* for quite a few reasons.

First, Ireland has world-class resources in abundance (wind and water being two obvious examples) but has yet to determine how best to develop these assets in a sustainable manner and to quantify the potential scale of the investment and export opportunities.

Second, the projected €80 billion in green economy investments (renewable energy, grid, forestry, water and waste etc.) in Ireland already announced could generate upwards of 80,000 jobs. To put it more bluntly, a fifth of the people who are currently unemployed could find jobs in green economy companies if the Government and its agencies got their collective act together. The top priority must be to lever private sector investment.

Third, current enterprise and jobs policies have not given the green economy sector the same priority (or resources as a consequence) as for example the food, ICT and pharmaceuticals sectors. In excess of €500 billion will be invested in green economy projects in the UK and Northern Ireland and there is no reason why Irish entrepreneurs cannot get a share of this vast 'green' market. State agency support is not geared up for Irish enterprises to take full advantage of this opportunity.

Finally, project promoters (of which there are very many) need policy certainty, a consistent approach to regulation, incentives and taxation policy and a 'whole of government' approach to the twin issues of climate change (and energy security) and the green economy. A revised NCCS along with the energy policy framework will go a long way towards informing future investment decisions.

While we await the NESC review, the Government might wish to consider the following options that are largely Exchequer cost-neutral but which if acted upon promptly could give a significant and short-term boost to Ireland's fledgling green economy sector.

First, concentrate all the state's efforts (including R&D) into one agency. SEAI is the obvious candidate as the primary delivery agent given its credentials and reputation as a 'can-do' organisation. The underused engineers, technicians and planners in the NRA, RPA and local authorities should be transferred to SEAI as part of the Croke Park Agreement and tasked with facilitating the construction of the necessary infrastructure and the development of the emerging technologies, including ICT convergence. The naysayers to such a radical proposal might check out what the UK's Department of Energy and Climate Change is doing.

Second, a share (say 50 per cent) of the Exchequer's revenue from carbon taxation and the auctioning of emissions permits should be recycled into potentially commercial and sustainable projects: some €1 billion in additional 'green' revenue may be collected annually by 2020. Who in government has the courage to bring forward a financing plan to expand Ireland's green economy as a major exporter using this largely windfall revenue as a key lever to secure significant private investment? A working hypothesis is that €10 billion may be collected between 2015 and 2025; the Government might seek the views of stakeholders as to how best a portion of this sum (say €5 billion for argument's sake) could be deployed to support green economy investments.

Third, the enterprise agencies should be instructed not to grant aid companies (other than by way of competitive tendering) but instead to finance (by way of competitive tendering) all the sub-sector networks that advise and support these innovating cleantech/greentech companies. Would it be a better use of scarce resources to provide €10 million to five networks than to spend the same money on supporting one company? Specialist staff in the agencies could be better employed working in these networks than processing application forms.

Fourth, require by way of a PSO that the electricity generators co-finance a nationwide programme of retrofitting for energy efficiency in some 1 million households. A complication is that the banks will not lend because that are not comfortable with the proposed ESCO model.

Fifth, what is the China dimension? Could Ireland make the business proposition that we become a European hub for the deployment of Chinese green economy technologies into the EU?

Finally, Ireland should introduce incentives (all approved under EU state aid rules) to support R&D, the wider use of environmental technologies, and ICT convergence that many competitor governments already offer to their businesses.

The green economy is happening. It is real. Jobs are being created. For example, according to Bloomberg New Energy Finance, some $41 billion was spent on clean energy investments in the third quarter of 2011 across the globe despite of (or because of one might argue) the economic down turn. In addition, $2.2 billion was invested in just three months in renewable energy projects by venture capitalists. The UNEP,[565] the European Commission, the OCED[566] and many developed countries (including the UK, the Scandinavian countries, Germany[567] and China) have adopted low-carbon strategies that are already resulting in a surge of investment. Sorry to say but Ireland is playing catch-up with its competitors. The fact that Ireland does not feature as investors look elsewhere for 'green' investments should be a matter of concern for everyone.

The green/cleantech sector will not lift off and create much needed employment unless the well-documented barriers and obstacles facing many companies are addressed and resolved by government action. For example, the planning and development legislation for offshore wind is based on the antiquated provisions of the Foreshore Acts dating from 1933 that never envisaged such projects. This legislation, which is not 'fit for purpose', was a reason why R&D on an Irish ocean energy project was moved to Scotland. Primary legislation is also needed if Ireland's geothermal resources can be exploited. The absence of a regulatory framework for waste is discouraging investors. The rules by which the CER processes applications for grid connections (Gate 3) have also been criticised. Even if projects are approved, grid connections take years to happen. While there are limited subsidies to support renewable projects (REFIT) the levels are below those of competitor economies. A significant number of AD plants were stalled pending a Government decision about the appropriate level of REFIT. Another complication is that the banks will not lend to potential biomass/CHP project promoters because of the weakness of the balance sheets of start-up companies and what they perceive as insufficient guarantees over fuel supply.

This country has more strategies than counties. Some have been on the shelf for years. Very few are being fully implemented. Most have no budget or a detailed implementation plan. The much-needed *National Low Carbon Plan 2050* should not fall into the same trap. We need to identify and to plot a sustainable and affordable pathway to transition Ireland as a low-carbon country and to be a world leader where we have a natural competitive advantage. This ambition will not happen unless the Government engages with the private and public investors who have projects in the pipeline (despite their frustration at the Government's inability to get their plans to a shovel-ready state).

Nobody is advocating a BAU approach as the IEA are forecasting a one-third rise in energy demand, with China and India being two of the growing economies seeking scarce fossil fuel resources. BAU as a policy option has been banished thankfully.

The cost-compliance burden resulting from the implementation of EU environmental, energy and climate change Directives is high and will get higher and has already had a significant impact on investors' decisions.[568] On the other side of the equation, the need to respect environmental rules and greater corporate awareness about sustainable development – both largely driven by consumer behaviour – is rapidly changing the way certain sectors are conducting their commerce, in particular as regards sustainability requirements being pushed onto suppliers.

While all green economy sub-sectors have prospects, Exchequer resources are limited so therefore priorities will have to be set. This does not mean that any sub-sector should be ignored by the state agencies. Rather a higher priority should be given to a limited number of niche areas within sub-sectors that have the greatest potential to make a breakthrough into what is a very competitive European market.

In this regard, the following screening criteria could be used in assessing the green economy goods and services with the greatest potential:

- Clear demonstration of growth prospects in European markets

- Companies in the sub-sectors have the scale to export into European markets

- Exploitation of natural resources or technical experience is achievable

- Clear regulatory drivers exist with high levels of enforcement

- Emerging technologies and product development are attracting venture capital investments.

As the vast majority of green economy companies are satisfying demand on the island, it will take a major effort over several years to grow exports unless the sector gets the attention it warrants. Where business opportunities are identified in the domestic market initially, this will enable companies to develop and expand capabilities and expertise to test products and services that may provide the launchpad for exports. The task of growing exports should be greatly facilitated as the UK – Ireland's largest export market – expects its green economy sector to grow by nearly 100 per cent to £46 billion by 2015. With an adjacent, large, growing and dynamic market, this suggests that the priority should be to secure an ambitious market share of the UK overall green economy market as a first step for potential Irish exporters.

Environmental policy, in particular the climate change agenda, has been, and is expected to continue to be, of critical importance in influencing the future direction of the sector. For this reason, it is important that government provides and articulates – importantly in close consultation with stakeholders – a clear and consistent strategic policy framework as regards how best the green economy sector will be developed. This is an essential precondition in order to provide certainty and confidence as regards the long-term prospects for the sector to stimulate investment in the provision of new goods and services. Clear and consistent policy direction can help to reduce the risk associated with the development of new products and services. Risk can be reduced and some market failures overcome by creating a robust, long-term policy and taxation framework that gives business the time and confidence to invest in finding new solutions to environmental goals.[569]

It is evident that the regulatory framework has been the most important driver of growth for virtually all sectors to date. While other factors are also now coming into play in some sectors (e.g. climate change, energy pricing and life-cycle costs), there is no doubt that regulation will continue to play an extremely important role going forward.

The Government needs to raise the bar by designating the green economy sector as a priority industry on par with life sciences and the ICT sector. A strategic policy framework that drives investment both domestic and FDI; that facilitates enterprise development; and one that promotes access to new markets and exploits new business opportunities needs to be prepared along with a fully resourced project implementation plan. Such a strategy must be informed by businesses who are active in the sector. High-level engagement between the green economy sub-sectors and the state agencies tasked to support enterprise is a precondition if the ambition that Ireland becomes a green economy centre of excellence is to have a prospect of success.

Initially through the UK, companies in the green economy arena – whether or not they are Irish owned – need to harness the market dynamics that are evident in priority green economy sub-sectors and to build a sector that will position the island as a major player in niche environmental goods and services.

Setting credible targets; seeking to exploit a comparative advantage; refocusing state supports; and articulating a strategic intent to become a player in the global green economy market will set the right framework conditions essential to secure FDI; to unlock investment; to raise the level of R&D; and to convince Ireland's entrepreneurs that the green economy sector is a growth area of the future.

Many international institutions are calling for a new policy focus. For example, the UNEP notes that:

....to bring about a transition to a green economy, Governments should level the playing field for greener products by phasing out antiquated subsidies; by reforming policies and providing new incentives; strengthening market infrastructure and market based mechanisms; redirecting public investment; and greening public procurement.

It is expected that the revised NCCS, the energy policy framework and Ireland's low-carbon plan will become the key pillars of the Government's strategy to position Ireland as a resource-efficient economy.

A word of caution is needed by way of final comment. Many of Ireland's green economy sub-sectors are playing catch-up and as a consequence the proposed strategic framework needs to be realistic. Despite having a potential comparative advantage in niche areas, Ireland does not have first-mover advantage in respect of any green economy technology (apart perhaps from wave and tidal). Furthermore, there are no major indigenous players of scale in the private sector that, for the present at least, could challenge on the global market. We also need to reskill many people to take advantage of green economy jobs. Finally, as the sector was not a government priority until recently, FDI activity, R&D investment and eco-innovation levels are well below what exists in competitor economies.

Despite these weaknesses, the sector is on a strong potential growth path so the challenge is the transformation of the sector as a key driver of new economic activity on the island.

Climate change is one of the greatest challenges facing mankind.

The green economy that is responding to this challenge is also the source of new investment and job opportunities.

# Notes

1. Action Plan for Jobs, ch. 7 (The Green Economy), February 2012. The estimate provided by the UK Government's Green Economy Strategy, (2011) *Enabling the Transition to a Green Economy: Government and Business Working Together*, is much higher at £4 trillion by 2015.
2. Brennan, P. and Curtin, J. (eds) (2008), The Climate Change Challenge: Strategic Issues, Options and Implications for Ireland, Institute of International and European Affairs.
3. Australian Academy of Science (2010), The Science of Climate Change, Questions and Answers. This publication contains an extensive list of references about the science of climate change.
4. This is the definition used by the UNFCCC. The IPCC has a more subtle definition as follows: 'climate change refers to any change in climate over time, whether due to natural variability or as a result of human activity'.
5. Flannery, T. (2005), The Weather Makers: The History and Future Impact of Climate Change, Text Publishing.
6. Fealy, R. (2008) with contributions from Ray Bates (UCD), Laura McElwain, John Sweeney and Conor Murphy (NUI Maynooth), *The Science of Climate Change*, Occasional Paper, Institute for International and European Affairs. This section draws heavily on the occasional paper.
7. Hart, M.H. (1978), 'Evolution of atmosphere of Earth', *Icarus* 33: 23–39.
8. Roberts, N. (1998), *The Holocene*, Blackwell. These cycles were initiated by subtle variations in the Earth's orbit that altered the pattern of absorbed sunlight. Measurements from ice cores and other sources suggest that as temperatures changed, other changes were triggered that had an amplifying effect: during warm periods for example, $CO_2$ and methane were released into

the atmosphere and ice sheets receded and so reflected less sunlight into space.

[9] Clark, P.U., et al. (2004), 'Rapid Rise of Sea Level 19,000 Years Ago and Its Global Implications', *Science* 304: 1141–4.

[10] Schwartz, P. and Randall, D. (2004), 'An Abrupt Climate Change Scenario and Its Implications for US National Security'. Another major tipping point is the massive release of methane from the sea floor.

[11] Contribution of Working Groups I, II and III to the Fourth Assessment Report of the Intergovernmental Panel on Climate Change, IPCC, Geneva, 2007. The IPCC was set up in 1988 to advise governments on the emerging problem of climate change. It produced its first report in 1990 and three more since. Its three working groups assess the science; impacts and the response to global warming respectively.

[12] Climate Research Unit (2008), 'Global Temperature Record', University of East Anglia.

[13] Schneider, S.H. (2001), 'What Is 'Dangerous' Climate Change?', *Nature*, 411: 17–19; Schneider, S.H. (2002), 'Can we estimate the likelihood of climatic changes at 2100?'. *Climate Change*, 52: 441–51; and Dessai, S., Adger, W.N., Hulme, M., Koehler, J., Turnpenny, J. and Warren, R. (2003), Defining and experiencing dangerous climate change, Tyndall Centre for Climate Change Research, Working Paper 28.

[14] Schneider, S.H. and Lane, J. (2005), An Overview of 'Dangerous' Climate Change, Stanford University.

[15] Tirpak, D., Ashton, J., Dadi, Z., Gylvan Meiro Filho, L., Metz, B, Parry, M, Schnellnhuber, J, Seng Yap, K, Watson, R., Wigley, T. (2005), Avoiding Dangerous Climate Change: International Symposium on the Stabilisation of Greenhouse Gas Concentrations, Report of the International Scientific Steering Committee.

[16] McElwain, L. and Sweeney, J. (2007), Implications of the EU climate protection target for Ireland, EPA.

[17] Patwardhan, A., Schneider, A.H. and Semenov, S.M. (2003), *Assessing the Science to Address UNFCCC Article 2: A Concept Paper Relating to Cross Cutting Theme Number Four*, IPCC.

[18] Wild, M., Calanca, P., Scherrer, S.C. and Ohmura, A. (2003), 'Effects of polar ice sheets on global sea level in high-resolution greenhouse scenarios', *Journal of Geophysical Research*, 108(D5): 4165 and McElwain and Sweeney (2007).

[19] Oppenheimer, M. and Alley, R. (2005), 'Ice sheets, global warming and Article 2 of the UNFCCC'. *Climatic Change*, 68: 257–67; and Oppenheimer, M. and Alley, R.B. (2004), 'The West Antarctic Ice Sheet and long term climate policy', Climate Change 64, 1–10.

[20] McElwain and Sweeney (2007).

[21] Hansen, J. (2004), 'Diffusing the global warming time bomb', *Scientific American*, 290 (3): 68–77.

[22] Meinshausen, M. (2005), On the risk of overshooting 2°C, paper presented at Scientific Symposium Avoiding Dangerous Climate Change, Met Office, Exeter, 1–3 February 2005.

[23] European Commission (2005), Winning the Battle Against Global Climate Change, Communication from the Commission to the Council, the European Parliament, the European Economic and Social Committee and the Committee of the Regions, COM (2005) 35 Final, 9 February 2005.

[24] Lovelock, J. (2009), *The Vanishing Face of Gaia: A Final Warning*, Allen Lane. See also his books (1979), *Gaia: A New Look at Life on Earth*, Oxford University Press; (2000), *Homage to Gaia: The Life of an Independent Scientist*, Oxford University Press; and (2005), *Gaia: Medicine for an Ailing Planet*, Gaia Books, London. The first book was written while Lovelock lived in Ireland.

[25] Polovina, J. (2008), *Geophysical Research Letters* (American Geophysical Union).

[26] IPCC Report from Working Group II, 2007.

[27] Tocker, T. and Plattner, G.K. (2007), The Physical Science Basis of Climate Change: Latest Findings to be Assessed by WG1 in AR4, IPCC.

[28] Ahlstrom, D., *The Irish Times*, 8 December 2011.

[29] IPCC (2011), Managing the Risks of Extreme Events and Disasters to Advance Climate Change, A Special Report of Working Group I and Working Group II.

[30] UNEP (2010), The Emissions Gap Report, A Preliminary Assessment. See also UNEP/World Resources Institute (2011), Building the Climate Change Regime: Survey and Analysis of Approaches.

[31] EPA (2009), Climate Change in Ireland: Refining the Impacts for Ireland, STRIVE Report prepared by NUI Maynooth (John Sweeney ed.). The EPA was allocated a €8m budget in 2007 for a Climate Change Research Programme. Regular calls for proposals in relation to climate change research have been issued under the STRIVE Programme (2007–2013). The funding is provided by the Inter-Departmental Committee for the Strategy for Science, Technology and Innovation. In addition, the EPA has set up a national climate research data archive under the Environmental Research Centre, an open resource that complies with the EU INSPIRE Directive. The EPA has also hosted a climate change lecture series. Top international experts from the worlds of science, politics and economics have

contributed. UCD's Metrology and Climate Centre, with Met Éireann, is engaged in the Community Climate Change Consortium for Ireland (C41), which is examining future changes in the Irish climate using high resolution computer models.

32  The Irish Climate Change and Research Unit produce some of Ireland's most valuable research on climate change.

33  Fealy, R. (2008) with contributions from Ray Bates (UCD), Laura McElwain, John Sweeney and Conor Murphy (NUI Maynooth), *The Science of Climate Change*, Occasional Paper, Institute for International and European Affairs.

34  McElwain and Sweeney (2007), Key Meteorological Indicators of Climate Change in Ireland, Environmental Research Centre-ERC Report 6, EPA, Johnstown Castle, Co. Wexford, Ireland. Much of the data about observed changes in climate in Ireland are based on this report.

35  Fealy, R. and Sweeney, J. (2007), 'Statistical downscaling of precipitation for a selection of sites in Ireland employing a generalised linear modelling approach', *International Journal of Climatology*, 2083–94.

36  Murphy, C., Fealy, R., Charlton, R. and Sweeney, J. (2006), 'The reliability of an "off-the-shelf" Conceptual Rainfall Runoff model for use in climate impact assessment: uncertainty quantification using Latin Hypercube sampling', *Area*, 38.1: 65–78; and Steele-Dunne, S., Lynch, P., McGrath, R., Semmler, T., Wang, S., Hanafin, J. and Nolan, P. (2008), 'The impacts of climate change on hydrology in Ireland', *Journal of Hydrology*, 356: 28–45.

37  Holden, N.M. and Brereton, A.J. (2003), 'The Impact of Climate Change on Irish Agriculture', in J. Sweeney, et al, Climate Change: Scenarios and Impacts for Ireland, EPA, 33–80.

38  Holden, N.M., Brereton, A.J. and Fitzgerald, J.B. (2009), 'Impact of Climate Change on Irish Agricultural Production Systems', in J. Sweeney (ed.), *Climate Change: Refining the Impacts for Ireland*, EPA.

39  Gulev, S.K., Hasse, L. (1999), 'Changes of wind waves in the North Atlantic over the last 30 years', International Journal of Climatology, 19(10).

40  Houghton, J.T., Ding, Y., Griggs, D.J., Noguer, M., van der Linden, P.J. and Xiaosu, D. (eds) (2001), Climate Change 2001: The Scientific Basis, contribution of Working Group I to the Third Assessment Report of the IPCC, Cambridge University Press.

[41] McGrath, R., Nishimura, E., Nolan, P., Semmler, T., Sweeney, C. and Wang, S. (2005), Climate Change: Regional Climate Model Predictions for Ireland, EPA, ERTDI Report Series No. 36.

[42] Farrell, G. (2007), *Impact on Coastal Areas Ireland at Risk: The Impact of Climate Change on the Water Environment*, IAE.

[43] Purser, P.M., Byrne, K.A. and Farrell, E.P. (2003), 'The Potential Impact of Climate Change on Irish Forestry', in J. Sweeney et al., Climate Change: Scenarios and Impacts for Ireland, EPA, 121–40.

[44] Brennan, P. and Curtin, J. (eds) (2008), The Climate Change Challenge: Strategic Issues, Options and Implications for Ireland, Institute of International and European Affairs, ch. 1.

[45] Stern, N. (2006), The Stern Review on the Economics of Climate Change, HM Treasury.

[46] The Fourth Assessment Report (November 2007) is the culmination of six years' work by 450 lead authors, 800 contributing authors and 2,500 expert scientific reviewers from 130 countries. Previous reports were published in 1990, 1995 and 2001.

[47] Damro, C. and Mende, P.L. (2003), 'Emissions Trading at Kyoto: From EU Resistance to Union Innovation', *Environmental Politics*, 12(2), Taylor & Francis Online.

[48] UNFCCC, Kyoto Protocol, Article 6.1.d; Article 17 (2007).

[49] FOX News, 'Bush Dubs Kyoto "Lousy Deal" For America', aired 11 July 2005.

[50] Netherlands Environmental Assessment Agency (2007), 'China Now No. 1 in CO2 Emissions; USA in Second Position'.

[51] G8 Summit, Chair's Summary (Heiligendamm, 8 June 2007).

[52] UNFCCC, The United Nations Climate Change Bali Conference (2007), COP 13.

[53] Curtin, J. and Hanrahan, G. (2010), What Can Cancún Deliver: Pre-Summit Briefing, Institute of International and European Affairs.

[54] Stern, T., the US Climate Envoy, *Associated Press*, 21 September 2010, 'Big powers talk climate, no grand deal sighted'.

[55] Conclusions of EU Environment Ministers, 14 March 2011.

[56] Interview with Tosi Mpanu-Mpanu, chair of the Africa Group on Climate Change, May 2011.

[57] Santarius, T. et al (2011), One Step Forward and Two Sideward: Regional Analysis of Climate Policy in 2010 and the Cancún Climate Conference, Heinrich Boll Stiftung.

[58] McDonald, F., *The Irish Times*, December 2010. See also editorial dated 13 December 2010.

[59] Masters, L. (June 2011), 'A Complex Exercise in Climate Diplomacy for South Africa', www.boell.org.za.

60   CDC Climat (December 2011), 'Durban: One small promising step for climate by 2020', *Climate Brief.*

61   Since 2001, over 3,600 CDM projects in 70 countries have been registered and 860 million CERs issued. The majority of CERs originate from China and India. There has been some controversy that some CERs are based on investments in coal power plants.

62   Presentation by Martin Hession, member of the CDM Executive Board, to the IIEA Climate Change Working Group, 13 February 2012.The deadline for submissions was 5 March 2012.

63   Cormier, A. and Bellassen, V. (2012), CDC Climat Research, The Risks of CDM Projects: How did only 30 per cent of expected credits come through, Working Paper No. 2012–11.

64   European Commission (2012), *Preparing the EU's QELRO based on the EU Climate and Energy package*, Staff Working Document, SWD (2012) 18 final, 13 February 2012.

65   Presentations by Owen Ryan (Department of the Environment, Community and Local Government), Pat Finegan (Grian) and Matthew Kennedy (SEAI) to the IIEA's Climate Change Research Group, 17 January 2012.

66   Brennan, P. and Curtin, J. (eds) (2008), The Climate Change Challenge: Strategic Issues, Options and Implications for Ireland, Institute of International and European Affairs, ch. 1.

67   European Commission, Staff Working Paper, *Towards a Comprehensive Climate Change Agreement in Copenhagen*, Annex 5, SEC (2009) 101, January 2009.

68   Malta and Cyprus are Annex 2 countries and consequently have no reduction commitments.

69   European Commission, Communication to the European Parliament, the Council, the European Economic and Social Committee and the Committee of the Regions (2009), Stepping up International Climate Finance: A European Blueprint for the Copenhagen Talks, SEC (2009) 1172, 11 September 2009.

70   Briefing by Martin Lidegaard, Denmark's Climate and Energy Minister, European Policy Centre, Brussels, 24 January 2012.

71   For background information: Profeta, T. (Nicholas Institute for Environmental Policy Solutions) and Kelly, C. (German Marshall Fund of the United States) (2008), *The US Climate Policy Debate: How climate politics are moving forward on Capitol Hill and in the White House*, The German Marshall Fund of the United States.

72   The April 2007 Supreme Court case, *Massachusetts v EPA* found that the EPA has the authority to regulate GHG emissions under the Clean Air Act if the Agency found that such emissions posed a threat to human health and welfare. The EPA's 'endangerment

finding' is the subject of a public consultation which has just closed.

73 On 30 September 2009 the EPA issued two new proposals regulating GHGs under the Clean Air Act. They concern the so-called 'tailoring rule', and a reconsideration of what is called the Johnson memorandum. Both proposals are fraught with legal and policy uncertainty and come at a time when the debate about the EPA's role under US climate change legislation is contentious.

74 This implies that developed countries as a group should reduce their GHG emissions below their 1990 levels through domestic and complementary international efforts by 25–40 per cent by 2020 and by 80–95 per cent by 2050, while developing countries as a group should achieve a substantial deviation below the currently predicted emission growth rate of 15–20 per cent by 2020.

75 European Commission, Communication to the European Parliament, the Council, the Economic and Social Committee and the Committee of the regions, Investing in the Development of Low-Carbon Technologies Plan (SET-Plan), SEC (2009) 1295, 7 October 2009, sets out the EU's level of ambition.

76 The Council will provide a new framework for deepening trans-atlantic dialogue on strategic energy issues of mutual interest. It will also provide a platform for cooperation on energy policies and strengthening collaboration on energy technologies. Members include the European Commissioners for External Relations, for Energy and for Science and Research, as well as the EU Presidency and, on the US side, the Secretary of State and the Secretary of Energy.

77 Address to the Annual Forum of Parliamentarians for Global Action, Washington, 21 October 2009.

78 A border tax adjustment would, if enacted, impose a levy on imported goods proportionate to their embedded carbon. This was another US 'red line' issue given the sensitivities of many Senators with carbon-intensive manufacturing industries in their constituencies. It dominated the agenda of the US's bilateral meetings with many countries. However, when subject to scrutiny, it appears EU and Canadian products account for the bulk of the imports in the covered sectors (iron and steel, non-ferrous metals, cement and glass, paper and pulp and basic chemicals), which account for more than 50 per cent of carbon emissions from manufacturing but account for less than 2 per cent of nationwide employment. To soften the impact of any accusations of protectionism, and to make it WTO compatible,

some senators supported the proposal that the revenue collected should become a funding source for the Global Adaptation Fund. Making the border tax WTO compatible is a challenge. China is strongly opposed to US proposal about introduction of a GHG-related border tax.

79 China's National Climate Change Programme, June 2007. China has dedicated almost a third of its stimulus package towards infrastructure projects that will promote energy efficiency.

80 A special report published by *The Economist* on 24 October 2010 provides an assessment of the current state of the relations between China and US.

81 MacGregor, R., 'China's Data on Soaring Energy Use Give a Shock', *The Financial Times*, February 2007.

82 Lewis, I.J. (2007) China's Climate Change Strategy, Jamestown Foundation. See also more recent research from the Foundation (2012).

83 For more information please see the European Parliament Article (November 2007).

84 Harvey, F., 'Yo Kyoto: Bush Shifts His Stance on Global Warming', *The Financial Times*, 2 October 2007.

85 China Briefing News, 5 April 2011.

86 'China says climate talks stalled over lack of commitments to cut emissions', Bloomberg, 8 October 2010.

87 The Pew Trust (2010), Who is Winning the Clean Energy Race?, Washington.

88 'India Rejects Greenhouse Gas Limits', Terra Daily, 28 May 2007.

89 Living on Earth, 10 August 2007.

90 Capoor, K. and Ambrosi, P. (2005), State and Trends of the Carbon Market 2007, World Bank.

91 Hughes, L. (2011), Climate Change and Japan's post-Copenhagen Challenge, The Brookings Institute.

92 The policy is influenced by the Treasury's economic modelling of the carbon price.

93 Trocaire, Changing Lives, Climate Change in the Developing World, Dublin.

94 Arnold,T., CEO Concern (20 November 2009) *Impact of Climate Change on Developing Countries*.

95 European Commission, Communication to the European Parliament, the Council, the European Economic and Social Committee and the Committee of the Regions (2009), Towards a Comprehensive Climate Change Agreement in Copenhagen.

96 UNEP, Oxfam and the World Resource Institute (2011), Adapting for a Green Economy: Companies, Communities and Climate Change, UN Global Compact.

97 UNFCCC (2007), Climate Change: Impacts, Vulnerabilities and Adaptation in Developing Countries.

98 European Commission (2009), Supporting a Climate for Change: the EU and Developing Countries Working Together.

99 Adaptation is different from mitigation in as far as the direct benefits of adaptation actions are local or regional, while the benefits of mitigation actions are shared globally.

100 European Commission (2007), EU Action Against Climate Change: Working With Developing Countries to Tackle Climate Change.

101 See also European Commission (2008), Implementation Framework of the GCCA, Staff Working Document, SEC (2008) 2319, 15 July 2008.

102 Brennan, P., IIEA, Occasional Paper No. 2 (2008) provides a short explanation of flexible mechanisms such as CDMs and JIs.

103 European Commission, Environment and Natural Resources Thematic Programme, 2011–2013 Strategy Paper and Multiannual Indicative Programme, DG for Development and Relations with ACP countries, as approved by the DCI on 29 October 2010. ENRTP commitments are equal to 40 per cent of Member States' total pledges to both the GEF and the MLF over the period 2006–2010.

104 CDC Climat Research (February 2012), Financing climate actions in developing countries: What role is there for NAMAs?.

105 The Economics of Ecosystems and Biodiversity, a study involving the UNEP, the German government and the Commission through the ENRTP. A comparable study on the economics of desertification, land degradation and drought (E-DLDD) is underway.

106 Reid, H., Huq, S. and Murray, L. (2010), Community Champions: Adapting to Climate Challenges, International Institute for Environment and Development, provides or a detailed account of CBA. Irish Aid supports the work of the IIED.

107 See p. 64 of the White Paper. The quote is from Ban Ki Moon, the UN Secretary General.

108 Mary Robinson, President of the Mary Robinson Foundation – Climate Justice, address to the Institute of International and European Affairs, 5 September 2011.

109 Directive 2009/29/EC of the European Parliament and of the Council of 23 April 2009 amending Directive 2003/87/EC so as

to improve and extend the greenhouse gas emission allowance trading scheme of the Community, OJ L140 dated 5 June 2009.

[110] Stern, N. (2007), *The Economics of Climate Change*, The Stern Review, Cambridge University Press.

[111] Jamet, S. and Corfee-Morlot, J. (2009), Assessing the Impacts of Climate Change: A Literature Review, OECD Economics and Environment Departments.

[112] An externality is the cost or benefit accruing to an agent as a result of a transaction to which they were not a party. Externalities result in sub-optimal outcomes for society.

[113] OECD (2009), The Economics of Climate Change Mitigation.

[114] This assumes all GHGs are covered. If reductions in $CO_2$ only were achieved, the cost to world GDP rises to 7 per cent in 2050.

[115] Jones, B., Keen, M., Norregaard, J. and Strand, J., IMF Fiscal Affairs Department (October 2007), 'The Economics of Climate Change', IMF Survey Magazine.

[116] Helm, D. and Hepburn, C. (2009), The Economics and Politics of Climate Change, Oxford University Press.

[117] Weitzman, M.L. (2010), 'Risk-Adjusted Gamma Discounting', *Journal of Environmental Economics and Management*, 60(1): 1–13.

[118] Cox, S. and Vadon, R., 'Running the Rule over Stern's Numbers', BBC Radio 4, 26 January 2007.

[119] A 'discount rate' is necessary to compute all relevant future costs and benefits in present-value terms. Most commonly, the discount rate used for present-value calculations is an interest rate taken from financial markets.

[120] Quiggin, J.C. (2006), Stern and the Critics on Discounting, University of Queensland.

[121] Ecological economics is a trans-disciplinary field of academic research within economics that aims to address the interdependence between human economies and natural ecosystems.

[122] Quoted in IPCC Fourth Assessment Report, Working Group 3, ch. 2, p. 137.

[123] See, for example, Professor Hans Joachim Schellenhuber , Potsdam Institute for Climate Impact Research, who argued to the IIEA Climate Change Working Group that some impacts are in fact 'high probability, high impact'.

[124] IPCC Fourth Assessment Report, Working Group III, Summary for Policy Makers, p. 12.

[125] Nordhaus, W. (2007), 'The Stern Review on the Economics of Climate Change', *Journal of Economic Literature*, 45(3): 686–702.

[126] OECD (2009).

[127] Duval, R. (2008), A Taxonomy of Instruments to Reduce GHG Emissions and Their Interactions, Economics Department Working Paper No. 636, OECD.

[128] National Environmental Research Institute, University of Aarhus (2007), Competitiveness Effects of Environmental Tax Reforms, final report to the European Commission.

[129] Brennan, P. and Curtin, J. (eds) (2008), The Climate Change Challenge: Strategic Issues, Options and Implications for Ireland, Institute of International and European Affairs, ch. 4 (which addresses measures and instruments and policy options to reduce Ireland's GHG emissions).

[130] European Environment Agency (2011), Environmental tax reform in Europe: Opportunities for eco-innovation, EEA Technical Report No. 17/2011.

[131] European Commission (2011), Proposal for a revision of the EU Energy Tax Directive, COM (2011) 169 final, 7 June 2011.

[132] Directive 2003/96/EC.

[133] Under Article 17 of the Renewable Energy Directive (2009/28/EC) and in Article 7b of the Fuel Quality Directive (209/30/EC).

[134] European Commission (2011), Impact Assessment to the Proposal for a Council Directive amending Directive 2003/96/EC Restructuring the Community Framework for the Taxation of Energy Products and Electricity, Staff Working Paper, SEC 409, vols 1 and 2.

[135] European Commission (2009), The Support of Electricity from Renewable Energy Sources, Staff Working Paper.

[136] Deutsche Bank (2009), Global Climate Change Policy Tracker, Deutsche Bank's Climate Change Advisors' reports are top class.

[137] Deutsche Bank (2009), Paying for Renewable Energy: TLC at the Right Price – Achieving Scale through Efficient Policy Design.

[138] After the conclusion of the Durban COP (December 2011), Canada's Environment Minister Peter Kent announced that Canada will not take on a second commitment under the Kyoto Protocol as the Cancún Agreements (covering three-quarters of global emissions) are more comprehensive and more effective than Kyoto. Canada is making significant progress towards its target of reducing GHG emissions by 17 per cent over 2005 levels by 2020.

[139] Cosbey, A., and Tarasofsky, R. (2007), Climate Change, Competitiveness and Trade: A Chatham House Report, The Royal Institute of International Affairs.

[140] OECD (2009).

Notes

141 European Commission, Communication to the European Parliament, the Council, the European Economic and Social Committee and the Committee of the Regions (2010), Analysis of options to move beyond 20 per cent greenhouse gas emission reductions and assessing the risk of carbon leakage, COM (2010) 265 final, 26 May 2010.

142 Stiglitz, J. (2006), 'A New Agenda for Global Warming', *The Economists' Voice*, 3(7).

143 Point Carbon (March 2007), A New Climate for Carbon Trading.

144 Department of Trade and Industry (UK), Meeting the Energy Challenge, White Paper, 2007; uses a €20 per tonne of carbon estimate for 2012.

145 Harris, P., Head of Natural Resources Risk Management, Bank of Ireland Global Markets.

146 European Commission, Communication to the Council. The European Parliament, the European Economic and Social Committee and the Committee of the Regions (2007), Limiting Global Climate Change to 2 Degree Celsius; the way ahead for 2020 and beyond, COM (2007) 2 final, 10 January 2007.

147 Check www.pointcarbon.com to get the latest carbon price.

148 CDC Climat Research (October 2011), 'The factors that determine the carbon price: An econometric analysis', *Tendances Carbone*.

149 O'Kane, K. (2011), 'The Changing Face of CDM post-2012: a European Utilities Perspective', unpublished.

150 European Commission (2009), Towards a Comprehensive Climate Change Agreement in Copenhagen, Staff Working Paper, Part I (p. 73), SEC (2009) 101.

151 European Commission (2012), Analysis of options beyond 20 per cent GHG emission reductions: Member States results, Staff Working Paper, SWD 5 final.

152 CDC Climat Research (February 2012), 'Understanding the link between macroeconomic environment and the EU carbon price', *Tendances Carbone*.

153 Thomson Reuters Point Carbon (2012) Carbon 2012.

154 CDC Climat Research (February 2012), 'The EU ETS carbon price: To intervene or not to intervene?'.

155 Centre for European Policy Studies (2012), *The EU ETS as a Driver for Future Carbon Markets*.

156 A gigatonne is $10^9$ tonnes.

157 The authors state that the possible costs of implementing the options have not been included. These would include transactions costs.

[158] Most studies produce a social cost of carbon that increases over time, the logic being that as concentrations of GHGs increase, the impacts associated with each additional unit of carbon increase. In 1996, the IPCC's Working Group III produced a figure of between $6–160 (in 2000 prices) for each tonne of carbon emitted between 1991 and 2000. The range increases to $9–197 for each tonne of carbon emitted between 2001 and 2010.

[159] European Environmental Agency (1996), Communication on Community Strategy on Climate Change.

[160] European Council of Ministers, Presidency Conclusions, Brussels, 8–9 March 2007.

[161] For more information see Dr R.K. Pachauri's presentation to the IIEA's Carbon Day, 1 June 2007.

[162] European Commission, Communication to the Council. The European Parliament, the European Economic and Social Committee and the Committee of the Regions (2007), Limiting Global Climate Change to 2 Degree Celsius: The way ahead for 2020 and beyond, COM (2007) 2 final, 10 January 2007.

[163] Between 435 and 535ppm/ $CO_2$-e.

[164] 450ppm/$CO_2$-e.

[165] Between 500–550 ppm/$CO_2$-e.

[166] Professor H.J. Schellenhuber's presentation to the IIEA, Dublin, June 2007.

[167] Weale, A. (1996), 'Environmental Rules and Rule-Making in the European Union', *Journal of European Public Policy*, 3(4): 598.

[168] Treaty of Lisbon amending the Treaty on European Union and the Treaty establishing the European Community, OJ C 306, 17 December 2007.

[169] Damro, C. and Mendes, P.L. (2003), 'Emissions Trading at Kyoto: From EU Resistance to Union Innovation', *Environmental Politics*, 12(2).

[170] In fact, both the EU and its Member States were signatories to the Kyoto Protocol, leading to some ambiguity as to who was ultimately responsible for implementation.

[171] The foreign minister of the country holding the Presidency of the Council, the Commissioner for External Relations and the High Representative of the Common Foreign and Security Policy.

[172] Ringius, L. (1997), Differentiation, Leaders and Fairness: Negotiating Climate Change Commitments in the European Community, CICERO Report 1997, Oslo.

[173] European Commission (2008), Impact Assessment accompanying the package of implementation measures for the EU's objectives on climate change and renewable energy for 2020,

Staff Working Document, SEC 85/3. This analysis provides a lot of primary data that could assist with research into climate change policies.

[174] Community Guidelines on State aid for Environment Protection (2008/C 82/01), OJ C 82/1, 1 April 2008.

[175] Decision 406/2009/EC on the effort of Member States to reduce greenhouse gas emissions to meet the Community's greenhouse gas emission reduction commitments up to 2020, OJ L 140/136, 5 June 2009.

[176] Department of the Environment, Community and Local Government (2011), Review of National Climate Policy.

[177] Teagasc has conducted significant research into potential abatement options.

[178] Department of Transport (2009), Smarter Travel – A Sustainable Transport Future: A new Transport Policy for Ireland 2009–2020.

[179] The case for an ambitious electric vehicles programme was set out in a report Drive for Zero, approved by the Oireachtas Joint Committee on Climate Change and Energy Security, April 2009; Simon Coveney, T.D., was rapporteur.

[180] Department of the Environment, Community and Local Government (2011), Review of National Climate Policy.

[181] Directive 2009/28/EC of 23 April 2009 on the promotion of the use of energy from renewable sources and amending and subsequently repealing Directives 2001/77/EC and 2003/30/EC, OJ L 140/16, 3 June 2009.

[182] DCENR (2010), National Renewable Energy Action Plan.

[183] Report from the Commission to the Council and European Parliament on sustainability requirements for the use of solid and gaseous biomass sources in electricity, heating and cooling, COM (2010) 11 final, 25 February 2010.

[184] European Communities (Renewable Energy) Regulations 2011, SI 147 of 2011 and Sustainable Energy Act 2002 (Section 8 (2)) (Conferral of Additional Functions) Renewable Energy Order 2011, SI 148 of 2011. The elements of the directive transposed include the provisions relating to access to and operation of the grid; guarantees of origin and the exemplary role of public bodies regarding public buildings. SI 148 of 2011 confers additional functions on the SEAI concerning renewable energy related information and training; promotion and encouragement of renewable energy use by public bodies; and promotion of certain renewable technologies.

<sup>185</sup> Presentation on the European Energy Roadmap 2050 by Philip Lowe, European Commission, Director General, DG Energy, IIEA Dublin, 10 November 2011.

<sup>186</sup> By the end of 2011, Ireland had 1,900 MW of renewable generation on the grid, including 1,630 MW of wind connected; 234 MW of hydro; and 46 MW from other sources.

<sup>187</sup> This breakdown reflects the priorities set down in the 2007 Energy White Paper and was not derived from robust economic analysis.

<sup>188</sup> DG Energy's website provides full details about the EU's energy-efficiency policies.

<sup>189</sup> European Commission (2011), *Proposal for a Directive on energy efficiency and repealing Directives 2004/8/EC and 2006/32/EC*, COM (2011) 370 final, 22 June 2011. See also the accompanying Impact Statement, SEC (2011) 779 final.

<sup>190</sup> Smart meters have been estimated to pay for themselves in less than four years through increased productivity, as a result of increased customer awareness and energy price signals.

<sup>191</sup> A typical family spends €1,000 a year heating their home. Grants of up to €5,560 are available for a comprehensive up-grade package. On average every home uses around 30 MWh or primary energy equivalent per annum. Some 150,000 homes have completed upgrade works (September 2011), with an investment of €300m.

<sup>192</sup> Curtin, J. and Maguire, J. (eds) (2011), Thinking Deeper – Financing Options for Home Retrofit, Institute for International and European Affairs. Two pay as you save options are assessed in detail, one which attaches the loan to the property (based on a US trial) and another which attaches the loan to the energy meter (based on upcoming UK data). See also presentations made to the IIEA's September 2011 conference on retrofitting.

<sup>193</sup> European Commission, Communication to the European Parliament, the Council, the European Economic and Social Committee and the Committee of the Regions (2010), Analysis of options to move beyond 20 per cent greenhouse gas emission reductions and assessing the risk of carbon leakage, COM (2010) 265 final, May 2010. Of particular interest to researchers is the accompanying background information and analysis, SEC (2009) 101 of 28 January 2009.

<sup>194</sup> The European Council in December 2008 confirmed: 'the European Union's commitment to increasing this reduction to 30 per cent within the framework of an ambitious and comprehensive global agreement in Copenhagen on climate change for the period after 2012 on condition that the other developed

countries undertake to achieve comparable emission reductions and that the economically more advanced developing countries make a contribution commensurate with their respective responsibilities and capabilities.'

195 UNFCCC, press release, 1 February 2010.
196 Data based on Member State's inventories, without LULUCF, but with aviation included.
197 These figures represent an additional energy cost, not a reduction of GDP. It includes additional investments needed, as well as energy savings. It does not include air quality benefits.
198 In the analysis presented in 2008, EU GDP over the period 2005–2020 was assumed to grow yearly at an average rate of 2.4 per cent. In this updated analysis, this average yearly growth over the same period has decreased to 1.7 per cent. For more information see table 4 of Part II of the Staff Working Document, SEC (2010) 650, accompanying the Communication.
199 The Commission's impact assessment projected a carbon price of some €32 (2008 prices) in the ETS, in case of full implementation of the package (including renewables policies and maximum use of international credits). New projections show a carbon price of €16 in 2020 (including renewables policies to meet the 20 per cent target, without necessitating international credits).
200 Reaching the goal of staying under a 2°C temperature increase will also require developing countries as a group, in particular the more advanced among them, to achieve a substantial and quantifiable deviation below the currently predicted emissions growth rate, in the order of 15–30 per cent below BAU by 2020.
201 World Energy Outlook 2009, estimate: US$ 500 billion.
202 European Commission, Communication to the European Parliament, the Council, the European Economic and Social Committee and the Committee of the Regions (2010), A digital agenda for Europe, COM (2010) 245 final, 19 May 2010.
203 Article11.a (5) of the ETS Directive (2009/29/EC) contains the legal basis for the Community to conclude agreements with third countries for the provision of sectoral credits in the event that the negotiations on an international agreement on climate change are not concluded by 31 December 2009.
204 A multiplier of e.g. 2 for 1 would mean that for every tonne emitted in an ETS installation, two tonnes of CDM credits would have to be surrendered. In this way every CDM credits used to cover a tonne emitted in Europe would as a by-product result in another tonne reduced in a developing country.

205 Cost estimate includes the achievement of the 20 per cent renewables target.
206 European Commission (2012), Analysis of options beyond 20 per cent GHG emission reductions: Member States results, Staff Working Paper, SWD 5 final, 1 February 2012.
207 European Commission (2010), Europe 2020: A European Strategy for Smart, Sustainable and Inclusive Growth. The Commission's recommendations for Ireland under *Europe 2020* are set out in a Staff Working Paper, SEC (2011) 716 final, 7 June 2011.
208 Directive 2003/87/EC establishing a scheme for GHG emission allowance trading within the Community and amending Council Directive 96/61/EC dated 13 October 2003.
209 The term 'trading sector' refers to sectors covered by the EU ETS; this currently includes energy activities (power generators, combustion installations with a rated thermal input exceeding 20MW, mineral oil refineries, coke ovens), production and processing of ferrous metals, mineral industries (cement, clinker, glass and ceramic bricks), and pulp, paper and board activities. 11,000 installations and 41 per cent of EU GHG emissions are covered by the EU ETS. In addition, emissions from international aviation are also covered.
210 Directive 2004/101/EC amending Directive 2003/87/EC establishing a scheme for greenhouse gas allowance trading within the Community, in respect of the Kyoto Protocol's project mechanisms, OJ L 228/18, 13 November 2004.
211 European Commission, Communication to the European Parliament, the Council, the European Economic and Social Committee and the Committee of the Regions (2006), *On the assessment of National Allocation Plans for the allocation of greenhouse gas emission allowances in the second period of the EU ETS*, COM (2006) 725 final, 29 November 2006.
212 Confusingly, 1990 was replaced by 2005 – the latest year for which verifiable emissions figures are available – as the baseline for measurements.
213 See for example, The EU ETS in Perspective, Pew Centre on Global Climate Change; EU ETS Review II CEPS, and the most recent by the Scottish Government.
214 Directive 2009/29/EC of 23 April 2009 amending Directive 2003/87/EC so as to improve and extend the GHG emission allowance trading scheme of the Community, OJ L 140/63, 5 June 2009.
215 Commission Regulation (EU) 1031/2010 on the timing, administration and other aspects of auctioning GHG allowances

pursuant to Directive 2003/87/EC, Official Journal L 302/1, 18 November 2010.

[216] Committee on Climate Change (2008), *Building a Low-Carbon Economy – The UK's Contribution to Tackling Climate Change.* See also www.carbonretirement.com

[217] European Commission (2012), Analysis of options beyond 20 per cent GHG emission reductions: Member States results, Staff Working Paper, SWD (2012) 5 final, 1 February 2012, Table 7.

[218] European Commission, Communication to the European Parliament, the Council, the European Economic and Social Committee and the Committee of the Regions (2008), Addressing the challenges of deforestation and forest degradation to tackle climate change and biodiversity loss, COM (2008) 645 final.

[219] Macken, K. (2011), The EU ETS: A Review of the First Six Years of Operation, EPA.

[220] DECLG, Climate Change Section, Draft Regulatory Impact Analysis on the Revised EU ETS Directive, July 2011.

[221] The European Communities (Greenhouse Gas Emissions Trading) (Amendment) Regulations 2010, SI 161 of 2010 and European Communities (Greenhouse Gas Trading) (Amendment) Regulations 2011, SI 127 of 2011.

[222] Directive 2008/101/EC amending Directive 2003/87/EC so as to include aviation activities in the scheme of GHG emission allowance trading within the Community, OJ L8/3, 13 January 2009. This Directive was transposed into Irish law by SI 261 of 2010, European Communities (Greenhouse Gas Trading) (Aviation) Regulations, 2010. The implementation of the Aviation ETS Directive was the subject of a partial Regulatory Impact Assessment.

[223] Ryanair, press release, 11 January 2012.

[224] Merrill Lynch, Aviation in the EU ETS: An incentive for efficiency, September 2008 and IATA (2010).

[225] See Virgin Atlantic's carbon-offset scheme for example. [226] A lot of modelling has been done on the relationship between allowance prices and power prices. The major uncertainty is the future price of EAUs and this depends to a significant extent on regulatory certainty.

[227] Commission Decision 2020/634/EU adjusting the Union-wide quantity of allowances to be issued under the ETS for 2013 and repealing Decision 2010/384/EU, Official Journal L 279/34, 23 October 2010.

[228] Commission Decision 2011/278/EU determining transitional Union-wide rules for harmonised free allocation of emission

allowances pursuant to Article 10a of the Directive 2003/87/ EC, Official Journal L 130/1, 17 May 2011.

[229] Department of Environment, Heritage and Local Government (2007), National Climate Change Strategy 2007–2012.

[230] Decision No. 280/2004/EC of the European Parliament and of the Council of 11 February 2004 concerning a mechanism for monitoring Community greenhouse gas emissions and for implementing the Kyoto Protocol.

[231] SEAI (2011), Energy Forecasts for Ireland to 2020.

[232] ESRI (2010), Recovery Scenarios for Ireland.

[233] The Carbon Fund was set up under the Carbon Fund Act 2007 to purchase carbon credits on behalf of the Government.

[234] Department of Agriculture Food and the Marine (2010), Food Harvest 2020: A Vision for Irish Agri-food and Fisheries.

[235] DCENR (2009), Maximising Ireland's Energy Efficiency: The National Energy Efficiency Action Plan 2009–2020.

[236] DCENR (2010), *National Renewable Energy Action Plan: Ireland,* submitted to the European Commission under Article 4 of Directive 2009/28/EC.

[237] European Commission (2011), Progress towards achieving the Kyoto objectives, Report to the European Parliament and the Council (required under Article 5 of Decision 280/2004/EC) COM (2011) 624 final, 7 October 2011.

[238] EPA (2008), Ireland's National Allocation Plan for Emission Trading 2008–2012, Final Allocation Decision.

[239] Comptroller and Auditor General Annual Report, Accounts of Public Services 2008, September 2009.

[240] 69.3 Mt of $CO_2$e (total 2005 national emissions) – 22.4 tonnes of $CO_2$ (2005 ETS emissions without de-minimis) = 46.8 Mt of $CO_2$e (2005 non-ETS emissions) - 20 per cent = 37.5 Mt of $CO_2$e. However, some further adjustment of this figure is anticipated due to corrections for alterations to the scope of the ETS.

[241] Walker, N. (2012) 'Climate Mitigation Policy – a business perspective', presentation to the IIEA's Carbon Day, 16 April 2012.

[242] Department of Transport, Tourism and Sport (2009), *Smarter Travel – A Sustainable Transport Future: A new Transport Policy for Ireland (2009–2020).*

[243] European Commission (2011), Roadmap to a Single Transport Area – Towards a Competitive and Resource Efficient Transport System, COM (2011) 144 final, March 2011.

[244] EPA (2009), Municipal Solid Waste – Pre-treatment and Residuals Management, an EPA Technical Guidance Document.

[245] Waste Management (Food Waste) Regulations 2009. SI 508 of 2009.

246 SEAI (2011), Energy in Ireland 1990–2010.

247 Howley, M., ó Gallachóir, B., and Dennehy, E. (2010), Understanding Electricity and Gas Prices in Ireland, SEAI.

248 Presented in December 2010 by the Minister for the Environment, Heritage and Local Government.

249 Each year the time series from 1990 is revised to reflect changes in methodology; the 2011 carbon budget used a later inventory record.

250 European Environmental Agency (2011), Greenhouse gas emission trends and projections in Europe 2011, EEA Report No. 4/2011.

251 EPA, 'EPA Announces Final Decision for Ireland's National Allocation Plan', 5 March 2008.

252 The authority's five-year strategic plan should be consulted for details.

253 Department of the Taoiseach (2007), An Agreed Programme for Government, pp 19–20.

254 European Commission (2009), Adapting to climate change: Towards a European framework for action, White Paper COM (2009) 147 final, 1 April 2009.

255 Forfás (August 2010), Adaptation to Climate Change: Issues for Business.

256 The research was completed by a consortium led by H.R. Wallingford and included eleven sector reports and an overarching technical evidence report.

257 The UK has legislated for a steadily rising carbon floor price which will inevitably result in higher carbon costs than elsewhere in the EU.

258 Which had, for illustrative purposes, predicted a best-case scenario target of -2 per cent for the whole economy on 1990 levels by 2020.

259 DECLG, Review of National Climate Change Policy, 3 November 2011:

260 If, for example, a car runs on electricity rather than petrol, the emissions would be counted in the EU ETS sector – where the electricity was generated – rather than in the transport sector. Emissions from transport would be reduced; the company producing the electricity would have to purchase permits on the carbon market to cover its increase in emissions.

261 European Commission, Communication to the European Parliament, the Council, the European Economic and Social Committee and the Committee of the Regions (2011), A roadmap for moving to a competitive low carbon economy by 2050, COM (2011) 112 final, 8 March 2011.

[262] Reid, L., 'Government underestimated effect of abandoned carbon tax', *The Irish Times*, 29 November 2004.

[263] Scott, S. and Eakins, J. (2004), *Carbon Taxes: Which Households Gain or Lose?*, report for the EPA, ESRI.

[264] World Resource Institute (2011), Building the Climate Change Regime – Survey and Analysis of Approaches.

[265] ETUC (2010), Climate Change and Employment, Impact of Employment in the EU-25 of Climate Change and Carbon Emission Reduction Measures by 2030.

[266] Houses of the Oireachtas, Fifth Report of the Joint Committee on Climate Change and Energy Security, Second Report on Climate Change Law, October 2010, Liz McManus TD was rapporteur.

[267] The Group comprises 12 industry leaders who presented a communiquÉ on climate change to the Taoiseach on the occasion of the diaspora leaders' meeting in Farmleigh (2010).

[268] Department of the Environment, Community and Local Government, press release, 'Hogan Issues Roadmap for Climate Policy and Legislation', 23 January 2012.

[269] Curtin, J. and Hanrahan, G. (2012), Why Legislate? Designing a Climate Law for Ireland, IIEA.

[270] Stavins, R.N. (2004), Discussion Paper, *Resources for the Future, Can an Effective Global Climate Change Treaty be Based on Sound Science, Rational Economics and Pragmatic Politics, Resources for the Future.*

[271] Scott and Eakins (2004).

[272] Tol, R.S.J., Callan, T., Conefrey, T., FitzGerald, J.D., Lyons, S., Malaguzzi Valeri, L. and Scott, S. (2008), A Carbon Tax for Ireland, ESRI.

[273] Report of the Commission on Taxation, 2009.

[274] For full details refer to the *Revenue Commissioner's Guide* (2010). The operation of the NGCT is governed by Chapter 2 of Part 3 of the Finance Act 2010. The rate (based on net calorific value) is derived from the rate of €15 per tonne of $CO_2$ emitted and is calculated by multiplying the emission factor of natural gas, expressed in kilograms of $CO_2$ per terajoule (56,873), by the number of terajoules per MWh (0.0036) and multiplying the resultant figure by a rate of 1.5 cent per kilogram of $CO_2$ emitted.

[275] Department of Finance, TSG Paper 01/22.

[276] Sweden, Denmark, Norway and the UK either exempt ETS sites completely, or pass through between 10 per cent and 20 per cent of the carbon tax to such enterprises.

[277] Dail Statement by the Minister for the Environment, Heritage and Local Government on the occasion of the presentation of the Carbon Budget 2011.

[278] Section 76A of the Taxes Consolidation Act 1997.

[279] Section 90A of the Stamp Duties Consolidation Act 1999.

[280] Section 6(1)(a) of Schedule 1, Value Added Tax Consolidated Act 2010.

[281] As with all schemes involving Exchequer support it had to be approved under EU State aid rules. The Commission's decision (September 2007) provides a good description about the main features of the scheme and the conditions that were attached to it.

[282] Gorecki, P.K. (2011), The Internal EU Electricity Market: Implications for Ireland, Research Series No. 23, ESRI.

[283] *Farmers Journal*, 27 August 2011. The Government approved the scheme on 21 February 2012.

[284] Reply to a parliamentary question, 18 January 2012.

[285] Departments of Environment, Community and Local Government and Public Expenditure and Reform (2012), An Action Plan for Green Procurement.

[286] European Commission, Communication to the European Parliament, the Council, the European Economic and Social Committee and the Committee of the Regions (2011), A resource-efficient Europe – Flagship initiative under the Europe 2020 Strategy, COM (2011) 21, January 2011.

[287] European Commission, Communication to the European Parliament, the Council, the European Economic and Social Committee and the Committee of the Regions (2011), A roadmap for moving to a competitive low carbon economy by 2050, COM (2011) 112 final, 8 March 2011.

[288] European Commission, Communication to the European Parliament, the Council, the European Economic and Social Committee and the Committee of the Regions (2011), Energy Efficiency Plan 2011, COM (2011) 109 final, 8 March 2011.

[289] Taking into account necessary efforts from developing countries, this will allow a global reduction of 50 per cent in emissions by 2050.

[290] European Commission (2011), Roadmap to a Single European Transport Area – Towards a competitive and resource-efficient transport system, White Paper COM (2911) 144 final, 28 March 2011.

[291] Poland blocked the adoption of Ministers' conclusions on the Low Carbon 2050 Roadmap at the EU Environment Council held on 9 March 2012.

[292] As agreed by the Emissions Trading Directive 2003/87/EC (as amended by Directive 2009/29/EC) and the effort-sharing decision (Decision 406/2009/EC).

[293] European Commission, Communication to the European Parliament, the Council, the European Economic and Social Committee and the Committee for the Regions (2009), *Investing in the development of low carbon technologies* (SET-Plan). COM (2009) 519 final, 7 October 2009.

[294] *Practical Guide to a Prosperous Low-Carbon Europe* (2010), ECF.

[295] IEA (2011), World Energy Outlook 2011.

[296] European Commission, Communication to the European Parliament, the Council, the European Economic and Social Committee and the Committee for the Regions (2011), Energy Roadmap 2050, COM (2011) 885 final, December 2011.

[297] Directive 2003/87/EC as amended by Directive 2009/29/EC foresees a linear reduction of the cap of 1.74 percentage points per year. This reduction is legally enshrined in the ETS and continues after 2020.

[298] European Commission, Communication to the European Parliament, the Council, the European Economic and Social Committee and the Committee for the Regions (2010), Energy infrastructure priorities for 2020 and beyond – A Blueprint for an Integrated European Energy Network, COM (2010) 677.

[299] The level of reductions in the bill for fossil fuel imports depend on future fossil fuel price developments and diversification of supply sources.

[300] Directive 2010/31/EU of 19 May 2010 on the energy performance of buildings.

[301] European Commission, Communication to the European Parliament, the Council, the European Economic and Social Committee and the Committee of the Regions (2011), Analysis of options to move beyond 20 per cent GHG emission reductions and assessing the risk of carbon leakage, COM (2011) 265 final, 26 May 2010.

[302] Article 10a (13) of Directive 2003/87/EC as amended by Directive 2009/29/EC.

[303] European Commission, Communication to the European Parliament, the Council, the European Economic and Social Committee and the Committee of the Regions (2010), The CAP towards 2020 – meeting the food, natural resources and territorial challenges of the future, COM (2010) 672 final, 18 November 2010.

[304] Eurostat, National Accounts.

[305] World Bank Indicators.

306 If it constitutes state aid, public funding will have to comply with and be approved under EU state aid rules.

307 European Commission, Communication to the European Parliament, the Council, the European Economic and Social Committee and the Committee of the Regions (2010), An Agenda for New Skills and Jobs – A European Contribution Towards Full Employment, COM (2010) 682 final, 23 November 2010.

308 This assumes an accelerated implementation of that the NREAP.

309 A resource efficiency project funded by the EPA as part of the National Waste Prevention Programme.

310 *ENDS Directory 2008*, UK, CEED Global Market Estimate.

311 UK Commission on Environmental Markets and Economic Performance, BERR/DEFRA Report, November 2007.

312 Environmental Business International Inc (2010), *EBI Report: The Climate Change Industry*.

313 Leflevre, X., OECD, presentation at 'Today's Environmental Research, Tomorrow's Environmental Protection', EPA Conference on Irish Environmental Research Dublin, February 2008.

314 US Department of Commerce.

315 Vickery, G. and Iarrera, M. (1996), *The Global Environmental Goods and Services Industries*, OECD.

316 UK CEED (2006), Emerging Markets in the Environmental Industries Sector, Report for the UK Department for the Environment, Food and Rural Affairs.

317 CleanEdge Inc. (2011), Clean Energy Trends 2011.

318 Report of the Commission on Environmental Markets and Economic Performance, November 2007.

319 New Energy Finance, White Paper, April 2007.

320 Bloomberg New Energy Finance.

321 Renewable Energy Global Status Report.

322 EICTA (2008), 'High Tech: Low Carbon – The role of technology in tackling climate change'. ICT Ireland is a member of EICTA. Citing several studies, EICTA points out that the application of ICT solutions could reduce energy consumption in the EU from 10 per cent to 25 per cent by 2020: (2008) 'Intellect, High Tech: Low Carbon.'

323 European Commission, Communication to the European Parliament, the Council, the European Economic and Social Committee and the Committee of the Regions (2008), Addressing the challenge of energy efficiency through Information and Communication Technologies, COM (2008) 241 final, 13 May 2008.

324 IEA (2010), Energy Technology Perspectives, Scenarios and Strategies to 2050.

# Notes

325 European Commission (2005), Assessing Opportunities for ICT to Contribute to Sustainable Development, DG Information Society.

326 A&L Goodbody Consulting and the Clean Technology Centre (2005), *Assessment of the Potential to Develop Environmental State Aid Supports for Enterprise*, a report for Forfás, unpublished.

327 European Commission, Community Guidelines on State Aid for Environmental Protection, 23 January 2008. OJ C 82 dated 1 April 2008.

328 REN21, 'Renewable energy policy network for the 21st century'.

329 European Wind Energy Association, Wind in Power, 2011 European Statistics, February 2012.

330 European Commission (2007), A European Strategic Energy Technology Plan, Staff Working Document, SEC 1511, 22 November 2007.

331 'EU report see bio-fuel giving 3.4 per cent of 2020 needs', commentary on leaked draft EEA report, *Reuters*, 4 July 2008.

332 European Parliament, Environment Committee, List of key compromise amendments, 7 July 2008.

333 'Secret report: bio-fuel caused food crisis', *The Guardian*, 4 July 2008.

334 Ringel, M. (2006), 'Fostering the use of renewable energies in the EU; the race between feed-in tariffs and green certificates', *Renewable Energy*, 31: 1–17.

335 Carbon Trust (2006), Future Marine Energy.

336 US Department of Commerce (2010), Measuring the Green Economy.

337 Avery, B. et al. (2004), 'Global Demand for US Environmental Goods and Services', Journal of Agricultural and Applied Economics.

338 US Energy Information Agency.

339 Renewable Fuels Association, April 2007.

340 Bourne, J.K. (2007), 'Green Dreams: Making fuel from crops could be good for the planet–after a breakthrough or two', National Geographic.

341 Department of Energy (2011), Biomass Supply for a Bio-energy and Bio-products Industry.

342 National Renewable Energy Laboratory, 2009.

343 Department of Energy, Washington, National Energy Renewable Laboratory.

344 Massachusetts Institute of Technology, 2009.

345 US Government Executive Order 13423.

346 US DOE/EERE, 15 January 2007.

347 *Bloomberg Business*, November 2007.

348 Chatham House Report, Who Owns Our Low Carbon Future: Intellectual Property and Energy Technologies, September 2009.

349 Climate Change Business Journal, 18 January 2008.

350 Library House research report, *Cleantech Goes Mainstream*, September 2007.

351 Thomson Financial, National Venture Capital Association, November 2007.

352 Bloomberg New Energy Finance, 'Sustainable Development Technology Canada forecast that the global environmental industry is now worth in excess of $4 trillion'.

353 Carus, F., 'Venture Capital: Patience is a virtue in hunt for game-changing "Green Google"', *Financial Times*, 28 October 2011.

354 Estimate of the UN's Environmental Programme.

355 Koppl, A. (2006), *The Austrian Environmental Industry Summary of Results WIFO*.

356 Ernst and Young, *Eco-industry, its size, employment, perspectives and barriers to growth in an enlarged EU* European Commission DG Environment, Brussels, 2006.

357 Bundesministerium für land- und forstwirtschaft, umwelt und wasserwirtschaft land niederösterreich *MUT Masterplan Uumwelttechnologie Österreichische: umwelttechnologie auf dem weg in die zukunft.* 2007.

358 The Corporate Leaders Group on Climate Change comprises major UK and international companies, including ABN Amro, Centrica, Shell, Tesco and Vodafone.

359 European Research Centre (UK) (2007), Investment in Electricity Generation: The role of costs, incentives and risks.

360 Presentation by Barbara Swann, Department of Enterprise, Trade and Investment, MRIA Conference, 10 February 2012.

361 *All-Island Energy Market: Renewable Electricity – A '2020' Vision*, preliminary consultation document, July 2005.

362 DCENR and the Department of Enterprise, Trade and Investment (2008), All-island Grid Study.

363 The UK's CCAR reviewed the evidence for more than 700 potential climate change impacts on the UK economy, society and environment, with over 100 of these impacts taken forward for more detailed analysis. A list of the most important impacts for Northern Ireland was subsequently developed through a process of consultation with stakeholders.

364 Forfás and InterTradeIreland (2008), Environmental Goods and Services Sector on the Island of Ireland, Enterprise Opportunities and Policy Implications.

[365] European Commission, DG Environment, *Eco-industry, its size, employment, perspectives and barriers to growth in an enlarged EU*, Ernst & Young, September 2006.

[366] National Industrial Symbiosis Programme case studies, 2007.

[367] CEMEP, case study: Scott Brothers, Impetus Waste Management and Plasrec, 2007.

[368] Carbon Trust, case study, 2007.

[369] Philips Sustainability Report (2006), Improving Lives, Delivering Value.

[370] Carbon Trust (2006), *Carbon Footprints in the Supply Chain: The Next Steps for Business.*

[371] Discussions with EPS Consulting as part of their research fieldwork in completing a report for Forfás/InterTrade Ireland on Business Opportunities in the Environmental Goods and Services Sector, 2008.

[372] Interview with Regina Breheny (2008), Irish Venture Capital Association

[373] Leflaive, X., OECD, EPS Research Conference, Dublin, February 2008.

[374] Matthews, N., '41 Shades of Green', *Business and Finance*, 18 January 2008.

[375] Expert Group on Future Skills Needs (2010), Future Skills Needs of Enterprise within the Green Economy in Ireland.

[376] Martin, J.P., Director, Employment, Labour and Social Affairs, OECD, presentation at Belgium Ministerial Conference on Transition Towards a Competitive Low Carbon and Green Economy, Brussels, 2010.

[377] SEAI, press release, 28 March 2012.

[378] Department of Environment, Heritage and Local Government (2006), Ireland's National Roadmap for the Implementation of the Environmental Technologies Action Plan (ETAP) .

[379] Kelly, D. and Ryan, J. (CIRCA Group Europe Ltd) (2007), Environmental Technologies: Guidelines on How to Take a Pilot Project to Market (2005-ET-DS-25-M3) Final Report, EPA.

[380] Coakley, T. et al. (Clean Technology Centre) (2007), Investigation into why existing environmental technologies are underused (2005-ET-DS-19-M3) Final Report, EPA.

[381] Forfás (March 2012), Report of the Research Prioritisation Steering Group.

[382] The Ecology Foundation (2010), Energy Security: Ireland on the Edge.

[383] Eirgrid 25, A strategy for the development of Ireland's electricity grid for a sustainable and competitive future.

[384] Commission for Energy Regulation (2011), Smart Metering Information Paper 4.
[385] SEAI. An earlier (pre-recession) forecast suggested a requirement for 6 GW of installed capacity.
[386] SQQenergy (2010), Economic Study for Ocean Energy Development in Ireland, a report for SEAI and Invest Northern Ireland.
[387] Houses of the Oireachtas, Joint Committee on Climate Change and Energy Security (April 2009), Drive for Zero: Electric vehicles are a Winning Proposition.
[388] By the end of 2011 just 50 electric vehicles had been purchased despite the availability of an Exchequer subsidy.
[389] Department of Transport, Smarter Travel – a Sustainable Transport Future Policy: A new Transport Policy for Ireland 2009–2020.
[390] Forfas (2011), Intelligent Infrastructure: Delivering the Competitiveness Benefits and Enterprise Opportunities.
[391] Curtin, J. and Maguire, J. (eds) (2011), Thinking Deeper: Financing Options for Home Retrofit, IIEA.
[392] SEAI, press release, 12 March 2012.
[393] DECLG (2012), Reform of the Water Sector in Ireland, position paper.
[394] A PwC report addressed the regulatory arrangements for water in Ireland and identified the business model required to generate the investment needed, including domestic water meters.
[395] DECLG (2011), Towards a New National Waste Policy, discussion document.
[396] HM Government (2011), Enabling the Transition to a Green Economy: Government and Business Working Together.
[397] European Cluster Observatory, Europe Innova, Eco-Innovation and National Cluster Policies in Europe: a Qualitative Review, July 2011. See also Cluster Benchmarking Report from the South West Regional Authority, June 2009.
[398] Global Green Interchange (2011), Securing Ireland's Competitive Advantage in the Transition to a Global Low Carbon Economy.
[399] Department of Jobs, Enterprise and Innovation (2011), Progress Report on the Implementation of the recommendations of the Report of the High Level Group on Green Enterprise.
[400] Meadows, D.H., Meadows, D.L., Randers J. and Behrens III, W.W. (1992), The Limits to Growth, Club of Rome. The book echoes some of the concerns and predictions of the reverend T.R. Malthus in An Essay on the Principle of Population (1798).
[401] The Sixth EAP expires in mid-2012. EU environment policy was listed as an EU Treaty competence in the Single European Act 1987.

402 UN documents on sustainable development.
403 Jacquier, J. (2005), 'On Relationships Between Integrated Policies for Sustainable Urban Development and Urban Governance', Royal Dutch Geographical Society 96(4).
404 Economist Intelligence Unit (2007), Action or Aspiration? Sustainability in the Workplace.
405 Eurostat (2011), Sustainable Development in the European Union: 2011 Monitoring Report of the EU Sustainable Development Strategy.
406 Department of the Environment, Heritage and Local Government (2007), *National Climate Change Strategy 2007–2012*.
407 Department of Communications, Energy and Natural Resources (2007), Energy White Paper, *Delivering a Sustainable Energy Future for Ireland*.
408 SEAI (2010), Renewable Energy In Ireland, 2010 Update. In fact, in the early part of 2012 the share rose to nearly 20 per cent.
409 Walsh, A. (January 2012), *Climate Change and the Role of Banking*, unpublished.
410 'Paradigm Change Capital LLP Forms Group to Promote Low Carbon Bonds', *Bloomberg*, 19 July 2011.
411 Ernst & Young (2010), Business Risk Report 2010.
412 Kyte, R., Vice-President and Head of Network, Sustainable Development, World Bank.
413 Paradigm Change Capital Partners LLP.
414 Paul Harris, Bank of Ireland, 2011.
415 HSBC (2010), Sizing The Climate Economy.
416 Swiss Federal Institute of Technology, Zurich (2009), Banking and Climate Change: Opportunities and Risks – An analysis of climate strategies in more than 100 banks worldwide.
417 Gaskin, F. (2012), *'Do Investors and Consumers Care if a Company Goes Green?'*, unpublished.
418 The Global Investor Survey on Climate Change (2010), Annual Report on Actions and Progress.
419 PwC (UK) (2008), Sustainability: Are Consumers Buying It?
420 KPMG (2011), Corporate Sustainability: A Progress Report.
421 Gaskin (2012).
422 Cohn & Wolfe, Landor Associates and Penn, Schoen & Berland (2011), The 2011 Green Brands Survey.
423 Mintel, March 2010.
424 PwC (UK) (2008), *Sustainability: Are Consumers Buying It*.
425 Business in the Community Ireland (2009), Green Ireland: The Business of Climate Change.

426 Department of the Environment, Community and Local Government (2011), A Framework for Sustainable Development for Ireland, a draft for public consultation.

427 Forfas (2010), Adaptation to Climate Change: Issues for Business.

428 European Commission (2009), Adapting to Climate Change: Towards a European Framework for Action, White Paper COM (2009) 147 final, April 2009.

429 To keep up to date with developments check out this regular newsletter.

430 European Commission, Communication to the European Parliament, the Council, the European Economic and Social Committee and the Committee of the Regions (2011), Rio+2-: Towards the Green Economy and Better Governance, COM (2011) final, 20 June 2011.

431 The EU's principal documents on sustainable development.

432 European Commission, Communication to the European Parliament, the Council, the European Economic and Social Committee and the Committee of the Regions (2011), A Resource-Efficient Europe – Flagship Initiative under the Europe 2020 Strategy, COM (2011) 21, 26 January 2011.

433 D/ECLG engaged in a stakeholder consultation on the rNSDS. Further details about the Government's policy on sustainable development can be found on this site.

434 DCENR (2012), NREAP, First Progress Report. The figure represents the share of renewable energy in gross final energy consumption.

435 Department of Energy, Communication and Natural Resources (2012), *Strategy for Renewable Energy (2012–2020)*.

436 His speech to the IIEA (24 February 2012), The Future of Energy Policy in Ireland and Europe set out his wider strategic approach.

437 SEAI (2011), Energy in Ireland 1990–2010, 2011 Report.

438 SEAI claims that 89 per cent of Ireland's energy is derived from imported supplies and that Ireland is 'the least self-sufficient country in the industrialised world (for energy production/consumption)'.

439 At present, the production of electricity from fossil fuels is cheaper than from any renewable source (nuclear energy is the cheapest source of electricity). However, other countries are leading the race to develop commercially-viable renewable energy. In this sense, Ireland is being left behind and is becoming a 'technology-importer' and, with a few exceptions, is missing the associated income and development potential that

comes with patents, copyrights and commercial sales of this technology.

440 Statement from CER on a proposed direction and comments/ response paper on the treatment of renewable projects in Gate 3 of the group processing approach to network connection, 11 July 2008.

441 DCENR, Government White Paper (2007), Delivering a Sustainable Energy Future for Ireland.

442 Department of the Taoiseach (2008), Building Ireland's Smart Economy.

443 The baseline scenario is akin to a business as usual scenario, against which alternative policy scenarios can be compared. The *White Paper Plus* scenario assumes the achievement of renewable energy targets and power generation fuel diversity targets in the Government's Energy White Paper, as well as subsequent Government targets for renewable electricity and the share of electric cars by 2020. The *Exploratory* scenario makes all of the same assumptions as the *White Paper Plus* scenario, but further assumes that all of the wind energy generation plant in the Gate 3 process is accepted (which would give wind a 52 per cent share in electricity production in 2020).

444 DCENR (2012), NREAP, First Progress Report.

445 Houses of the Oireachtas, Sixth Report of the Joint Committee on Climate Change and Energy Security (2011), Report on the National Renewable Energy Action Plan.

446 SEAI (2003), Attitudes to Wind Farms and Wind Energy in Ireland.

447 SEAI (2011), *Energy in Ireland 1990–2010, 2011 Report.*

448 Eirgrid (November 2011), *Irish Electricity System – Summary of All Generators.*

449 Eirgrid (December 2009), Monthly Availability Report.

450 Eirgrid (December 2011), Annual Renewable Report 2011.

451 Eirgrid (2011), Offshore Grid Study, Analysis of the Appropriate Architecture of an Irish Offshore Network.

452 DCENR (2011), Offshore Renewable Energy Development Plan.

453 Kjaer, C. (2007), Wind energy – why businesses should say yes, EWEA, Climate Action.

454 *Sunday Business Post*, 9 October 2011, quoting George Bennett, IDA Ireland's Head of Cleantech.

455 Reply to a parliamentary question, 18 January 2012.

456 *Sunday Business Post*, 9 October 2011, quoting David Gunning, CEO of Coillte, suggests that Ireland will not meet this target.

457 Micro-generation is classified by ESB Networks as grid-connected electricity generation up to a maximum rating of 11kW

when connected to the three phase grid (400V). The vast majority of domestic and agricultural customers are connected at single phase (230V) and for these customers to be classified as micro-generators the maximum rating permitted is 5.75kW. These ratings are in line with Irish conditions prescribed in European standard.

[458] SEAI provides information on the Greener Homes Scheme, the Home Energy Saving Scheme, the Warmer Homes Scheme and the Low Carbon Homes Programme.

[459] All Maxol garages in Ireland now stock 'E5' petrol at the same price as regular unleaded petrol that contains 5 per cent domestically-produced bio-ethanol. All retailers are required that petrol and diesel contain at least 4 per cent bio-fuels; much of which is imported.

[460] Directive on the Promotion of the use of bio-fuels and other renewable fuels for transport (Directive 2003/30/EC).

[461] DCENR (2007), Bio-energy Action Plan for Ireland. Willow, miscanthus, hemp and reed canary grass have been identified by Teagasc as suitable for agricultural growth as biomass in the Irish climate.

[462] Environment Commissioner Dimas echoed concerned of the House of Commons that the production of bio-fuels was causing farmers in developing nations to replace food crops with fuel crops, causing increased food prices, and was causing deforestation in order to clear land for crop growing.

[463] COFORD (2003), Strategic Study, Maximising the Potential of Wood Use for Electricity Generation in Ireland.

[464] Houses of the Oireachtas, Seventh Report of the Joint Committee on Climate Change and Energy Security, Report on Biogas Energy in Ireland, January 2011. The report cites the European Biomas Association as a useful source of information

[465] Dr Jerry Murphy, UCC.

[466] Irish Bio-energy Association (2012), The Economic Benefits from the Development of Bio-energy in Ireland to Meet the 2020 Targets.

[467] EPA, Strategic Policy Unit (2005), Anaerobic Digestion: Benefits for Waste Management, Agriculture, Energy and the Environment.

[468] DCENR, Renewable Energy Development (2006), An Overview of Policy and Strategy Evolution.

[469] Houses of the Oireachtas, Fourth Report of the Joint Committee on Communications, Energy and Natural Resources, The Development of Anaerobic Digestion in Ireland, January 2011.

[470] Greenstar newsletter, December 2009.

471 Presentation by Donal McNioclais, CEO, AER Sustainable Energy, to the Dublin Chamber Green Economy Group, 21 February 2012.
472 Deverell, R., McDonnell, K., Ward, S., and Devlin, G. (2009), 'An Economic Assessment of Potential Ethanol Production Pathways in Ireland', *Energy Policy*, 37–10.
473 (2009) Bio-energy News, 4, provides a summary of the state of play of Ireland's bio-fuels sector.
474 www.cso.ie; 703 flexi-fuel vehicles were registered in 2009 and 2,255 registered in 2010 (January–July).
475 European Commission (2010), Consultation on the Future of Trans-European Transport Network Policy, COM (2010) 212 final, May 2010.
476 European Commission (2010), A European strategy on clean and energy efficiency vehicles, Communication to the European Parliament, the Council and the European Economic and Social Committee, COM (2010) 186 final, April 2010.
477 DCENR, Regulatory Impact Assessment, Bio-fuels Obligation Scheme.
478 Statement by Minister for State Tony Killeen during an adjournment debate on VRT, Seanad Debates, 12 May 2010.
479 Commission on Taxation, Report 2009, ch. 9.
480 Hennessy, H. and Tol, R.S.J (2010), The Impact of Climate Policy on Private Car Ownership in Ireland, ESRI, Working Paper Series Paper.
481 The Earth's core emits energy in the form of heat at a rate of 44.2 TW, and is replenished at a rate of 30 TW due to radioactive decay of minerals. The net outflow of energy is far greater than the entire energy consumption of mankind, but it is only possible to tap into a small proportion of this. Thus, the Earth is very slowly cooling, and so geothermal energy is not strictly 'renewable'. However, given the extremely long time frame in question, it is reasonable to call this 'sustainable' energy (see Pollack H. et al. (1993), 'Heat Flow from the Earth's Interior: Analysis of the Global Data Set', Review of Geophysics, 31(3)).
482 In an interview with Gareth Jones, Secretary of the Geothermal Association of Ireland, 27 January 2009.
483 This plant is at Aughinish Island, Askeaton, Co. Limerick and is run by UC Rusal, the world's largest producer of Aluminium and Alumina, in order to run a smelter. The plant has the capacity to produce 130 MW of energy
484 Presentation by Martin McAdan, CEO Aquamarine, MRIA Ocean Energy Industry Forum, 10 February 2012. As a rule of thumb some eight jobs are created for every MW installed.

[485] Marine Renewable Industry Association (2012), submission to government, Our Ocean Wealth; towards an integrated marine plan for Ireland.

[486] SEAI, press release, 28 March 2012.

[487] Presentation by Martin McAdam, chief executive officer, to the MRIA Ocean Energy Industry Forum, 10 February 2012.

[488] It is interesting to note that large government grants for the production and use of solar panels in some countries, particularly Germany, have concentrated much of the world's photovoltaic technology in areas where it is inefficiently employed.

[489] IAE (2009), Review of Ireland's Energy Policy in the Context of the Changing Economy.

[490] Smart metering involves the replacement of mechanical meters for measuring electricity consumption with sophisticated meters offering a range of benefits to both consumers and utility suppliers, by providing real-time information on customer's energy consumption and cost.

[491] CER, 'Irish Consumers Get Smart', press release, 20 January 2010.

[492] Rate impact analyses are often carried out prior to many capital investments in order to determine how this investment will affect tariffs for consumers.

[493] IAE (2006), Report on Future Energy Policy in Ireland.

[494] IAE (2011), Energy Policy and Economic Recovery 2010–2015.

[495] DCENR, Minister's Brief (released under the Freedom of Information Act), March 2011.

[496] European Commission, Energy 2020: A strategy for competitive, sustainable and secure energy.

[497] DG Energy's web site provides full details about the EU's energy efficiency policies.

[498] European Commission, Communication to the European Parliament, the Council, the European Economic and Social Committee and the Committee of the Regions, Energy 2020: a strategy for competitive, sustainable and secure supply, SEC (2010) 1346 639 final, 10 November 2010.

[499] European Commission, Communication to the European Parliament, the Council, the European Economic and Social Committee and the Committee of the Regions, Energy Roadmap 2050.

[500] European Commission (2011), Proposal for a Directive on energy efficiency and repealing Directives 2004/8/EC and 2006/32/EC, COM (2011) 370 final, 22 June 2011. See also the accompanying impact statement, SEC (2011) 779 final.

[501] Directive 2006/32/EC on energy end-use efficiency and energy services (repealing Council Directive 93/76/EEC), OJ L 114/64, 27 April 2006.

[502] DCENR, Energy End-Use Efficiency and Energy Services Regulations 2009, SI 542 of 2009.

[503] DCENR, Energy Performance of Buildings Regulations 2006, SI 666 of 2006.

[504] Directive 2010/31/EU on the energy performance of buildings, OJ L 153, 18 June 2010.

[505] DCENR (2011), *NEEAP 2 Energy Saving Measures and Tables*.

[506] European Council for an Energy Efficient Europe, views on a future European Energy Efficiency Action Plan (2010).

[507] IEA (2010), Energy Technology Perspectives 2010: scenarios and strategies to 2050.

[508] SEAI (2005), Assessment of the Potential for ESCOs in Ireland.

[509] Curtin, J. (2009), *Greenprint for a National Energy Efficiency Retrofit Programme*, Institute for International and European Affairs. See also Curtin, J. and Maguire, J. (eds) (2011), *Thinking Deeper – Financing Options for Home Retrofit*, IIEA. Two pay-as-you-save options are assessed in detail, one which attaches the loan to the property (based on a US trial) and another which attaches the loan to the energy meter (based on upcoming UK data). See also presentations made to the IIEA's September 2011 conference on retrofitting.

[510] Statement by Sean Connick, Minister of State, Department of Agriculture, Fisheries and Food, to the Joint Oireachtas Committee on Climate Change and Energy Security, 26 November 2010.

[511] European Commission, *Green Paper on Forest Protection – Preparing Forests for Climate Change*, SEC (2010) 163 final.

[512] Oireachtas Joint Committees on Climate Change and Energy Security and Agriculture, Fisheries and Food, July 2010. Deputy Andrew Doyle TD was rapporteur.

[513] Oireachtas Joint Committee on Climate Change and Energy Security, Eighth Report on public hearings on sustainable Forestry and Forest Carbon Sequestration, January 2011.

[514] Peter Wehrheim, Head of Climate Finance and Deforestation, DG Climate Action, European Commission explained the situation at a briefing to the Institute for International and European Affairs, April 2011.

[515] Some €70m in 2010 and €114.5 in 2011.

[516] Briefing provided to the Joint Committee by EcoSecurities Group plc and Bank of Ireland Global Markets.

[517] Ecosystem Marketplace (2011), State of Forest Carbon Markets 2011, from Canopy to Currency.

[518] There are now at least sixteen such groupings in existence.

[519] A full list of EU waste legislation can be found on this site.

[520] The proximity principle is set out in EU Framework Directive 91/156/EEC. Member states must establish an integrated and adequate network of disposal installations so that waste can be disposed of in one of the nearest appropriate installations, by means of the most appropriate methods and technologies to ensure a high level of protection for the environment.

[521] Proxied from UK data: Department of Trade and Industry (2006), *Emerging Markets In the Environmental Industries Sector.*

[522] The *KOMPASS Business Directory* lists 100 companies involved in waste collection (excluding local authorities) and 104 engaged in recycling. In addition, 25 companies are listed as being providers of waste equipment and machinery.

[523] Interview with the Irish Waste Management Association (2008).

[524] Eunomia Research and Consulting Ltd., in association with TOBIN Consulting Engineers (2007), Waste Policy, Planning and Regulation in Ireland, Final Report for Greenstar.

[525] Directive 2008/98/EC on waste was transposed into Irish law by European Communities (Waste Directive) Regulations 2011, SI 126 of 2011, 31 March 2011.

[526] European Commission (2010), Communication on Future Steps in Bio-waste Management in the EU, COM (2010) 235 final.

[527] Comprehensive Expenditure Report 2012–14, 2012 Estimates for Public Services and Summary Public Capital Programme, Government Publications Sales Office, November 2011.

[528] Department of the Environment, Community and Local Government (2009), International Review of Waste Management, Eunomia and Associates.

[529] The report argued that MBT is the only internationally proven technology solution that can play a major role in helping Ireland meet its EU waste targets. AEA Technology, in a report for the European Commission has evaluated technology options.

[530] Department of the Environment, Community and Local Government (2011), Towards a New National Waste Policy, discussion document.

[531] EPA (2011), National Waste Report (2009), 2011.

[532] Forfás, National Competitiveness Council (2011), Ireland's Competitiveness Challenge 2011, January 2012.

[533] O'Toole, Dr F. (2007), Household Waste Collection: An Economics of Competition Policy Perspective, Trinity College Dublin.

[534] Irish Waste Management Association, press statement, June 2006.

[535] Forfás (August 2009), Waste Management in Ireland: Benchmarking Analysis and Policy Priorities (updated in October 2010).

[536] EPA (2007), National Waste Report (2006), Table 6. It appears recent statistics about exports have not been published.

[537] Calculations made at prevailing prices in January 2012 based on Brent crude. There are 159 litres in a barrel of oil. The assumed price of the drinking water is 55c/litre.

[538] McKinsey Water Resources Group (2009), Charting Our Water Future; economic frameworks to inform decision-makers.

[539] Siemens Financial Services (2007).

[540] EPA (2009), A Summary of the State of Knowledge on Climate Change Impacts for Ireland, Climate Change Research Programme.

[541] IAE (2009), Ireland at Risk: Critical Infrastructure – Adaptation for Climate Change.

[542] Ofwat UK (2007), International Comparison of Water and Sewerage Services. This report provides comparisons of the financial performance of water and sewage companies.

[543] Department of the Environment, Community and Local Government (2012), Reform of the Water Sector in Ireland: Position Paper. The deadline for submissions was 24 February 2012.

[544] Forfás (2007), Overview of the Main Infrastructure Issues for Enterprise.

[545] PwC (Ireland) (2011), Irish Water: Phase 1 Report.

[546] EPA (2009), The Provision and Quality of Drinking Water in Ireland.

[547] Directive 2000/60/EC establishing a framework for Community action in the field of water policy, OJ L 327/1, 22 December 2000.

[548] EPA (2010), Water Quality in Ireland 2007–2009.

[549] HM Government, Department for Environment, Food and Rural Affairs (2011), Water for Life.

[550] Presentation by Trevor Haslett, CEO, NI Water, iQuest National Water Summit, December 2011.

[551] UNESCO (2009), *The United Nations World Development Report*.

[552] Water Resources Group, 2008. The group was set up in 2008 to contribute new insights to what was seen then as the 'increasingly critical issue of water resource scarcity'. Membership includes the World Bank and a consortium of business partners.

[553] Carbon Disclosure Project, Water Disclosure Global Report 2011. Some 500 large corporate were surveyed but none were from Ireland.

[554] The only published statistics relate to NACE 41 which covers the collection, purification and distribution of water. Figures from the CSO Census of Industrial Production indicate that in 2006, the number of local units was 64, there were 2,449 persons engaged in the sector and the gross output of the sector was valued at €168 million.

[555] *KOMPASS* lists 245 companies involved in water products and services provision (excluding local authorities) with 26 companies listed as being providers of effluent services.

[556] European Commission, DG ENVIR Environment Study on Eco-industry, its size, employment, perspectives and barriers to growth in an enlarged EU final report, August 2006.

[557] Frost and Sullivan (2008), Climate Change in Europe: Investment Opportunities.

[558] PwC (Ireland) (2011), Irish Water: Phase 1 Report.

[559] Speech by Phil Hogan, Minister for the Environment, Community and Local Government, IIEA Water Seminar, 9 November 2011.

[560] OECD (2010), Environmental Performance Review: Ireland.

[561] Tol, R. (2012), 'The hidden depths of the water charge', *Sunday Business Post*, 22 April 2012.

[562] Frost and Sullivan (2008).

[563] KPMG (2011), Delivering Water Infrastructure Using Private Finance.

[564] Department of the Environment, Community and Local Government (2011), Review of National Climate Policy.

[565] UNEP (2011), Towards a Green Economy: Pathways to Sustainable Development and Poverty Eradication – A Synthesis for Policy-makers.

[566] OECD (2011), Towards Green Growth.

[567] C.C. Jaeger et al. (German Federal Ministry for the Environment, Nature Conservation and Nuclear Safety) (2011), A New Growth Path for Europe: Generating Prosperity and Jobs in the Low Carbon Economy, European Climate Forum Report.

[568] As articulated by speakers at the Business Europe Conference on 'Greening the Environment' held in Brussels on 21/22 February 2008.

[569] Ibid.

# Bibliography

A&L Goodbody Consulting and the Clean Technology Centre (2005), *Assessment of the Potential to Develop Environmental State Aid Supports for Enterprise*, a report for Forfás, unpublished.

Ahlstrom, D. (2011), 'Santa Seeks New Headquarters', *The Irish Times*, 8 December 2011.

Arnold, T. (2009), 'Impact of Climate Change on Developing Countries', presentation to the Climate Change Forum, European Parliament Office, Dublin.

Australian Academy of Science (2010), The Science of Climate Change, Questions and Answers.

Avery, B., et al. (2004), 'Global Demand for US Environmental Goods and Services', *Journal of Agricultural and Applied Economics*.

Bloomberg (2007), *New Energy Finance*, White Paper.

Bloomberg (2011), www.newenergyfinance.com

Bloomberg, 'Paradigm Change Capital LLP Forms Group to Promote Low Carbon Bonds', 19 July 2011.

Bourne, J.K. (2007), 'Green Dreams: Making fuel from crops could be good for the planet—after a breakthrough or two', *National Geographic*, October.

Brennan, P. (2008), 'Flexible Mechanism, Ireland's Carbon Fund and the Carbon Market', Institute of International and European Affairs, Occasional Paper No. 2.

Brennan, P., and Curtin, J. (eds.), (2008) The Climate Change Challenge: Strategic Issues, Options and Implications for Ireland, Institute of International and European Affairs.

Business in the Community Ireland (2009), Green Ireland: The Business of Climate Change.

Capoor, K., and Ambrosi, P. (2005), State and Trends of the Carbon Market 2007, World Bank.

Carbon Disclosure Project (2011), Water Disclosure Global Report 2011.

Carbon Trust (2006), Carbon Footprints in the Supply Chain: The Next Steps for Business.

Carbon Trust (2006), Future Marine Energy.

Carus, F. (2011), 'Venture Capital: Patience is a virtue in hunt for game-changing "Green Google"', *Financial Times*, 28 October.

CDC Climat Research (2011), 'Durban: One small promising step for climate by 2020', *Climate Brief*.

CDC Climat Research (2011), 'The factors that determine the carbon price: An econometric analysis', *Tendances Carbone*.

CDC Climat Research (2012), Financing climate actions in developing countries: What role is there for NAMAs?

CDC Climat Research (2012), 'The EU ETS carbon price: To intervene or not to intervene?'

CDC Climat Research (2012), 'Understanding the link between macroeconomic environment and the EU carbon price', *Tendances Carbone*.

Centre for European Policy Studies (2012), *The EU ETS as a Driver for Future Carbon Markets*, Task Force Report, Brussels.

Chatham House Report (2009), Who Owns Our Low Carbon Future: Intellectual Property and Energy Technologies.

China Briefing News, 5 April 2011.

Clark, P.U., et al. (2004), Rapid Rise of Sea Level 19,000 Years Ago and Its Global Implications, *Science* 304: 1141–4.

CleanEdge Inc. (2011), Clean Energy Trends 2011.

Coakley, T., et al. (Clean Technology Centre) (2007), Investigation into why existing environmental technologies are underused (2005-ET-DS-19-M3), Final Report, EPA.

COFORD (2003), Strategic Study, Maximising the Potential of Wood Use for Electricity Generation in Ireland.

Cohn & Wolfe, Landor Associates and Penn, Schoen & Berland (2011), The 2011 Green Brands Survey.

Coillte (2010), Presentation to the Oireachtas Joint Committee on Climate Change and Energy Security.

Commission for Energy Regulation (2011), Smart Metering Information Paper 4.

Committee on Climate Change (2008), *Building a Low-Carbon Economy* – The UK's Contribution to Tackling Climate Change.

Cormier, A., and Bellassen, V. (2012), CDC Climat Research, The Risks of CDM Projects: How did only 30 per cent of expected credits come through, Working Paper No. 2012–11.

Cosbey, A., and Tarasofsky, R. (2007), Climate Change, Competitiveness and Trade: A Chatham House Report, The Royal Institute of International Affairs.

Cox, S., and Vadon, R., 'Running the Rule over Stern's Numbers', BBC Radio 4, 26 January 2007.

Curtin, J. (2009), *Greenprint for a National Energy Efficiency Retrofit Programme*, Institute for International and European Affairs.

Curtin, J. and Hanrahan, G. (2010), What Can Cancún Deliver: Pre-Summit Briefing, Institute of International and European Affairs.

Curtin, J. and Hanrahan, G. (2012), Why Legislate? Designing a Climate Law for Ireland, Institute of International and European Affairs.

Curtin, J. and Maguire, J. (eds.) (2011), Thinking Deeper: Financing Options for Home Retrofit, Institute for International and European Affairs.

Damro, C., and Mendes, P.L. (2003), 'Emissions Trading at Kyoto: From EU Resistance to Union Innovation', *Environmental Politics*, 12(2).

Department of Agriculture, Food and the Marine (Government of Ireland) (2010), Food Harvest 2020: A Vision for Irish Agri-food and Fisheries.

Department of Communications, Energy and Natural Resources (Government of Ireland) (2007), Bio-energy Action Plan for Ireland.

Department of Communications, Energy and Natural Resources (Government of Ireland) (2007), Delivering a Sustainable Energy Future for Ireland, White Paper.

Department of Communications, Energy and Natural Resources (Government of Ireland) (2009), Maximising Ireland's Energy Efficiency. The National Energy Efficiency Action Plan 2009–2020.

Department of Communications, Energy and Natural Resources (Government of Ireland) (2010), *National Renewable Energy Action Plan: Ireland*.

Department of Energy, Communications and Natural Resources, Renewable Energy Development (Government of Ireland )(2006), An Overview of Policy and Strategy Evolution.

Department of Energy, Communications and Natural Resources (Government of Ireland) (2006), Energy Performance of Buildings Regulations 2006, SI 666 of 2006.

Department of Energy, Communications and Natural Resources and the Department of Enterprise, Trade and Investment (Government of Ireland) (2008), All-island Grid Study.

Department of Energy, Communications and Natural Resources (Government of Ireland) (2009), Energy End-Use Efficiency and Energy Services Regulations 2009, SI 542 of 2009.

Department of Energy, Communications and Natural Resources (Government of Ireland) (2011), Offshore Renewable Energy Development Plan.

Department of Energy, Communications and Natural Resources (Government of Ireland) (2012), NREAP, First Progress Report.

Department of Enterprise, Jobs, and Innovation (Government of Ireland) (2011), Progress Report on the implementation of the recommendations of the Report of the High Level Group on Green Enterprise.

Department of Environment, Community and Local Government (Government of Ireland) (2011), A Framework for Sustainable Development for Ireland, a draft for public consultation.

Department of Environment, Community and Local Government (Government of Ireland) (2011), Draft Regulatory Impact Analysis on the Revised EU ETS Directive.

Department of Environment, Community and Local Government (Government of Ireland) (2011), Review of National Climate Policy.

Department of Environment, Community and Local Government (Government of Ireland) (2011), Towards a New National Waste Policy, discussion document.

Department of Environment, Community and Local Government (Government of Ireland) (2012), 'Hogan Issues Roadmap for Climate Policy and Legislation', press release, 23 January.

Department of Environment, Heritage and Local Government (Government of Ireland) (2006), Ireland's National Roadmap for the Implementation of the Environmental Technologies Action Plan (ETAP).

Department of Environment, Heritage and Local Government (Government of Ireland) (2007), National Climate Change Strategy 2007–2012.

Department of Jobs, Enterprise and Innovation (Government of Ireland) (2011), Progress Report on the Implementation of the recommendations of the Report of the High Level Group on Green Enterprise.

Department of the Taoiseach (Government of Ireland) (2007), An Agreed Programme for Government.

Department of the Taoiseach (Government of Ireland) (2008), Building Ireland's Smart Economy.

Department of Transport (Government of Ireland) (2009), Smarter Travel – A Sustainable Transport Future: A new Transport Policy for Ireland 2009–2020.

Departments of Environment, Community and Local Government and Public Expenditure and Reform (Government of Ireland) (2012), An Action Plan for Green Procurement.

Departments of Environment, Community and Local Government and Public Expenditure and Reform (Government of Ireland) (2012), Reform of the Water Sector in Ireland, position paper.

Dessai, S., Adger, W.N., Hulme, M., Koehler, J., Turnpenny, J., and Warren, R. (2003), Defining and experiencing dangerous climate change, Working Paper 28, Tyndall Centre for Climate Change Research.

Deutsche Bank (2009), Global Climate Change Policy Tracker, 26 October.

Deutsche Bank (2009), Paying for Renewable Energy: TLC at the Right Price – Achieving Scale through Efficient Policy Design.

Deverell, R., McDonnell, K., Ward, S., and Devlin, G. (2009), 'An Economic Assessment of Potential Ethanol Production Pathways in Ireland', *Energy Policy*, 37–10.

Duval, R. (2008), A Taxonomy of Instruments to Reduce GHG Emissions and Their Interactions, Economics Department Working Paper No. 636, OECD.

Ecosystem Marketplace (2011), State of Forest Carbon Markets 2011: From Canopy to Currency.

EICTA (2008), *High Tech: Low Carbon – The role of technology in tackling climate change.*

Eirgrid (2009), Monthly Availability Report.

Eirgrid (2010), Eirgrid 25, A strategy for the development of Ireland's electricity grid for a sustainable and competitive future.

Eirgrid (2011), Annual Renewable Report 2011.

Eirgrid (2011), Irish Electricity System – Summary of All Generators.

Eirgrid (2011), Offshore Grid Study, Analysis of the Appropriate Architecture of an Irish Offshore Network.

Environmental Business International Inc (2010), *EBI Report: The Climate Change Industry.*

EPA (2005), Anaerobic Digestion: Benefits for Waste Management, Agriculture, Energy and the Environment.

EPA (2007), National Waste Report (2006).

EPA (2008), Ireland's National Allocation Plan for Emission Trading 2008–2012, Final Allocation Decision.

EPA (2009), A Summary of the State of Knowledge on Climate Change Impacts for Ireland, Climate Change Research Programme.

EPA (2009), Climate Change in Ireland: Refining the Impacts for Ireland, STRIVE Report prepared by NUI Maynooth (John Sweeney ed.).

EPA (2009), Municipal Solid Waste – Pre-treatment and Residuals Management, an EPA Technical Guidance Document.

EPA (2009), The Provision and Quality of Drinking Water in Ireland.

EPA (2010), Water Quality in Ireland 2007–2009.

EPA (2011), Ireland's Greenhouse Gas Emissions Projections 2010–2020.

EPA (2011), National Waste Report (2009), 2011.

EPA (2011), Presentation to the Oireachtas Joint Committee on Climate Change and Energy Security.

EPA (2011), Verified Emissions 2008–2010.

EPA (2012), 'Greenhouse Gas Projections', Presentation by Laura Burke, Director General, Institute of International and European Affairs, Carbon Day.

EPA (2012), Ireland's Greenhouse Gas Emissions Projections 2011–2020.

EPS Consulting (2008), *Business Opportunities for the Environmental Goods and Services*, Report for Forfás/InterTrade Ireland.

EPS Consulting (2010), 'Construction Opportunities in the Green Economy', Presentation to the Construction Industry Federation Annual National Conference.

Ernst and Young (2006), *Eco-industry, its size, employment, perspectives and barriers to growth in an enlarged EU*, European Commission DG Environment, Brussels.

Ernst & Young (2010), Business Risk Report 2010: The Top 10 Risks for Business.

ESRI (2010), Recovery Scenarios for Ireland.

ETUC (2010), Climate Change and Employment: Impact of Employment in the EU-25 of Climate Change and Carbon Emission Reduction Measures by 2030.

Eunomia Research and Consulting Ltd., in association with TOBIN Consulting Engineers (2007), Waste Policy, Planning and Regulation in Ireland, final report for Greenstar.

European Climate Foundation (2010), Practical Guide to a Prosperous Low-Carbon Europe.

European Commission (2005), Winning the Battle Against Global Climate Change, Communication from the Commission to the Council, the European Parliament, the European Economic and Social Committee and the Committee of the Regions, COM (2005) 35 final.

European Commission (2005), Assessing Opportunities for ICT to Contribute to Sustainable Development, DG Information Society.

European Commission (2006), Communication to the European Parliament, the Council, the European Economic and Social Committee and the Committee of the Regions, On the assessment of National Allocation Plans for the allocation of greenhouse gas emission allowances in the second period of the EU ETS, COM (2006) 725 final.

European Commission (2007), A European Strategic Energy Technology Plan, Staff Working Document, SEC (2007) 1511.

European Commission (2007), Communication to the Council. The European Parliament, the European Economic and Social Committee and the Committee of the Regions (2007), Limiting Global Climate Change to 2 Degree Celsius: The way ahead for 2020 and beyond, COM (2007) 2 final.

European Commission (2007), EU Action Against Climate Change: Working With Developing Countries to Tackle Climate Change.

European Commission (2008), Communication to the European Parliament, the Council, the European Economic and Social Committee and the Committee of the Regions, Addressing the challenge of energy efficiency through Information and Communication Technologies, COM (2008) 241 final.

European Commission (2008), Communication to the European Parliament, the Council, the European Economic and Social Committee and the Committee of the Regions, Addressing the challenges of deforestation and forest degradation to tackle climate change and biodiversity loss, COM (2008) 645 final.

European Commission (2008), Implementation Framework of the GCCA, Staff Working Document, SEC (2008) 2319.

European Commission (2008), Impact Assessment accompanying the package of implementation measures for the EU's objectives on climate change and renewable energy for 2020, Staff Working Document, SEC 85/3.

European Commission (2009), Adapting to climate change: Towards a European framework for action, White Paper, COM (2009) 147 final.

European Commission (2009), Communication to the European Parliament, the Council, the European Economic and Social Committee and the Committee of the Regions, Investing in the Development of Low Carbon Technologies (SET-Plan), COM (2009) 519 final.

European Commission (2009), staff working document, Communication to the European Parliament, the Council, the Economic and Social Committee and the Committee of the Regions, Investing in the Development of Low-Carbon Technologies Plan (SET-Plan), SEC (2009) 1295.

European Commission (2009), Communication to the European Parliament, the Council, the European Economic and Social Committee and the Committee of the Regions Stepping up International Climate Finance: A European Blueprint for the Copenhagen Talks, SEC (2009) 1172.

European Commission (2009), Communication to the European Parliament, the Council, the European Economic and Social Committee and the Committee of the Regions, Towards a Comprehensive Climate Change Agreement in Copenhagen.

European Commission (2009), Supporting a Climate for Change: the EU and Developing Countries Working Together.

European Commission (2009), The Support of Electricity from Renewable Energy Sources, Staff Working Paper.

European Commission (2009), Towards a Comprehensive Climate Change Agreement in Copenhagen, Staff Working Paper, Part I, SEC (2009) 101.

European Commission (2010), A European strategy on clean and energy efficiency vehicles, Communication to the European Parliament, the Council and the European Economic and Social Committee, COM (2010) 186 final.

European Commission (2010), Communication on Future Steps in Bio-waste Management in the EU, COM (2010) 235 final.

European Commission (2010), Communication to the European Parliament, the Council, the European Economic and Social Committee and the Committee of the Regions, A digital agenda for Europe, COM (2010) 245 final.

European Commission (2010), Communication to the European Parliament, the Council, the European Economic and Social Committee and the Committee of the Regions, An Agenda for New Skills and Jobs – A European Contribution Towards Full Employment, COM (2010) 682 final.

European Commission (2010), Communication to the European Parliament, the Council, the European Economic and Social Committee and the Committee of the Regions, Analysis of options to move beyond 20 per cent greenhouse gas emission reductions and assessing the risk of carbon leakage, COM (2010) 265 final.

European Commission (2010), Communication to the European Parliament, the Council, the European Economic and Social Committee and the Committee of the Regions, Energy 2020: a strategy for competitive, sustainable and secure supply, COM (2010) 639 final.

European Commission (2010), Communication to the European Parliament, the Council, the European Economic and Social Committee and the Committee of the Regions, Energy infrastructure priorities for 2020 and beyond – A Blueprint for an Integrated European Energy Network, COM (2010) 677.

European Commission (2010), Europe 2020: A European Strategy for Smart, Sustainable and Inclusive Growth. The Commission's recommendations for Ireland under Europe 2020 are set out in a Staff Working Paper, SEC (2011) 716 final.

European Commission (2010), *Preparing Forests for Climate Change: Forest Protection and Information in the EU*, Green Paper SEC (2010) 163 final.

European Commission (2010), Report from the Commission to the Council and European Parliament on sustainability requirements for the use of solid and gaseous biomass sources in electricity, heating and cooling, COM (2010) 11 final.

European Commission (2010), Communication to the European Parliament, the Council, the European Economic and Social Committee and the Committee of the Regions, The CAP towards 2020 – meeting the food, natural resources and territorial challenges of the future, COM (2010) 672 final.

European Commission (2011), A roadmap for moving to a competitive low carbon economy by 2050, COM (2011) 112 final.

European Commission (2011), Communication to the European Parliament, the Council, the European Economic and Social Committee and the Committee of the Regions, A resource-efficient Europe – Flagship initiative under the Europe 2020 Strategy, COM (2011) 21.

European Commission (2011), Communication to the European Parliament, the Council, the European Economic and Social Committee and the Committee of the Regions, Energy Efficiency Plan 2011, COM (2011) 109 final.

European Commission (2011), Communication to the European Parliament, the Council, the European Economic and Social Committee and the Committee of the Regions, Energy Roadmap 2050, COM (2011) 885 final.

European Commission (2011), Communication to the European Parliament, the Council, the European Economic and Social Committee and the Committee of the Regions, Rio+2-: Towards the Green Economy and Better Governance, COM (2011) final.

European Commission (2011), Impact Assessment to the Proposal for a Council Directive amending Directive 2003/96/EC Restructuring the Community Framework for the Taxation of Energy Products and Electricity, Staff Working Paper, SEC (2011) 409.

European Commission (2011), Progress towards achieving the Kyoto objectives, Report to the European Parliament and the Council (required under Article 5 of Decision 280/2004/EC), COM (2011) 624 final.

European Commission (2011), Proposal for a Directive on energy efficiency and repealing Directives 2004/8/EC and 2006/32/EC, COM (2011) 370 final.

European Commission (2011), Proposal for a revision of the EU Energy Tax Directive, COM (2011) 169 final.

European Commission (2011), Roadmap to a Single European Transport Area – Towards a competitive and resource-efficient transport system, White Paper COM (2011) 144 final.

European Commission (2012), Analysis of options beyond 20 per cent GHG emission reductions: Member States results, Staff Working Paper, SWD 5 final.

European Commission (2012), *Preparing the EU's QELRO based on the EU Climate and Energy package*, Staff Working Document, SWD (2012) 18 final.

European Council for an Energy Efficient Europe (2010), views on a future European Energy Efficiency Action Plan.

European Council of Ministers (2007), Presidency Conclusions.

European Council of Ministers (2011), Conclusions of EU Environment Ministers.

European Environmental Agency (1996), *Communication on Community Strategy on Climate Change*.

European Environmental Agency (2005), The European Environment, State and Outlook.

European Environment Agency (2011), Environmental tax reform in Europe: Opportunities for eco-innovation, EEA Technical Report No. 17/2011.

European Environmental Agency (2011), Greenhouse gas emission trends and projections in Europe 2011, EEA Report No. 4/2011.

European Research Centre (UK) (2007), Investment in Electricity Generation: The role of costs, incentives and risks.

European Union's Publications Office (2000), Directive 2000/60/EC establishing a framework for Community action in the field of water policy, OJ L 327/1, 22 December 2000.

European Union's Publications Office (2003), Directive 2003/87/EC establishing a scheme for GHG emission allowance trading within the Community and amending Council Directive 96/61/EC dated 13 October 2003.

European Union's Publications Office (2003) Directive 2003/30/EC on the promotion of the use of bio-fuels and other renewable fuels for transport.

European Union's Publications Office (2004), Directive 2004/101/EC amending Directive 2003/87/EC establishing a scheme for greenhouse gas allowance trading within the Community, in respect of the Kyoto Protocol's project mechanisms, OJ L 228/18, 13 November 2004.

European Union's Publications Office (2004), Decision No. 280/2004/EC of the European Parliament and of the Council of 11 February 2004 concerning a mechanism for monitoring Community greenhouse gas emissions and for implementing the Kyoto Protocol.

European Union's Publications Office (2006), Directive 2006/32/EC on energy end-use efficiency and energy services (repealing Council Directive 93/76/EEC), OJ L 114/64, 27 April 2006.

European Union's Publications Office (2007), Treaty of Lisbon amending the Treaty on European Union and the Treaty establishing the European Community, OJ C 306, 17 December 2007.

European Union's Publications Office (2008), Community Guidelines on State aid for Environment Protection (2008/C 82/01), OJ C 82/1, 1 April 2008.

European Union's Publications Office (2009), Decision 406/2009/EC on the effort of Member States to reduce greenhouse gas emissions to meet the Community's greenhouse gas emission reduction commitments up to 2020, OJ L 140/136, 5 June 2009.

European Union's Publications Office (2009), Directive 2008/101/EC amending Directive 2003/87/EC so as to include aviation activities in the scheme of GHG emission allowance trading within the Community, OJ L8/3, 13 January 2009.

European Union's Publications Office (2009), Directive 2009/28/EC of 23 April 2009 on the promotion of the use of energy from renewable sources and amending and subsequently repealing Directives 2001/77/EC and 2003/30/EC, OJ L 140/16, 3 June 2009.

European Union's Publications Office (2009), Directive 2009/29/EC of the European Parliament and of the Council of 23 April 2009 amending Directive 2003/87/EC so as to improve and extend the greenhouse gas emission allowance trading scheme of the Community, OJ L140 dated 5 June 2009.

European Union's Publications Office (2010), Commission Decision 2011/278/EU determining transitional Union-wide rules for harmonised free allocation of emission allowances pursuant to Article 10a of the Directive 2003/87/EC, Official Journal L 130/1, 17 May.

European Union's Publications Office (2010), Commission Regulation (EU) 1031/2010 on the timing, administration and other aspects of auctioning GHG allowances pursuant to Directive 2003/87/EC, Official Journal L 302/1, 18 November 2010.

European Union's Publications Office (2010), Directive 2010/31/EU on the energy performance of buildings, OJ L 153, 18 June 2010.

European Wind Energy Association (2012), Wind in Power, 2011 European Statistics.

# Bibliography

Eurostat (2011), Sustainable Development in the European Union: 2011 Monitoring Report of the EU Sustainable Development Strategy.

*Farmers Journal* (2011), 'The Government approved the scheme on 21 February 2012', 27 August.

Farrell, G. (2007), Ireland at Risk: The Impact of Climate Change on the Water Environment, IAE.

Fealy, R. (2003), 'The Impacts of Climate Change on Sea Level and the Irish Coast', in Sweeney et al., *Climate Change: Scenarios and Impacts for Ireland*.

Fealy, R. and Sweeney, J. (2007), 'Statistical downscaling of precipitation for a selection of sites in Ireland employing a generalised linear modelling approach', *International Journal of Climatology*, 2083–94.

Fealy, R. with contributions from Ray Bates (UCD), Laura McElwain, John Sweeney and Conor Murphy (NUI Maynooth) (2008), *The Science of Climate Change*, Occasional Paper, Institute for International and European Affairs.

Flannery, T. (2005), The Weather Makers: The History and Future Impact of Climate Change, Text Publishing.

Forfás (2007), Overview of the Main Infrastructure Issues for Enterprise.

Forfás (2009), Waste Management in Ireland: Benchmarking Analysis and Policy Priorities (updated in October 2010).

Forfás (2010), Adaptation to Climate Change: Issues for Business.

Forfás (2011), Intelligent Infrastructure: Delivering the Competitiveness Benefits and Enterprise Opportunities.

Forfás (2012), Report of the Research Prioritisation Steering Group, March.

Forfás and InterTradeIreland (2008), Environmental Goods and Services Sector on the Island of Ireland, Enterprise Opportunities and Policy Implications.

Forfás and the National Competitiveness Council (2011), Ireland's Competitiveness Challenge 2011.

FOX News, 'Bush Dubs Kyoto "Lousy Deal" For America', 11 July.

Frost and Sullivan (2008), Climate Change in Europe: Investment Opportunities.

Gaskin, F. (2012), 'Do Investors and Consumers Care if a Company Goes Green?', unpublished.

Global Green Interchange (2011), Securing Ireland's Competitive Advantage in the Transition to a Global Low Carbon Economy.

Gorecki, P.K. (2011), The Internal EU Electricity Market: Implications for Ireland, Research Series No. 23, ESRI.

Government of China (2007), China's National Climate Change Programme.

Government of Ireland (1997), Taxes Consolidation Act 1997, Section 76A.

Government of Ireland (1999), Stamp Duties Consolidation Act 1999, Section 90A.

Government of Ireland (2007), Carbon Fund Act 2007.

Government of Ireland (2009), Accounts of Public Services 2008, Comptroller and Auditor General Annual Report.

Government of Ireland (2009), Report of the Commission on Taxation.

Government of Ireland (2009), Waste Management (Food Waste) Regulations 2009, SI 508 of 2009.

Government of Ireland (2010), European Communities (Greenhouse Gas Trading) (Aviation) Regulations, 2010, SI 261 of 2010.

Government of Ireland (2010), Future Skills Needs of Enterprise within the Green Economy in Ireland, Expert Group on Future Skills Needs.

Government of Ireland (2010), Value Added Tax Consolidated Act 2010, Section 6(1)(a), Schedule 1.

Government of Ireland (2011), Comprehensive Expenditure Report 2012–14: 2012 Estimates for Public Services and Summary Public Capital Programme.

Government of Ireland (2011), European Communities (Greenhouse Gas Emissions Trading) (Amendment) Regulations 2010, SI 161 of 2010 and European Communities (Greenhouse Gas Trading) (Amendment) Regulations 2011, SI 127 of 2011.

Government of Ireland (2011), European Communities (Renewable Energy) Regulations 2011, SI 147 of 2011 and Sustainable Energy Act 2002 (Section 8 (2)) (Conferral of Additional Functions) Renewable Energy Order 2011, SI 148 of 2011.

Government of Ireland (2011), European Communities (Waste Directive) Regulations 2011, SI 126 of 2011, 31 March.

Government of Ireland (2012), Chapter 7: 'The Green Economy', Action Plan for Jobs.

Gulev, S.K. and Hasse, L. (1999), 'Changes of wind waves in the North Atlantic over the last 30 years', International Journal of Climatology, 19(10).

G8 Summit (2007), Chair's Summary, Heiligendamm, 8 June.

Hansen, J. (2004), 'Diffusing the global warming time bomb', Scientific American, 290(3): 68–77.

Hart, M.H. (1978), 'Evolution of atmosphere of Earth', Icarus, 33: 23–39.

Harvey, F. (2007), 'Yo Kyoto: Bush Shifts His Stance on Global Warming', *The Financial Times*, 2 October.

Helm, D., and Hepburn, C. (2009), 'Introduction', The Economics and Politics of Climate Change, Oxford University Press.

Hennessy, H., and Tol, R.S.J (2010), The Impact of Climate Policy on Private Car Ownership in Ireland, ESRI, Working Paper Series Paper.

Hession, M., (2012), 'Carbon Markets after Durban', Presentation to the Institute of International and European Affairs Climate Change Working Group.

HM Government (2006), Emerging Markets in the Environmental Industries Sector, UK Centre for Environment and Economic Development, Report for the UK Department for the Environment, Food and Rural Affairs.

HM Government (2007), *Emerging Markets in the Environmental Industries Sector*, Department of Trade and Industry.

HM Government (2007), International Comparison of Water and Sewerage Services, Ofwat UK.

HM Government (2007), Meeting the Energy Challenge, White Paper, Department of Trade and Industry.

HM Government (2007), UK Commission on Environmental Markets and Economic Performance, BERR/DEFRA Report.

HM Government (2011), Enabling the Transition to a Green Economy: Government and Business Working Together.

Hogan, P., Minister for the Environment, Community and Local Government, Speech to the Institute of International and European Affairs Water Seminar, 9 November 2011.

Holden, N.M., and Brereton, A.J. (2003), 'The Impact of Climate Change on Irish Agriculture', in J. Sweeney, et al, Climate Change: Scenarios and Impacts for Ireland, EPA, 33–80.

Holden, N.M., Brereton, A.J. and Fitzgerald, J.B. (2009), 'Impact of Climate Change on Irish Agricultural Production Systems', in J. Sweeney (ed.), Climate Change: Refining the Impacts for Ireland, EPA.

Houses of the Oireachtas (2009), Drive for Zero, First Report of the Joint Committee on Climate Change and Energy Security, Simon Coveney, T.D. rapporteur.

Houses of the Oireachtas (2010), Appendix to the 2011 Carbon Budget Statement presented by the Minister for the Environment, Heritage and Local Government to the Oireachtas.

Houses of the Oireachtas (2010), Second Report on Climate Change Law, Fifth Report of the Joint Committee on Climate Change and Energy Security, Liz McManus, T.D. rapporteur.

Houses of the Oireachtas (2011), Report on Biogas Energy in Ireland, Seventh Report of the Joint Committee on Climate Change and Energy Security.

Houses of the Oireachtas (2011), Report on the National Renewable Energy Action Plan, Sixth Report of the Joint Committee on Climate Change and Energy Security.

Houses of the Oireachtas (2011), Report on Public Hearings on Sustainable Forestry and Forest Carbon Sequestration, Eighth Report of the Joint Committee on Climate Change and Energy Security.

Houses of the Oireachtas (2011), The Development of Anaerobic Digestion in Ireland, Fourth Report of the Joint Committee on Communications, Energy and Natural Resources.

Houghton, J.T., Ding, Y., Griggs, D.J. et al. (eds.) (2001), Climate Change 2001: The Scientific Basis, contribution of Working Group I to the Third Assessment Report of the IPCC, Cambridge University Press.

Howley, M., Ó Gallachóir, B., and Dennehy, E. (2010), Understanding Electricity and Gas Prices in Ireland, SEAI.

HSBC (2010), Sizing the Climate Economy.

Hughes, L. (2011), Climate Change and Japan's post-Copenhagen Challenge, The Brookings Institute.

IEA (2009), World Energy Outlook 2009.

IEA (2010), Energy Technology Perspectives, Scenarios and Strategies to 2050.

IEA (2011), World Energy Outlook 2011.

Institutional Investors Group on Climate Change (2010), *The Global Investor Survey on Climate Change*, Annual Report on Actions and Progress.

IPCC (2007), Fourth Assessment Report.

IPCC (2011), Managing the Risks of Extreme Events and Disasters to Advance Climate Change, A Special Report of Working Group I and Working Group II.

Irish Bio-energy Association (2012), The Economic Benefits from the Development of Bio-energy in Ireland to Meet the 2020 Targets.

Irish Academy of Engineering (2006), Report on Future Energy Policy in Ireland.

Irish Academy of Engineering (2009), Ireland at Risk: Critical Infrastructure – Adaptation for Climate Change.

Irish Academy of Engineering (2009), Review of Ireland's Energy Policy in the Context of the Changing Economy.

Irish Academy of Engineering (2011), Energy Policy and Economic Recovery 2010–2015.

Jacquier, J. (2005), 'On Relationships Between Integrated Policies for Sustainable Urban Development and Urban Governance', Royal Dutch Geographical Society, 96(4).

Jaeger, C.C., et al. (German Federal Ministry for the Environment, Nature Conservation and Nuclear Safety) (2011), A New Growth Path for Europe: Generating Prosperity and Jobs in the Low Carbon Economy, European Climate Forum Report.

Jamet, S., and Corfee-Morlot, J. (2009), Assessing the Impacts of Climate Change: A Literature Review, OECD Economics and Environment Departments.

Jones, B., Keen, M., Norregaard, J. and Strand, J. (2007), 'The Economics of Climate Change', IMF Survey Magazine.

Kelly, D., and Ryan, J. (CIRCA Group Europe Ltd) (2007), Environmental Technologies: Guidelines on How to Take a Pilot Project to Market (2005-ET-DS-25-M3) Final Report, EPA.

Kjaer, C. (2007), Wind energy – why businesses should say yes, EWEA, Climate Action.

Koppl, A. (2006), *The Austrian Environmental Industry Summary of Results*, WIFO.

KPMG (2011), Corporate Sustainability: A Progress Report.

KPMG (2011), Delivering Water Infrastructure Using Private Finance.

Leflevre, X., OECD, 'Today's Environmental Research, Tomorrow's Environmental Protection', Presentation to the EPA Conference on Irish Environmental Research Dublin, February 2008.

Lewis, I.J. (2007), China's Climate Change Strategy, Jamestown Foundation.

Library House (2007), *Cleantech Goes Mainstream*, research report.

Lidegaard, M., (2012), Denmark's Climate and Energy Minister, Breakfast Policy Briefing, European Policy Centre, Brussels.

Lovelock, J. (1979), *Gaia: A New Look at Life on Earth*, Oxford University Press.

Lovelock, J. (2000), *Homage to Gaia: The Life of an Independent Scientist*, Oxford University Press.

Lovelock, J. (2005), *Gaia: Medicine for an Ailing Planet*, Gaia Books.

Lovelock, J. (2009), *The Vanishing Face of Gaia: A Final Warning*, Allen Lane.

Lowe, P. (2011), Presentation on the European Energy Roadmap 2050, Institute of International and European Affairs.

McAdam, M., CEO Aquamarine (2012), 'Oyster Progress', Presentation to the MRIA Ocean Energy Industry Forum, 10 February 2012.

McDonald, F., 'Global Warming Linked to Harsh Winters', *The Irish Times*, December 2010.

McElwain, L. and Sweeney, J. (2007), Implications of the EU climate protection target for Ireland, EPA.

McElwain, L. and Sweeney, J. (2007), Key Meteorological Indicators of Climate Change in Ireland, Environmental Research Centre-ERC Report 6, EPA.

McGrath, R., Nishimura, E., Nolan, P. et al. (2005), *Climate Change: Regional Climate Model Predictions for Ireland*, EPA, ERTDI Report Series No. 36.

MacGregor, R. (2007), 'China's Data on Soaring Energy Use Give a Shock', *The Financial Times*, February.

Macken, K. (2011), The EU ETS: A Review of the First Six Years of Operation, EPA.

McKinsey Quarterly Review (2007), 'A Cost Curve for Greenhouse Gas Reduction', July

McKinsey Water Resources Group (2009), Charting Our Water Future: Economic frameworks to inform decision-makers.

McNioclais, D., CEO AER Sustainable Energy, Presentation to the Dublin Chamber Green Economy Group, 21 February 2012.

Mann, M.E., Bradley, R.S., Hughes, M.K. (1999), 'Northern hemisphere temperatures during the past millennium: Inferences, uncertainties, and limitations', *Geophysical Research Letters* 26(6): 759.

Marine Renewable Industry Association (2012), submission to government, Our Ocean Wealth; towards an integrated marine plan for Ireland.

Martin, J.P., Director, Employment, Labour and Social Affairs, OECD, presentation at Belgium Ministerial Conference on Transition towards a Competitive Low Carbon and Green Economy, Brussels, 2010.

Masters, L. (2011), 'A Complex Exercise in Climate Diplomacy for South Africa', June, www.boell.org.za.

Mastrandrea, M.D. and S.H. Schneider, (2004), 'Probabilistic Integrated Assessment of "Dangerous" Climate Change', *Science*, 304, 571–5, 23 April 2004.

Matthews, N., '41 Shades of Green', *Business and Finance*, 18 January 2008.

Meadows, D.H., Meadows, D.L., Randers J. and Behrens III, W.W. (1992), The Limits to Growth, Club of Rome.

Meinshausen, M. (2005), On the risk of overshooting 2°C, paper presented at Scientific Symposium Avoiding Dangerous Climate Change, Met Office, Exeter, 1–3 February 2005.

Merrill Lynch (2008), Aviation in the EU ETS: An incentive for efficiency.

Mintel (2010), Press Release, March.

Murphy, C., Fealy, R., Charlton, R., and Sweeney, J. (2006), The reliability of an 'off-the-shelf' Conceptual Rainfall Runoff model for use in climate impact assessment: uncertainty quantification using Latin Hypercube sampling, *Area*, 38.1: 65–78.

National Environmental Research Institute (2007), Competitiveness Effects of Environmental Tax Reforms, final report to the European Commission, University of Aarhus.

NERI, Cambridge Econometrics, ESRI, IEEP, PSI and WIIW (2007), *Competitiveness Effects of Environmental Tax Reforms*, final report for the European Commission.

Netherlands Environmental Assessment Agency (2007), China Now No. 1 in CO2 Emissions; USA in Second Position.

Nordhaus, W. (2007), 'The Stern Review on the Economics of Climate Change', *Journal of Economic Literature*, 45(3): 686–702.

OECD (2009), The Economics of Climate Change Mitigation.

OECD (2010), Environmental Performance Review: Ireland.

OECD (2011), Towards Green Growth.

O'Kane, K. (2011), *The Changing Face of CDM post-2012: a European Utilities Perspective*, unpublished.

Oppenheimer, M. and Alley, R. (2004) 'The West Antarctic Ice Sheet and long term climate policy', *Climate Change*, 64, 1–10.

Oppenheimer, M. and Alley, R. (2005), 'Ice sheets, global warming and Article 2 of the UNFCCC', *Climatic Change*, 68: 257–67

O'Toole, Dr F. (2007), Household Waste Collection: An Economics of Competition Policy Perspective, Trinity College Dublin.

Patwardhan, A., Schneider, A.H., and Semenov, S.M. (2003), *Assessing the Science to Address UNFCCC Article 2: A Concept Paper Relating to Cross Cutting Theme Number Four*, IPCC.

Pew Trust (2010), Who is Winning the Clean Energy Race?

Philips Sustainability Report (2006), Improving Lives, Delivering Value.

Point Carbon (2007), A New Climate for Carbon Trading.

Pollack H. et al. (1993), 'Heat Flow from the Earth's Interior: Analysis of the Global Data Set', Review of Geophysics, 31(3).

Polovina, J. (2008), 'Ocean's least productive waters are expanding', *Geophysical Research Letters* (American Geophysical Union).

Profeta, T. (Nicholas Institute for Environmental Policy Solutions) and Kelly, C. (German Marshall Fund of the United States) (2008), *The US Climate Policy Debate: How climate politics are moving forward on Capitol Hill and in the White House*, The German Marshall Fund of the United States.

Purser, P.M., Byrne, K.A., and Farrell, E.P. (2003), 'The Potential Impact of Climate Change on Irish Forestry', in J. Sweeney et al., Climate Change: Scenarios and Impacts for Ireland, EPA, 121–40.

PwC (UK) (2008), Sustainability: Are Consumers Buying It?

PwC (Ireland) (2011), Irish Water: Phase 1 Report.

Quiggin, J.C. (2006), Stern and the Critics on Discounting, University of Queensland.

Reid, H., Huq, S. and Murray, L. (2010), Community Champions: Adapting to Climate Challenges, International Institute for Environment and Development.

Reid, L. (2004), 'Government underestimated effect of abandoned carbon tax', *The Irish Times*, 29 November.

Renewable Energy Policy Network (2011), *REN21 Renewables 2011 Global Status Report*.

Renewable Energy Policy Network (2011), 'Renewable energy policy network for the 21st century', REN21.

*Reuters*, 'EU report sees bio-fuel giving 3.4 per cent of 2020 needs', 4 July 2008.

Ringel, M. (2006), 'Fostering the use of renewable energies in the EU; the race between feed-in tariffs and green certificates', *Renewable Energy*, 31: 1–17.

Ringius, L. (1997), Differentiation, Leaders and Fairness: Negotiating Climate Change Commitments in the European Community, CICERO Report 1997, Oslo.

Roberts, N. (1998), *The Holocene: An Environmental History*, Blackwell.

Robinson, M. (2011), 'The role of climate justice', presentation to the Institute of International and European Affairs.

Ryan, O. (Department of the Environment, Community and Local Government), Finegan, F. (Grian) and Kennedy, M. (SEAI) (2012), panel presentations to the Institute of International and European Affairs' Climate Change Research Group.

Santarius, T., et al (2011), One Step Forward and Two Sideward: Regional Analysis of Climate Policy in 2010 and the Cancún Climate Conference, Heinrich Boll Stiftung.

Schneider, S.H. (2001), What is 'dangerous' climate change?, *Nature*, 411: 17–19.

Schneider, S.H. (2002), Can we estimate the likelihood of climatic changes at 2100?. *Climate Change*, 52: 441–51.

Schneider, S.H. and Lane, J. (2005), An Overview of 'Dangerous' Climate Change, Stanford University.

Schwartz, P. and Randall, D. (2004), An Abrupt Climate Change Scenario and its Implications for US National Security.

Scott, S. and Eakins, J. (2004), *Carbon Taxes: Which Households Gain or Lose?*, report for the EPA, ESRI.

SEAI (2003), Attitudes to Wind Farms and Wind Energy in Ireland.

SEAI (2005), Assessment of the Potential for ESCOs in Ireland.

SEAI (2010), Renewable Energy in Ireland, 2010 Update.

SEAI (2011), Energy Forecasts for Ireland to 2020.

SEAI (2011), Energy in Ireland 1990–2010.

SEAI (2012), 'Sustainable Energy Sector to Treble by 2020', Media Release.

Siemens Financial Services (2007), 'Private funds for public infrastructure – Ways to avoid the funding logjam.'

SQW energy (2010), Economic Study for Ocean Energy Development in Ireland, a report for SEAI and Invest Northern Ireland.

Stavins, R.N. (2004), *Can an Effective Global Climate Change Treaty be Based on Sound Science, Rational Economics and Pragmatic Politics?* Discussion Paper, Resources for the Future.

Steele-Dunne, S., Lynch, P., McGrath, R., et al. (2008), 'The impacts of climate change on hydrology in Ireland', *Journal of Hydrology*, 356: 28–45.

Stern, N. (2006), The Stern Review on the Economics of Climate Change, HM Treasury.

Stern, N. (2007), *The Economics of Climate Change: The Stern Review*, Cambridge University Press.

Stern, T. (2010), 'Big powers talk climate, no grand deal sighted', *Associated Press*, 21 September.

Stiglitz, J. (2006), 'A New Agenda for Global Warming', *The Economists' Voice*, 3(7).

Swann, B. (2012), Department of Enterprise, Trade and Investment, 'Northern Ireland's Offshore Renewable Energy Action Plan 2012-2020', presentation to the MRIA Conference, 10 February.

Swiss Federal Institute of Technology, Zurich (2009), Banking and Climate Change: Opportunities and Risks – An analysis of climate strategies in more than 100 banks worldwide.

The Ecology Foundation (2010), Energy Security: Ireland on the Edge.

*The Economist* (2010), 'The current state of the relations between China and US', 4 December, Special Report.

The Economist Intelligence Unit (2007), Action or Aspiration? Sustainability in the Workplace.

*The Guardian* (2008), 'Secret report: Bio-fuel caused food crisis', 4 July.

Thomson Reuters Point Carbon (2012), Carbon 2012.

Tirpak, D., Ashton, J., Dadi, Z., Gylvan Meiro Filho, L., et al. (2005), Avoiding Dangerous Climate Change: International Symposium on the Stabilisation of Greenhouse Gas Concentrations, Report of the International Scientific Steering Committee.

Tocker, T., and Plattner, G.K. (2007), The Physical Science Basis of Climate Change: Latest Findings to be Assessed by WG1 in AR4, IPCC.

Tol, R. (2012), 'The hidden depths of the water charge', *Sunday Business Post*, 22 April.

Tol, R.S.J., Callan, T., Conefrey, T., FitzGerald, J.D., Lyons, S., Malaguzzi Valeri, L. and Scott, S. (2008), A Carbon Tax for Ireland, ESRI.

Trocaire, Changing Lives, Climate Change in the Developing World, Dublin.

UNEP (2010), The Emissions Gap Report, A Preliminary Assessment.

UNEP (2011), Towards a Green Economy: Pathways to Sustainable Development and Poverty Eradication – A Synthesis for Policy-makers.

UNEP, Oxfam and the World Resource Institute (2011), Adapting for a Green Economy: Companies, Communities and Climate Change, UN Global Compact.

UNEP/World Resources Institute (2011), Building the Climate Change Regime: Survey and Analysis of Approaches.

UNFCCC (2007), Climate Change: Impacts, Vulnerabilities and Adaptation in Developing Countries.

UNFCCC (2007), Kyoto Protocol.

UNFCCC (2007), The United Nations Climate Change Bali Conference, COP 13.

United Nations (2010), Environmental Indicators.

US Department of Commerce (2010), Measuring the Green Economy.

US Department of Energy (2011), Biomass Supply for a Bio-energy and Bio-products Industry.

Vickery, G., and Iarrera, M. (1996), *The Global Environmental Goods and Services Industries*, OECD.

Walker, N. (2012), 'Climate Mitigation Policy – A Business Perspective', presentation to the Institute of International and European Affairs Carbon Day, 16 April 2012.

Walsh, A. (2012), *Climate Change and the Role of Banking*, unpublished.

Weale, A. (1996), 'Environmental Rules and Rule-Making in the European Union', *Journal of European Public Policy*, 3(4): 598.

Wehrheim, P., Head of Climate Finance and Deforestation, DG Climate Action, European Commission, 'Forestry, Agriculture and EU Climate Change Commitments', presentation to the Institute for International and European Affairs, April 2011.

Weitzman, M.L. (2010), 'Risk-Adjusted Gamma Discounting', *Journal of Environmental Economics and Management*, 60(1): 1–13.

Wild, M., Calanca, P., Scherrer, S.C., and Ohmura, A. (2003), 'Effects of polar ice sheets on global sea level in high-resolution greenhouse scenarios', *Journal of Geophysical Research*, 108 (D5): 4165 and McElwain and Sweeney (2007).

World Resource Institute (2011), Building the Climate Change Regime – Survey and Analysis of Approaches.